Hi Richard
Don't feel obliged to
stuff !! Looks good on ~~~~~~~~~~~ le
tho'.
Mike

THE UNIVERSAL UNITS OF THE MIND

How a simple data module underlies all our thoughts and perceptions

First Edition

MICHAEL JESSOP AND TERRY HILL

AMD Publishing (UK)

First published in 2018.

Published by AMD Publishing (UK). Sandon House, Gentlemans Lane
Ullenhall, Warwickshire, United Kingdom. B95 5RR.
Email: amdpublishinguk@gmail.com

ISBN 1-869937-03-1

Designed and typeset by Delicious Industries.
Copyedited by Carrie Walker.
Printed by Ashford Colour Press Ltd, Gosport, UK.

Preface

The biology of our brains is reasonably well understood through research and our knowledge of the laws of chemistry and ultimately physics. Our minds and our day-to-day experiences depend on the operation of the brain, yet the nature of these experiences has a quality that is somehow unlike the biological processes involved.

We are proposing in this book that there are two distinct entities at work here: biological processes that are governed by the laws of physics and chemistry, and information processes governed by a separate set of rules that underpin how information is structured and manipulated. It is only when these two processes fuse together, each operating under its own set of rules, that our minds come into being and we can actively experience the world.

We believe that the rules of the mind are abstract and universal in the same way that the laws of physics are abstract and universal. The rule for a circle is: the length of the circumference = the constant $\pi \times$ the circle's diameter. But the rule for a circle is not a circle itself. A circle is something made from physical stuff: it is made from the pencil lead on a piece of paper, or the rubber on the outside of a car tyre. Physical stuff becomes a circle when it obeys the rule for a circle and as a consequence the length of its circumference is equal to the length of its diameter times π.

So a square in the information system of the mind is *abstract*, it is not a square; it is an electrochemical code for a square. To see a square you must select the code for a square in your mind and let it direct you to the internal image of a square in your visual cortex, a part of your brain that is outside your mind.

The rules of the mind are *universal*. By this we mean that the exact same rules are applied whether they are in the mind of a cat or in the mind of an Oxford fellow. How well a mind executes the rules depends on the capacity of the physical structures supporting it, only a physical structure of limitless capacity can implement the rules perfectly. Our brains are probably near the bottom end of the physical spectrum so we implement the rules rather poorly, and as a result we experience a limited version of reality.

We believe there are about 20 rules. The most important of these is the rule that everything we experience is represented in our minds in a standard form. Not just objects such as cats and trees and mountains, but also Pythagoras' theorem, music and feelings of delight – a single data standard to represent movement, relationships in time and space, a structure for our memories, our ideas and our dreams. Only when information is held in this standard form can the rules of the mind produce for us that unity of consciousness we experience throughout our lives.

So we see the mind not as just a neuroscience problem or a psychology problem or even a philosophy problem – *but as essentially a software problem*; this is because the mind is an information system in the brain driven by software in much the same way that software drives your smartphone.

Contents

Movement and time

Long-term memory and reacting to events

18. Consciousness and the perfect mind?

Introduction

The mind is an information system. We receive information from the senses, interpret it, store it, retrieve it, merge it and manipulate it. We can combine complicated information streams such as vision, sound, movement and emotions, and, critically, we can generate actions and communicate with other minds. The variety of data being managed here and the types of manipulation involved create a formidable information-processing task. How do we maintain order amid such complexity without breakdown and confusion?

Digital computers provide reliable systems that also receive, interpret, store and transmit information. Their success is only possible because hardware and software designers work to a set of common standards that define precisely how data must be held and presented. For example, in ASCII coding the letter A is represented by the number 65, so if the A key is pressed on a keyboard, the number 65 will be transferred into the computer's memory and can be processed by whatever computer program is running at that time. The ASCII standard for encoding characters was established in 1963 by the American Standards Association and is still in use today (although mostly in an extended form).

More recently, in the early 1990s, Tim Berners-Lee developed international standards for screen design on the World Wide Web in order to unlock the power of the internet. This standard (HTML) provides software designers with a range of tags that they can insert, invisibly, into a screen, not only to control the way in which the text and graphics are displayed, but also to allow the presentation of sound and vision. Powerful tags can also be specified in the text that give users the ability to link from their current screen to any other HTML document on the Web with the click of a mouse.

The point is that these systems work effectively only because all the information held in their electronic components is structured according to a common set of rules. If this is necessary for information processed by electronic components, surely there must also be an underlying set of rules that manages the far more complex processing task carried out by the electrical components (neurons) that make up our brains? It would be most surprising if there were not a set of data standards defining how our brains represent and organise the information they receive and process, the equivalent of the data standards that support digital information systems.

But can we identify a common data structure underlying all our mental activities, a template that is capable of representing anything we could possibly experience in our lives? Not just objects such as cats and trees and mountains, but also Pythagoras' theorem, music and feelings of delight – a single data standard to represent movement, relationships in time and space, a structure for our memories, our ideas and our dreams.

In this book, we have developed a theory of mind using the approach a software developer would use in designing a software application; we are in effect reverse-engineering the procedures that enable us to think. One thing is clear from the outset – that our minds could not possibly handle the variety of information they encounter every day unless the supporting data were held in a standard form. In other words, there must be an underlying data structure that makes it possible for the hardware of our minds (neurons) to process, represent and integrate information in the same way that electronic systems do.

But before we get to that point, we have to consider where the data that get into our minds come from. In our computer analogy above, the A key on the keyboard is *out there* in the world; it is external to the computer. When we press the A key, this produces an electrical signal, and as a result the number 65 is stored internally in the computer's memory. This is then processed according to the standards that apply to *the computer's* internal world. The internal number 65 is nothing like an A key, but the computer is able to use '65' for whatever it is that As do.

Our minds too are an *internal* world. When we see something out there, like a leaf, we do not see it directly. What we see is the internal representation of that leaf. We can never know a leaf *directly* – we can only ever experience something inside our heads that equates to a leaf. But although we can never know exactly what it is that is *out there*, we must find some way of characterising it, because ultimately what is out there is the source of all our experiences.

To explain how this works, we will start by classing *everything* that exists as a *thing*. The use of the word *thing* in this context is chosen with care. At first glance, it may appear to be a trivial or even a throw-away title, but it is in fact a most appropriate and accurate description. So, for our explanation, the use of the word *thing* is all-encompassing. Thus, every individual tree out there in the world is a thing, and each one of the leaves on every tree is a thing. Every sound is a thing, and every playing of Beethoven's *Moonlight Sonata* is a thing. A rock on a planet 20 light-years away is a thing even though no one will ever see it. Things occur internally as well as out there, so a thought inside our heads is a thing, and every idea is a thing. Even our brains are things. Nothing exists that is not a thing because things are the class of everything that exists, did exist, will exist or conceivably could exist. Things are made from things because things are all there is.

And finally, no one thing is more important than any other thing. For example, a particular tree is no more significant than any one of its leaves, and the playing of Beethoven's *Moonlight Sonata* is no more significant than the sound of one of its notes. It is we who attach importance and order to things. Out there, no one thing is more important than any other thing; there is no order.

As well as assuming that there are only *things*, we make an important second assumption, which is that every thing has some characteristic or other: for example, that leaf is green, that note is loud, that coffee is hot. We will use the word *attribute* for the characteristics or qualities that things have. An attribute cannot exist on its own; it must be part of the description of a thing. So 'green', 'hot' and 'loud' cannot exist on their own – there are only green things, hot things and loud things. Consequently, there is no black, there are only black things.

In summary, there are just two entities: *things* and the *attributes* that describe them. A thing cannot exist unless it has an attribute, and an attribute cannot exist unless it is attached to the thing it describes.

Our senses pick up transmissions from external things and store them internally in our brains as internal things. So before we can experience an internal thing, we must first identify its characteristics or attributes, such as its shape or colour. If, for example, you look at a black square on a white piece of paper, it will transmit the image of a black square into your brain, but that internal image will become meaningful only when you identify its attributes. It is only then that you will see it as a black, square thing.

A similar process takes place in the computer example given earlier. When the A key is depressed, it transmits a unique electrical signal to the computer that identifies

the signal and codes it with the number 65, the internal equivalent of the letter A. Once we have identified the attributes in the image of the thing we are looking at, we encapsulate them in the *standard data packet*, a unit of information in the mind, that we will call a *datagram*. The origin of this term lies within internet protocol as a term for self-contained packets of information that act independently of the nature of the network carrying them.

Every datagram describes a single thing by listing its properties in two different ways: its *Whole* section describes the thing as a whole; its *Parts* section describes the characteristics of the parts from which it is made. So if you look at a black square, its internal image will be described by the attributes in its datagram as follows: the datagram's *Whole* section will have the attributes for Black and Square; its *Parts* section will have the attribute code Black because all the square's parts are black pixels:

Whole	*Parts*
Black Square	Black

If you look at a pattern of black dots against a white background, you will get an internal image that is coded with datagrams to describe the dots. Each black dot will have its own datagram: its *Whole* section attributes will give the dot's size and tell you that it is black; its *Parts* section will simply tell you that the dot's parts are all black. If the black dots are arranged so that they form a circle, an additional datagram will be created to describe the pattern as a whole: its *Whole* section will describe its circular shape and size, and its *Parts* section will describe the black dots making up the pattern.

Similarly, an internal image of four cats sitting in a row will create four datagrams, one for each cat. But the four cats together are a group so an additional datagram will be created to represent the row of cats as a whole, all of its *Parts* being cats and the *Whole* being a row that is, for example, 2 metres long.

Datagrams are the only form in which information is held in the mind, and therefore they are the source of all our experiences. Datagrams represent events, concepts and feelings as well as tangible things such as black squares, computer keyboards and rows of cats. If you are to be aware of any *thing*, even your own thoughts, there must be a description of it in your mind as a datagram with its data structured in the way we have just described.

The idea that things are a combination of their parts (substance) and their whole (form) goes back to the fourth century bc and the philosopher Aristotle. These ideas were developed further by St Thomas Aquinas in the thirteenth century as a contribution to Christian theology. Although it has an ancient pedigree, this way of looking at the nature of things, usually called hylomorphism or Thomism, is very much alive in current thinking on the philosophy of mind (see, for example, the publications of John Haldane listed in the Further reading).

However, we do not create datagrams for every piece of information in the brain regardless of its form. Only when information is structured in a very particular way is a datagram assigned to it so that it is presented in a form that can be experienced. A bundle of data is only assigned a datagram if all its component parts have something in common, a shared characteristic. Or, more precisely, the thing is made from component parts all of which belong to the same class. This means that the *Parts* sections of every datagram must contain *at least one attribute* that is present in every one of its components. So, in the examples we gave above, all the dots in the pattern were black, and each of the things in a row was a cat, and therefore we were able to provide them with datagrams.

So a single datagram describes each individual thing we see. But where do we hold these datagrams? The answer is that *the datagram that describes a thing is held in every part of the thing it describes!* Every pixel of the internal image of a black square holds a datagram telling you that this is a black square and these are its dimensions. If the square occupies 10,000 pixels in the image, 10,000 identical copies of its datagram will be placed in those pixels.

Is it possible that so simple a structure combined with just a small number of information-processing rules underlies something as enormously complex as our minds? We believe so. After all, the building blocks of life, our genes, are coded by our DNA using just four chemical bases. In much the same way that our DNA describes our biology, so datagrams describe our thoughts and perceptions.

This book is the culmination of a search for a single data standard and for the set of universal rules that will allow the mind to emerge. It is written for the general reader who, like ourselves, is fascinated by the puzzle of how we see the world and our place within it. The book is not a scientific treatise but a broad brush; no special knowledge of biology, neuroscience, psychology, computers, statistics or philosophy is required; all the reader needs is an open mind – and a little perseverance.

The book draws on research in a number of fields, in particular psychophysics (a branch of cognitive neuroscience) and philosophy of mind, and to a lesser extent computer vision. For those interested the first of these is covered comprehensively in Stephen Palmer's *Vision Science*. For those who wish to dig deeper there is *From Perception to Consciousness: Searching with Anne Treisman*, a collection of papers edited by Jeremy Wolfe and Lynn Robertson. But we must emphasise that it is not necessary to read either of these to understand the ideas being presented here.

The philosophical context is as important as the scientific one. Edward Feser, in his *Philosophy of Mind*, discusses with great clarity the philosophical issues that arise when you attempt a project of this field and, as with Stephen Palmer's *Vision Science*, the publications he recommends provide links to a broad range of ideas. Again, for those who wish to dig deeper there is *Consciousness, new philosophical perspectives*, a collection of articles edited by Quentin Smith and Aleksander Jokic. Certain works of Bertrand Russell have also been an important source throughout the life of the project; one book in particular – *An Inquiry into Meaning and Truth* – addresses many of the issues raised here.

The last publication we recommend is *The Object Primer* by Scott Ambler. This is a training manual for software developers that covers the analysis and design techniques they will need in tackling complex systems. Again, this is not necessary reading, but it may provide an insight into the methodology we have used in developing the ideas presented here.

In the body of the book, Chapters 1–18, we describe the flow of computational logic with very little discussion; this is so that the core principles stand out clearly. The downside of this approach is that it excludes much of the background thinking and strings of ifs and buts. However, in the Notes section towards the end of the book, we attempt to fill in some of the gaps by commenting on what has been written. We reference some of the literature we have used to develop these ideas in the Further reading section, but there is very little that is not covered by the books we mentioned earlier and by the references they provide.

Finally, we wish to stress that this is not an attempt to explain how the brain works, as we have neither the competence nor the intention to do this. But it is not necessary to understand the workings of the brain's hardware to understand the rules of the mind – any more than it is necessary to understand how a computer's hardware works to construct an email. So this book is not about the brain; it is instead a description of the underlying logic that enables us to understand the world and our place within it.

1

The raw data, source of everything we know

*For the Rays to speak properly are not coloured. In them there is nothing else than
a certain Power and Disposition to stir up a Sensation of this or that colour.*

(Sir Isaac Newton, *Optics, 1730*)

When you look out the window, let's say you see grass, trees and a house in the distance. You are able to see each of these things quite clearly without making any effort. You take for granted that these things are presented to you as they really are. You are completely unaware of the millions of operations performed by your brain every second to give you this picture, in the same way that you are unaware of the millions of instructions executed by your computer every time you open an email. These heavy processing loads are necessary because the raw inputs we have to work with are incredibly crude; they are just lists of numbers.

Each of your senses sends a stream of values – numbers – that represent the intensity of some outside event. These values travel along pathways of nerve fibres most of which eventually terminate in our cerebral cortex, a large region that extends along the top and back of the brain. So, for example, a rod receptor in the retina transmits an electrical signal up to the cerebral cortex that is proportional to the amount of light (the number of photons) hitting that receptor.

Each sense has its own particular region in the cortex. The electrical signals from the receptors in your eyes go to the region we call the visual cortex, the signals from your ears go to the auditory cortex, and the signals from the pressure receptors from under your skin go to a region called the somatic cortex.

Receptor cells that lie beside each other in the body, for example in the skin or in the retina of the eye, are connected to neurons in the cortex that also lie beside each other. This means that the neurons in the somatic cortex that receive signals from the pressure sensors in the skin produce an internal map of your body's surface, and the neurons in the visual cortex that receive signals from the eyes produce an internal image of the scene you are looking at – although there is some distortion because some parts of the internal image are shown in more detail than others.

Although you take in two images, one for each eye, the two versions of the scene are combined into a single internal image at the end of the nerve pathways that connect your retinas to your visual cortex. The visual cortex acts a bit like a digital camera in the way its pixels hold information. Together, these produce a single internal picture of what you are looking at. Thousands of experiments using dozens of procedures confirm the nature of this storage area. *When you look at a scene in the outside world, you do not see the scene itself; what you 'see' is the internal image of that scene encoded in the neurons of the visual cortex at the back of your brain.*

At this early stage, the internal image tells you nothing – it is simply a collection of separate independent pixels each containing an intensity value. If you look at a black square, you will get an internal image of a black square, but there is nothing there that pulls together the pixels of the black square so that it separates out from its background. So the first thing the brain does is to identify groups of pixels in your internal image that will, you hope, represent the individual objects in the scene you are looking at.

Let us now consider in more detail the black square on the white piece of paper that we mentioned in the Introduction. Light from the scene in front of you, of which the piece of paper is a part, projects an image on to the retina at the back of your eye. Each photosensitive cell in the retina reacts by transmitting a signal proportional to the light intensity into a corresponding storage point, a pixel of information, in your visual cortex. The result is a two-dimensional internal map of intensity values, an internal image representing the overall scene. Occupying a part of that image is a black square on a white piece of paper.

In our example, the visual cortex records the various intensities it receives from your eyes on a scale of 1 to 8: anything black produces an intensity of 1 and anything white an intensity of 8; intensities 2–7 represent the shades of grey in between the two. Thus, in Figure 1.1c, the pixels that have a low intensity value, '1', correspond to the position of the black square in the scene. Those which contain a high intensity value, '8', correspond to the white paper surrounding the square.

The intensities along the boundary between the black square and the surrounding white region will fall somewhere in between the two; these are shown as ‖ in Figure 1.1c. These pixels are not really points of

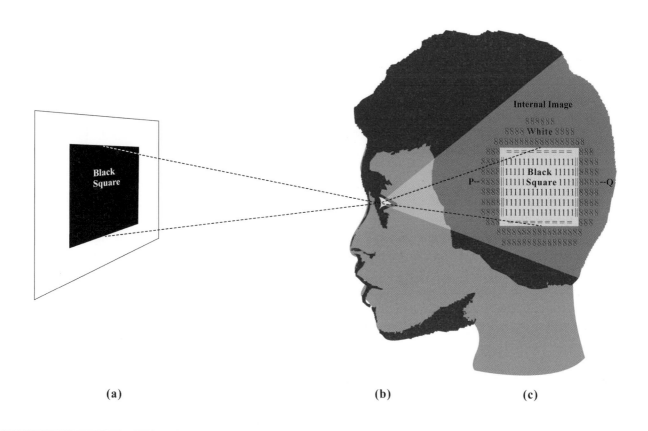

Figure 1.1 The internal image of a black square in the visual cortex. When you look at the black square on the white piece of paper, the reflected light produces an image of it on your retina, and nerve fibres then transmit this image into the visual cortex at the back of your brain. (a) The black square you are looking at. (b) The black square on the retina. (c) The internal image of the black square in your visual cortex.

intensity but are part of the boundary that separates the black square from the white region that surrounds it. The intensity values of these pixels have therefore been replaced by the marker ‖ to indicate that they are edges.

The black square is constructed from parts (pixels) all of which have something in common – they all have an intensity of '1'. So the black square is a thing that can be represented by a datagram and (eventually) experienced by the person looking at it. The square's boundary ‖ can also be represented by a datagram because all its parts are edge pixels.

The task now is how to organise this raw information so that (again eventually) it will deliver our experiences of the world. Essentially, we are turning a biological problem into an information-processing one, and just as the laws of physics and chemistry underpin the brain's biological processes, so there are rules of the mind that underpin how it processes information.

Of course, in nature things are seldom as simple as in this example. In reality, the pixel intensities you receive from your eyes are not as regular, and pre-processing is

necessary to convert them into uniform regions. The line of numbers below shows the intensity variation you might in reality see if you extended row PQ in the internal image in Figure 1.1c.

P–88987988786531201011201011123568897987898–Q

These raw numbers have to be manipulated to produce the regular pattern of a black square on a white piece of paper that you actually see on extended row PQ:

P–88888888888‖1111111111111111‖88888888888–Q

There is no master program that goes from pixel to pixel to do this; instead the way it is handled is that each pixel contains formulae that do the calculations for just that pixel. An idea of how this transformation is carried out is shown, step by step, in the Notes on Chapter 1 at the end of the book.

Much of our knowledge of these early processes originates in the pioneering work of Hubel and Weisel, for which they won the Nobel Prize in Physiology or

Medicine in 1981, and the computational approach to vision followed by David Marr before his early death in 1980 at the age of only 35 from leukaemia. This illustration of the pre-processing that takes place is grossly oversimplified as, in reality, our visual systems use a variety of strategies to segment the internal image into regions, and there are many more steps involved.

From this example, we see that the visual cortex is not simply a place where images are stored like photos on a computer, but is also where we process visual information to make it meaningful. The way this processing is managed is a bit like a computer spreadsheet in which formulae and data share the same pixels, but instead of being in electronic form they are represented in the brain by neurons. In these early stages, colour does not appear to play a significant role. Colour differences on their own do not produce good edges and therefore do not produce shapes – this is why a black and white photograph of a scene provides the same structural information as a coloured one. Your brain appears to create shapes from black and white edges first, and only then are colours applied, a bit like the way a child colours in the shapes between the lines in a colouring book. Colour may add richness to how we see the world, but it does not provide structure.

All we have created so far is a crude pixelated map of uniform regions. There is nothing there to tells us what anything is, for example that a particular cluster of black pixels, the '1's in Figure 1.1c, is a black square. The brain will now build layer upon layer of information on top of this internal image. Each additional layer has exactly the same pixel structure as the original image – they act as overlays, and taken together they give us the full picture of what we see.

The *internal* image we have described in this chapter is part of the *physical* world of sunsets, black squares and cats; the *iconic* image layers that overlay the internal image are in a separate *information* world, the world of the mind. The *physical* internal image contains no logic and the *iconic information* layers contain no sensations, but together they produce our experiences of the world because, within the structure of the brain, they share the same geometry.

Summary

Our sensory receptors transmit raw values to the cerebral cortex of the brain, where they are recorded in an internal storage area. Information from the different senses of vision, sound and touch, for example, are stored separately. The raw data in the internal image are partitioned into regions surrounded by edges that are 1 pixel wide. Together they form the foundation on which our minds build our understanding of the world.

This initial segmentation of the internal image into regions is an activity that takes place outside the information world of the mind and is therefore beyond the scope of this book. There do not appear to be a set of universal rules for segmentation but rather a collection of algorithms that are applied depending on the content of the image. The initial regions are continuously modified by feedback from inside the mind, and in later chapters we suggest how this might be achieved.

2

The emergence of meaning – datagrams

Of course it is happening inside your head, Harry, but why on earth should that mean it is not real?

(J. K. Rowling, *Harry Potter and the Deathly Hallows*)

Digital cameras capture the intensity and colour values in a scene and record them in an electronic pixel array. The camera does not try to identify the things that are in the picture it has captured. It does not, for example, label this group of black pixels as a square or that group of red pixels as a rose; it can only display the image back to you so you can work out what things are for yourself.

The raw internal image that we created in the last chapter is similar to the image in a digital camera; it is simply an array of intensities with no meaning. But the algorithms in the visual cortex are able to create regions in these raw data, identify their shapes and label them so we know what we are looking at. We call these labels *datagrams*, and they are held in the pixels of the things in the image that they describe. But datagrams are *not* held in the *internal image*; instead they are held in the *iconic image* that overlays the internal image – as the two images share the same pixels, they share the same geometry. Datagrams in the iconic image are in the information world of the mind, not in the material world of the internal image.

Each datagram holds a packet of *attributes*, and each attribute presents a single characteristic of the thing it represents – its shape or colour, for example. As described in the Introduction, attributes in datagrams are presented in two lists. The first list describes the thing as a *Whole*, and the second describes the *Parts* from which the thing is made. The two lists are encapsulated into a single packet (Figure 2.1a).

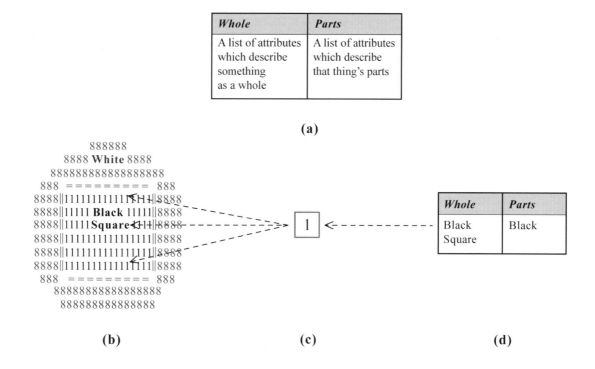

(a)

(b)   **(c)**   **(d)**

Figure 2.1 Datagrams. The datagram structure and an example of how a datagram would describe a black square. (a) The general structure of a datagram, its *Whole* section describes the object as a whole, and its *Parts* section describes its components. (b) The iconic image of a black square. (c) A single pixel in the black square. (d) The datagram held in every pixel of the iconic image of the black square.

The neurons in the visual cortex have identified the shape in Figure 2.1b as a black square and have created the datagram in Figure 2.1d for it. *A copy of this datagram is inserted into every pixel in the iconic image of the black square.* The attributes in this datagram tell us that, as a whole, this region is black and square, and that it is constructed from black pixels. *Every datagram in every pixel of the black square is identical – they all have exactly the same attributes.*

If your attention were drawn to any one of the datagrams in the pixels of the black square, you would get the same two *sensations* – one for black and one for square – and together they would tell you that the thing you are looking at is a black square. The only way you have of finding out about anything is through the attributes held in datagrams. Of course, the datagrams for the black square will have many more attributes, for example area and width, than the ones we have shown here, but to keep it simple we have limited its attributes to Black and Square.

Every pixel in our internal world is coded into datagrams in this way. These processes are taking place within our brains all the time even though we are not conscious of them; for this reason, we will refer to these processes as being pre-attentive. Their purpose is to convert the raw data into a form our minds can understand.

Attributes tell you what things look like, what things are and what they are doing. When you see a black shape and recognise it as a cat, it is because there is a datagram in its image that has an attribute code telling you that this is a cat (Figure 2.2a). If the cat is hissing at you, the attribute code for Hissing will be added to the list of attributes in all the cat's datagrams.

Attributes can also tell you how you should regard the information in the datagram you are looking at. Suppose that you are reading this page and you turn back and look again at the black square in Figure 1.1. This second time of looking at the black square will generate an additional attribute code of Same in the black square datagram (Figure 2.2b), which gives you the sensation that 'This is something I saw earlier.'

The attributes telling you what a thing is are carried in every pixel of that thing. Just as every cell in your body carries the genetic code, DNA, for the whole of your body, so every pixel of a thing in your mind carries a datagram that contains a description of the whole of that thing.

Edges

In the iconic image there are only regions and their boundaries, nothing else. We have described how we create datagrams for regions, and now we will show how we create datagrams for the edges that surround them.

In Figures 1.1 and 2.1, we marked the edges with a chain of ‖ 1 pixel wide – the reason we show edges as a chain of double vertical lines is because every pixel in a boundary holds two datagrams, one for each side of the edge.

Figure 2.3a shows the iconic image of the black square on a white piece of paper. The boundary of the square, ABCD, is marked by a chain of edge pairs '‖'. In each pixel in the chain, there are two datagrams, one for each side of the boundary. In Figure 2.3b, showing the vertical edge BC, the datagram to the left is in every pixel along the length of BC and marks the limit of the black square, whereas the datagram to the right, also in every pixel of BC, marks the limit of the surrounding white piece of paper. Both sets of datagrams tell you that the edge BC is vertical and 10 pixels long.

Please note that the shapes of things we are using to illustrate the text are not geometrically accurate – any more than the shapes of things in our visual cortex are geometrically accurate: it is attributes in datagrams, and

Whole	*Parts*
Black Cat Hissing	Black

(a)

Whole	*Parts*
Black Square Same	Black

(b)

Figure 2.2 Datagrams hold a wide range of attributes.
(a) There are attributes codes that tell you what things look like, what they are and what they are doing. (b) Other attribute codes like Same tell you something about the nature of the information itself.

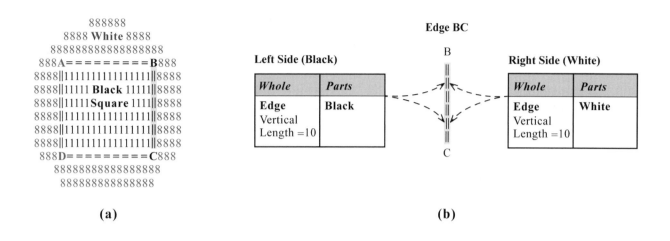

(a)   **(b)**

Figure 2.3 Edges are represented by datagrams in pairs, arranged in strings of single pixels. (a) The iconic image of the black square with the string of edge pixels along BC highlighted. (b) This shows that each of the pixels along edge BC holds two datagrams, one for each side of the edge.

not their physical presentation in the image, that tell us the shapes and sizes of things. The square in Figure 2.3a looks square-shaped but you will find that edge AB is 9 pixels long and BC is 6 pixels long even though they are two sides of the same square. This difference is, however, not relevant. The number of edge datagrams in an edge is not its length; instead its length is given by the length attribute in its datagrams – which in this example is 10.

In Figure 2.4a, we see two squares side by side, one grey, the other black; these are surrounded by a white region. The top edge, AC, separates the surrounding white

region from the connected grey and black squares below it. Edge AB separates the grey square from the white region above it, and edge BC separates the black square from the white region above it. Any position along AB can be seen either as part of length AC or as part of length AB; similarly, if we look at any position along BC, we can see it as part of either length AC or length BC. In fact, edge ABC has two lengths depending on which side of the edge you are looking at – but because there are two datagrams in each edge pixel, we are able to give an edge two lengths at the same point (Figure 2.5).

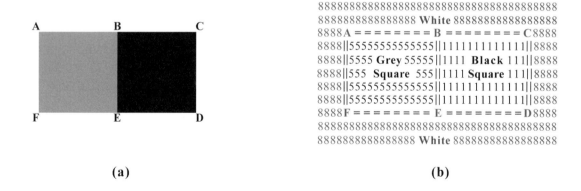

(a)   **(b)**

Figure 2.4 Edges of connected figures can have different lengths. We need two edge datagrams to describe an edge because an edge can have two different lengths at the same time. (a) A rectangle constructed from connected grey and black squares on a white background. (b) The two edge datagrams in each pixel along edge ABC in fact have different lengths. The top edge datagram for AC will say it is 17 pixels long, while the lower edges datagrams, for AB and BC, will each have a length of 8 pixels.

All the datagrams along the upper edge AC in Figure 2.5, which marks the limits of the white region, have a length of 17 pixels because that is the length of the white edge AC. All the datagrams along AB, which marks the limits of the grey square, have a length of 8 pixels, and all the datagrams along BC, which marks the limits of the black square, also have a length of 8 pixels. Together, this makes a total of 16 pixels. But the length of AC is 17 pixels, 1 pixel more than the sum of AB and BC. This is because the top edge AC is continuous through pixel B so the length of AC is 2 × 8 + 1 = 17. Conversely, pixel B is a termination point for edges AB and BC and is not included when the lengths of AB and BC are calculated. So this means that the two datagrams in every pixel of edge ABC show completely different lengths even though they are describing the same boundary – the length of the edge depends on which side of the boundary you choose to look at.

In real life, there are no perfect squares because some edges or corners are always missing. But if a region is square from the perspective of a particular pixel, the shape attribute in the datagram in that pixel will say that it is a square; if the *same* region from the perspective of another pixel appears shapeless, then the shape attribute in its datagram will say that this region has no shape. So ultimately the shape of a region depends on how you look at it; there is no attribute for 'squareish'. Iconic memory prioritises datagrams with shape attributes over those with no shape, and as a consequence we tend to see shape in things when they are not true forms.

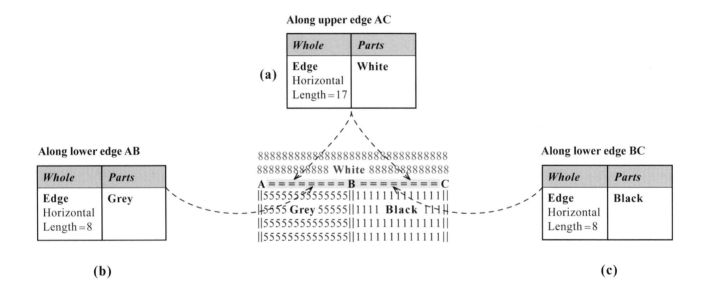

Figure 2.5 A boundary can have two lengths at the same point. The datagram for edge AC shown at the top of the figure gives a length of 17 pixels because it describes the top boundary of the rectangle; the datagrams for edges AB and BC, which share the same pixels as the datagrams for edge AC, both have lengths of 8 pixels because they describe the individual squares that make up the rectangle.

Where does this encoding take place in the brain?
For vision, these processes take place in the primary visual cortex at the back of the brain, the gold region in Figure 2.6a.

You will see from Figure 2.6a that the surface of the cortex looks rather lumpy, with grooves in between the lumps. This is due to the fact that the cortex is constructed of sheets of neurons folded over and over, rather like a multilayered blanket, so that they fit inside the casing of the skull. Unfolded to become flat, these neuron structures would reproduce the image projected on the retina. This *retinotopic image*, as it is usually called, is not, however, an exact projection of the image on the retina. It is distorted so that the central areas are magnified relative to the peripheral areas; nevertheless, areas that are adjacent on the retina remain adjacent in the internal image, and our brains automatically adjust for the distortion.

A cross-section through a folded neuronal sheet is shown in Figure 2.6b. Within the thickness of the folded sheet, the neurons are organised into layers that lie parallel

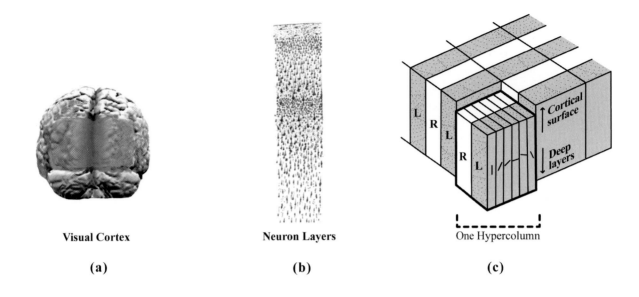

Visual Cortex

(a)

Neuron Layers

(b)

One Hypercolumn

(c)

Figure 2.6 Information structures in the visual cortex. (a) The visual cortex. (b) Neuron layers in the cortex. (c) Hypercolumns (after Palmer, 1999).

to the sheet's surface. There are six of these layers, although only three are shown in Figure 2.6b. Broadly speaking, each layer identifies a different attribute, for example the shape or orientation of an object.

Neurons, as well as being distributed horizontally in these attribute layers, are organised vertically through the sheet into what are called *hypercolumns* (Figure 2.6c). Hypercolumns are in effect the pixels of the internal image, so their geometry reproduces the layout of receptors in the retina. Where an attribute-detecting layer crosses a hypercolumn, it will identify a particular property at that point in the image and store it (in a datagram) in that hypercolumn.

One attribute-detecting layer in the visual cortex that has been well researched identifies edge orientation. This task layer is shown schematically in Figure 2.6c crossing a hypercolumn. The views from the left and right eyes are stored together because slight differences in orientation between the two provide the basis for calculating depth attributes.

Each hypercolumn has all the neural processors it needs to identify the attributes of the region surrounding it. This means that hypercolumns can process information in parallel and can complete a processing cycle in the length of time it takes just one hypercolumn to do so. Again, it is striking how similar these structures are to a computer spreadsheet arranged in three dimensions.

Summary

In this chapter, we defined the structure of the datagram – the mind's only source of information about the world. Datagrams hold attributes that describe the characteristics of the things we are looking at. The attributes in a datagram's *Parts* section describe the common characteristics of the parts that created the datagram, while those in its *Whole* section describe the characteristics of the thing as a whole.

The extent of a thing, the area it occupies in the iconic image, is defined by the extent of its datagrams. In the mind there are no longer any edges; there are only datagrams to tell you where edges are. The region has become a concept, its nature described by its datagrams and not by its physical presence.

3

Binding things into groups and the nature of space

Physical space – the space of physics – is not directly sensible,
but is definable by the relation to sensible spaces.

(Bertrand Russell, *An Inquiry into Meaning and Truth*)

Before we get to the point at which we can build datagrams to describe something as interesting as a cat or a house, we still have a lot more work to do on the basic iconic image we achieved at the end of Chapter 2. All we have managed so far is to identify some simple shapes among the raw numbers produced by our receptors.

Most of the things we are interested in and that make up the world we see are not stand-alone simple shapes, but are groups of shapes that come together to make up something. They are either groups of connected parts, in the way that trees are a collection of branches, or they are collections of separate items such as the keys on a keyboard – or a number of trees in a row at the side of the road. In essence, a group is a collection of different things bound together by something they have in common.

In the last chapter, we explained how datagrams are created in the iconic image to represent uniform regions and to describe their characteristics. We will now show how individual regions are able to come together to form groups whenever they share a common characteristic.

Groups of things that are separate

To illustrate how separate things combine together to make a group, let us look at a row of three black squares set against a white background, as shown in Figure 3.1a. The iconic image for these three squares is shown in Figure 3.1b.

The datagrams in the pixels of the three squares are all the same, as shown in Figure 3.1c; they simply say that this is a black square and nothing else. For instance, they do not tell you that this square is in a row of squares.

(a) Three black squares in a row

(b) The iconic image of the squares

Whole	Parts
Black Square	Black

(c) The datagram in the pixels of the squares

Figure 3.1 The representation of a row of black squares. This figure shows a row of three squares and the datagram that describes each of them. (a) The row of three black squares. (b) The iconic image of the three squares. (c) The datagram held in all the pixels of the iconic image of the three black squares.

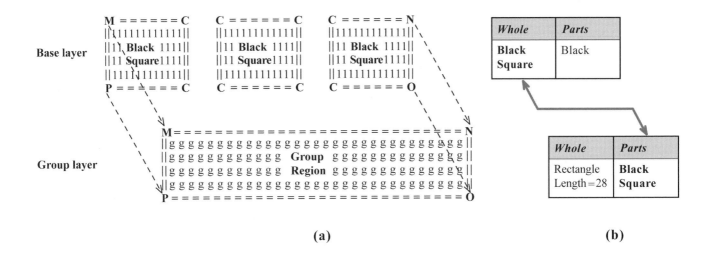

(a) **(b)**

Figure 3.2 Things in groups are represented by a group region in a separate group layer. (a) The row of three black squares in the base layer is shown overlaid by a single rectangular region that represents them as a group. (b) The top datagram shown here is in every pixel of the black squares and the bottom datagram is in every pixel of the group rectangle.

However, these three squares have something in common – they are all square and they are all black – which means that they can come together to form a group thing. The three squares automatically combine to create a group region that has the same area as the row of three squares. This group region is in a group layer that overlays the base layer in iconic memory in which the original image is held (Figure 3.2), and it has its own edges that mark the extent of the group as a whole.

The three squares, and the gaps in between them, have been overlaid by a single rectangular region that represents them as a group; the original image has not been replaced but remains in the base layer of iconic memory unchanged. The datagrams for the black squares are in the base layer, and the group datagrams for the row as a whole are in the group layer (Figure 3.2).

The *Whole* section of each group datagram tells us the overall shape and length of the row – 28 pixels – and its *Parts* section tells us that its components are black squares. The *Whole* sections in the datagrams in every one of the black squares also say they are black squares. *The attributes* **Black** *and* **Square** *are duplicated – as Parts attributes at the group level and as Whole attributes at the component level.* We

call this duplication the *binding*, and it is the universal linkage that ties components together so that they form a group.

So we have created a new region to represent the three squares as a group, but there are no attributes that tell us how the three squares are arranged – that they are in a row separated from each other by gaps 6 pixels long.

Two attributes are needed to describe the internal organisation of groups. The first attribute describes how the parts of the group are arranged, for example whether they are in a row, in a pair or in an array – we call this attribute the group's *distribution* type. The second attribute tells us the length of the gap between the parts that make up the group and is called the *interval*.

The distribution type and interval for our group of black squares are 'in a row' and '6' because the squares are in a row separated by 6 pixels from each other. The distribution type and interval attributes, written as iRow/6 are then inserted then into the *Parts* sections of all the group datagrams. But these distribution type and interval attributes – iRow/6 – *are also inserted into the Whole sections of the datagrams of the component squares,* and as a result every *component* square also has a description of the organisation of the row it is in (Figure 3.3).

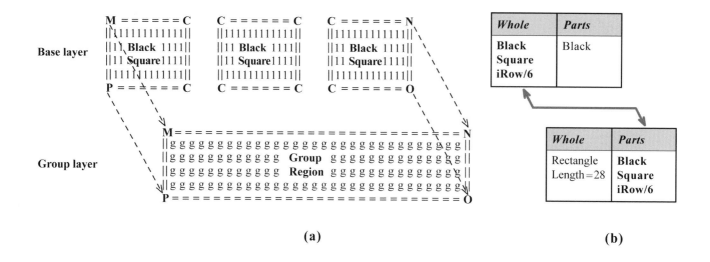

(a)   (b)

Figure 3.3 The attributes that bind things. There are two attributes that tell us the internal structure of a group: the distribution type tells us how the parts of the group are organised, and the interval tells us how far apart they are from each other. (a) In this example, the distribution attributes are distribution type **iRow** and interval **6** because the squares are in a row and they are 6 pixels apart – we show this in datagrams as **iRow/6**. (b) Distribution attributes **iRow/6** are shown duplicated in the group and component datagrams alongside **Black** and **Square** because they also are binding attributes.

The attributes for distribution type and interval, **iRow/6**, have been added to the *Parts* section of the group datagram, and to the *Whole* section of the datagrams of its component squares. The final *binding* attributes –**Black** and **Square** and **iRow/6** – are now the same in the two sets of datagrams. This form of duplication, *binding*, is the fundamental rule that defines groups of any type, not just groups of physical objects.

Because a group's internal distribution, **iRow/6** in this example, is carried by every one of its components, it is not necessary to go to the group level to find out how a group is organised; we can simply go to one of its components. In this example, each of the three black

squares says that it is in a row with other black squares at intervals of 6 pixels from each other.

Groups of things that are connected together

The previous example looked at groups of things that were separated from each other by gaps. But most things, including trees, cats and people, are groups of *connected* parts. Figure 3.4 shows the iconic image of two squares side by side; one is grey and one is black, and they share a common boundary, BE. The grey and black regions in Figure 3.4 are both squares, so they will come together to form a group region with **Square** as the binding attribute.

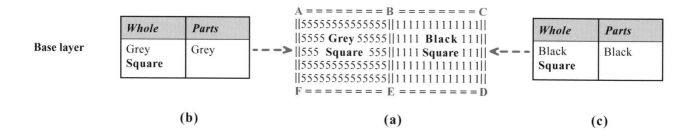

(b)   (a)   (c)

Figure 3.4 Connected things also form groups. The connected grey and black squares can form a group because they have the same shape, they are both square.

As a group, they are a pair of squares, so their *distribution* attribute is **iPair**, but what is the interval between them? When two regions that share a common boundary form a group, we always set an *interval* = 1, which is a gap of 1 pixel, the width of all boundaries. So in this example, the *binding* attributes that tie the two squares together so they form a group are **Square** and **iPair/1** (Figure 3.5).

The group region in the group layer represents the pair of squares as a whole. It is a rectangle, ACDF, and it covers the same area as the two squares. The group datagram's *Parts* section holds the two binding attributes **Square** and **iPair/1** and, as before, these attributes are duplicated in the *Whole* sections of the datagrams for the component grey and black squares in the base layer. The interval is **1** because the squares are separated by a distance of 1 pixel, the width of the edge that separates them.

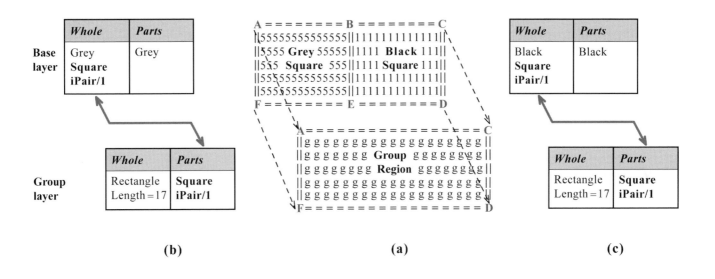

(b)   **(a)**   **(c)**

Figure 3.5 Connected things are separated by an interval of 1 pixel. The two component squares in the base layer combine to form a rectangular region in the group layer. The binding attributes, **Square** and **iPair/1**, are duplicated in component and group datagrams.

The nature of space

To describe space, we need two types of attribute. There are attributes that describe the dimensions of a thing; we call these *dimensional attributes*. Then there are the attributes we have been discussing in this chapter that describe the organisation of things that are in a group, and these are called *distribution attributes*.

Dimensional attributes in datagrams describe an object's internal geometry, for example a square's width and area. They include attributes that describe the three-dimensional nature of objects, in particular depth and volume. Dimensional attributes do not tell you anything about what lies outside an object's boundary; they only describe it internally.

Distribution attributes, on the other hand, only tell you the relationship that an object has with other similar objects in the space surrounding it. There are only two attributes available for describing the space around something – distribution type and interval.

There are many distribution types in addition to the two we have already mentioned – row and pair. Others include arrays in three dimensions; for example, a three-dimensional array would be used to describe a square stack of bricks, and a fan distribution to describe objects converging at a point, like spokes in a wheel or pins in a pin cushion.

Every datagram must hold a pair of distribution/interval attributes in its Whole section that describe the group organisation of which it is a part. But what if a thing exists on its own, if it is not part of a group? We assign the *distribution* 'Unit' to things on their own, and we assign the *interval* 'infinite' to them because nothing similar exists to mark where the interval ends. For example, Elizabeth II is the only living Queen of England; in that role, she is in a unit distribution, Unit, with an infinite interval.

It should be noted that we have not yet described the distribution attributes that bind together the pixels of the original regions of uniform intensity that we started with. What, for example, are the distribution/interval attributes that bind together the black pixels of our black squares so they come together to form a group, a square? In Figures 3.1–3.3, we have shown the *Parts* attributes of the black squares as simply Black. The full binding attributes in the *Parts* section of the black squares should be Black and iArray/0 because all the squares' parts (pixels) are black, and they are in a two-dimensional array with no gaps, or intervals, in between them.

The distribution attributes in the components of a row, iRow/6 for example, describe the internal structure of the row they are in but they do not tell you anything about the group, the row as a whole. What then is the attribute that tells you that a row, as a whole, is a row? Whenever you focus your attention on the distribution attribute iRow in the component of a row, this will match the iRow class code in your long-term memory, and as a result the attribute code for Row (not iRow) will be transferred into the *Whole* sections of all the datagrams in the *group* region of the row. The attribute Row in the group datagrams tells you that this thing is a row, but it does *not* tell you how the row is organised internally; to find that out you must go to the attributes iRow/6 in a datagram in one of the row's components.

Summary

In this chapter, we have shown how things, when they share a common characteristic, come together to form groups. The combining of things into a group produces a group region in a group layer that overlays its components. Group regions have datagrams to describe them, just as their components do. The duplication of attributes between the group and component layers is the binding that ties things together into groups.

The attributes in datagrams that describe space come in two forms: *dimensional attributes*, which describe the internal geometry of things, and *distribution attributes*, which describe the positions of things in relation to similar things around them. There are just two distribution attributes: the *distribution type*, which describes the organisation of components in a group, iRow for example; and the *interval*, which describes the distance between components – this is normally an average, for example 6. Together they are expressed as iRow/6.

The interval between two things is not itself a thing, it is an attribute of the things on either side of the gap. To find out the exact nature of a gap between two things, the gap must cease to be a gap and become a thing, in which case the things on either side cease to be things and become gaps.

In the Introduction, we made it absolutely clear that there are just two types of entity – there are *things* and there are *attributes*; there is nothing else. Distribution space, which describes the nature of the space that surrounds things, is an attribute of things, *not a thing itself*. So space *is not a thing*; there is no medium called *space* in which all things lie.

The grouping rules we describe here are universal in the sense that they apply to the creation of groups of any type. They facilitate how we create anything new – trees from branches, melodies from notes and new ideas from old.

Here we have somewhat simplified how things bind into groups in order to give a clearer account, but no fundamental principles have been excluded from the main narrative. A brief comment is provided in the explanatory Notes for this chapter, with particular reference to Anne Treisman's feature integration theory, and the subject is dealt with more fully in Chapters 7 and 10.

4
Minds, brains and rules

If the doors of perception were cleansed every thing would appear to man as it is, Infinite.

(William Blake, *The Marriage of Heaven and Hell*)

So far, we have looked at the way information is organised from two points of view, first as a sequence of computations, and second as processes taking place in the brain. The biology of our brains is reasonably well understood through research and our knowledge of the laws of chemistry and ultimately physics. Our minds and our day-to-day experiences depend on the operation of the brain, yet the nature of these experiences has a quality that is somehow unlike the biological processes involved.

We are proposing that there are two distinct entities here: biological processes that are governed by the laws of physics and chemistry, and information processes governed by a separate set of rules that underpin how information is structured and manipulated. It is only when these two processes fuse together, each operating under its own set of rules, that our minds come into being and we can actively experience the world.

The rules of the mind are abstract and universal in the same way that the laws of physics are abstract and universal. Let's explain. When you are typing an email, the nerves and muscles in your hands exert forces to move the bones in your fingers, which then hit the keys. The branch of physics called mechanics determines the amount and direction of the forces you apply. But the laws of mechanics are abstract; they cannot themselves press the keys without a physical hand to transmit the force.

The same principle applies to the rules of geometry. The rule for a circle is: the length of the circumference = the constant π × the circle's diameter. But the rule for a circle is not a circle itself. A circle is something made from physical stuff: it is made from the pencil lead on a piece of paper, or the rubber on the outside of a car tyre. Physical stuff becomes a circle when it obeys the rule for a circle and as a consequence the length of its circumference is equal to the length of its diameter times π.

Similarly information in the mind is abstract: a square in your mind is not a square, it is an electrochemical code that represents a square. To see a square, you must select a datagram in your mind holding the attribute code for a square and let it direct you to a physical square in the internal image, a part of your brain that is outside your mind.

The rules of the mind do not tell us how things should be physically represented or organised provided that the form of representation is adequate in terms of the demands the rules make. The way a computation is carried out by instructions in the neurons of brain is also irrelevant provided it delivers what the rules require.

There is no universal rule that says the physical sensation delivered for a particular attribute code has to be supplied by a particular release of chemicals. The only rule is that, within any one mind, every attribute code must be unique and must deliver a single unique physical sensation.

Similarly, there are no rules to say that we must be able to identify any particular property, for example that something is square or triangular. Bees cannot distinguish a square from a triangle, but they can find their way around, learn from other bees and remember things. Even though their brains are tiny, they appear to have minds of some sort. The rules of the mind are general, and there are no rules that are specific to any one sense; they all apply equally to, for example, vision, sound and taste.

So what are these rules? There appear to be around 20 rules governing the way information is processed in the mind, and we will introduce them progressively as we go through the book. The five that we have introduced so far are:

1. There are only things.

2. Things have attributes that describe them.

3. We can only identify those things that are made from components all of which have something in common.

4. The mind holds all information in a standard structure that we call here a datagram – there is no other form of representation.

5. When things combine into groups, the sharing of attributes between parent and component provides the binding that holds them together.

It is also a general rule that every datagram in a mind must have the capacity to communicate with every other datagram in that mind in a way that allows all the rules to be implemented. But, as we have already said, there is nothing to tell us how the information transmitted between datagrams should be structured.

The rules of the mind assume that they are implemented in a perfect physical system, whereas in fact we implement these rules rather poorly and as a result we have imperfect minds. So because our brains are not perfect, we have developed supporting procedures that organise the sense data we receive into a form that the rules of the mind will accept. For example, the rules assume that our eyes continuously transmit images into iconic memory. But we blink or make eye movements two or three times a second, and every time we do so the information pathways from our eyes to our visual cortex are shut down. To deal with this, we have procedures that create information and insert it into the breaks so that the transmission appears to be unbroken.

Datagrams are the only source of experience
Before moving on, let us re-emphasise the point that datagrams, implemented in our brains, are the only way in which anything can be described and therefore ultimately experienced. Each attribute value in a datagram is linked to a single unique sensation, so if a region is identified as a square, the unique attribute code for Square will be put into all its datagrams. If your attention goes to any one of

the datagrams in the square, you will experience the single unique physical sensation, outside the mind, of this being a square.

It is easy enough to understand how datagrams might represent simple things such as squares and rectangles, but how for instance might they represent something as complex as a cat? If you look at a black cat, it will project a set of connected black shapes into your internal image, and they will be overlaid in your iconic memory with datagrams describing its structure. You will then link these datagrams together and search your long-term memory to see if together they match the standard description of something. In this instance, they match the description of a cat, so a unique Cat attribute code will be automatically transferred from your long-term memory, as an attribute, *into the datagram in every pixel of the black cat region –* as shown in Figure 4.1.

Every pixel in the cat's image holds a datagram (Figure 4.1a) that describes it as black and as a cat. If you select any one of these datagrams, you will, as well as having the experience that you are looking at a black thing, get the unique sensation from the cat's attribute code **Cat** that you are looking at a thing that is a cat.

If you wished to find out more about the cat, you could go to a pixel in the curly shape at one end of the cat and find an additional datagram (Figure 4.1b) that will have an attribute code **Tail** extracted from long-term memory,

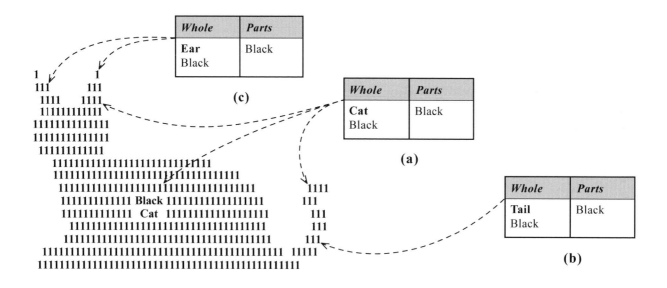

Figure 4.1 A black cat in the iconic image. When we recognise something in long-term memory, a unique attribute code is downloaded into its group datagrams and produces the unique sensation of what it is; in this example, it is a cat. (a) The group datagram with the attribute code for Cat from long-term memory. (b) The component datagram for the cat's tail. (c) The component datagram for the cat's ears.

and this will give you the unique sensation that this is a tail. You might then go to one of the triangular shapes on the top of its head and find a datagram (Figure 4.1c) with an attribute code **Ear**, giving you the sensation that this is an ear. If the cat's actions match the actions stored in your long-term memory of things that are friendly, a friendly attribute code giving you the sensation of friendly things will be inserted in all of the cat datagrams. This is now a friendly black cat. Datagrams for the cat as a whole are in *every* pixel of the cat image, including its tail, while the datagrams for its tail are only in the 'tail' part of the image.

It is possible that the attribute code you use for a cat is not the same as the one used by the person standing next to you, and that therefore the sensation you feel when you see a cat might not be exactly the same as the one that they feel. This does not matter: provided the sensations you feel always arise from the same data, they will always refer to the same thing.

We will see later that there are in fact three types of attribute. There are attribute codes that tell you *what a thing is*, there are sense attribute codes that tell *you what a thing looks like*, and there are other sense attribute codes that tell you the *precise positions* of things.

Attribute code numbers are class symbols as well as deliverers of sensations. In a datagram in the iconic image, the attribute code number for a cat is linked to the sensation that this is a cat; in long-term memory, *the same code number* is a class code for the class of all cats. The same applies to sense attributes. The attribute code number for the exact green of a particular leaf gives you the experience of that colour; in long-term memory, the same code number is a class code, a symbol, for all the things in the world that are coloured that exact shade of green.

We often say in this book that such and such an attribute code 'delivers' such and such a sensation, but of course it is not the attribute code itself that we experience. The sensations we experience are produced by physical states in the brain outside the mind. If, for example, you go to a datagram in a black cat in the *iconic* image, what you actually see is the captured blackness in the cat's *physical* internal image in the visual cortex; similarly, the Cat attribute code from long-term memory in the same datagram will deliver a 'this is a cat' sensation not in the mind, but in the cat's *physical* internal image that is outside the mind. It is the physical biology of our brains that makes us aware – but only when instructed to do so by information in our minds.

So how do we bridge the gap between this abstract world of information and the physical world we are familiar with? Later in the book, we discuss the special nature of information and suggest an interface connecting representations in the mind with their physical equivalents in the brain. But before we consider how our attention might be translated into responses in the physical world, we must first understand how the mind organises and evaluates the information in its abstract world.

Summary

Our experience of the world arises from the merging of two processes, one biological, the other information based; each operates within its own set of rules. Datagrams and the rules of the mind define how information is organised logically, while the structure and biology of our brains determine how we implement the rules physically. But our biology limits our ability to fully implement the rules, so our minds are imperfect; we have, however, evolved procedures that, to an extent, compensate for these limitations.

In the information world of the mind, there are no longer any physical edges; there are only datagrams that tell you where edges are. The extent of the thing you see is simply the extent of its datagrams. There are no colours or shadows, no artefacts; nothing physical persists from the outside; all these have been replaced by code numbers. Nothing remains, only pure information.

5

The singular nature of attention

The shuttle began to weave a carpet more beautiful than anyone had ever beheld.
Roses and lilies blossomed…

(Spindle, Shuttle, and Needle; *The Complete Fairy Tales,* translated by J. Zipes)

When a clam's eyes, which are just inside its shell, pick up a shadow passing overhead, they automatically activate a siphon that jets it away from possible danger. The clam does not think, 'Is that a squid or a bird, no it's a whale and whales don't eat clams so I will stay where I am because the food is good here.' It just reacts to the shadow. But we respond differently, using the raw information we receive from our senses to make judgements before we react. We need the ability to turn complicated arrangements of regions and edges into things we can identify separately as squid, birds and whales.

One way to do this is to list every possible combination of all the elements in a scene and then match every possible result against every description in long-term memory of what things look like. The problem with this approach is that you could be eaten by a tiger before completing the calculations needed to recognise it. The sheer volume of processing required is far beyond the capacity of modern computers, let alone our relatively slow brains. And quite apart from the number of elements that need to be processed, the attributes of an object can change as our viewpoint changes.

The alternative approach is to rely on an 'attention stream' that selects only those elements in a scene that are likely to build into something significant. An attention stream does this by going from one image element (datagram) to another until it has constructed something that matches a description stored in long-term memory.

For example, to identify a daisy as a daisy, you would transfer your attention to a datagram of one of its petals in the iconic image and record its shape and colour. You would then follow this with visits to datagrams in (say) two other petals to establish that the petals are in a fan distribution. Finally, you would transfer your attention to a datagram at the centre of the flower and record that its centre is circular and yellow. This information should be sufficient to give you a match to the description of a daisy

Figure 5.1 Eye movements reflect attention transfers between datagrams. The tracks on the left reflect eye movements recorded while scanning the face of the young girl on the right. Eye movements *follow* the attention movements taking place in the iconic image to ensure that our region of interest stays within the high-definition area at the centre of the retina. (From Yarbus, 1965.)

in your long-term memory. In carrying out this task, you would have visited something like 10 datagrams, each of which will have taken you around 50 milliseconds (a 20th of a second) to process.

No physical movements take place during the attention transfer from one datagram to the next. Attention transfers across the iconic image of the flower are realised entirely by electrical transmissions between neurons in the brain. You make eye movements (called saccades) as a consequence of these attention transfers, but this is simply to make sure that what is being attended stays in the high-definition area at the centre of your retina. Typically, you make around 20 attention transfers a second, but only three eye movements a second. Eye movements, therefore, reflect the path that attention takes in the internal image and provide a valuable insight into how attention is sequenced internally. Figure 5.1 shows the tracks made by a person's eye when scanning the face of a young girl. These eye movements reflect attention transfers within the visual cortex.

Priorities in attention-sequencing

Your attention transfers to a single datagram and processes it, then transfers to another datagram and processes it and so on. The path that attention takes is driven by *priority values placed in every datagram in the image*. Your attention will *always* go to the single datagram with the highest priority. Priorities are reset across your entire iconic memory before each and every attention transfer.

To demonstrate how this works, let us assume that the black square in Figure 5.2 has the highest priority in the image of the overall scene you are looking at. The datagrams in this diagram show the situation *just before* your attention transfer to the black square takes place. A *Priority* section has now been added to all the datagrams in the pixels of the image, which includes those in the black square. The higher the priority value in a datagram, the more likely it is that your attention will go to it – but remember that your attention will select only one datagram out of the millions available in the image.

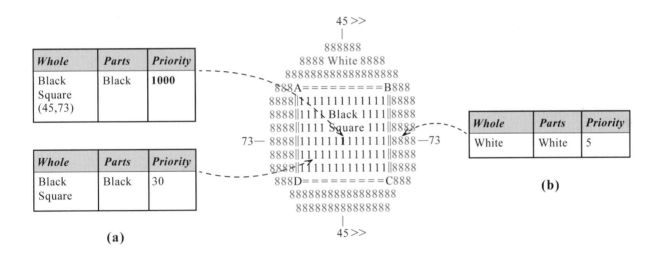

Figure 5.2 Priorities in datagrams control how your attention moves around the iconic image. Before every attention movement, priority values are inserted into every datagram in the image to indicate the path your attention should take. This figure shows the datagrams in the square just before your attention transfers to it.

The top datagram on the left of Figure 5.2, which has a priority of **1000**, is held in the pixel at the centre of the square. The datagram below it is in a different pixel of the black square, its priority being 30. The datagram on the right relates to a pixel in the surrounding white area and has a low priority – just 5.

So why do datagrams in different pixels of the same square have different priority values when the priority is simply to go to the square? Why should it matter which datagram in the square you go to when all the datagrams in the square are identical?

It's all about position. When you select something to attend, you need to know its position in the image because ultimately that tells you where it is in the overall scene you are looking at. The problem is that you can only record the position of a thing as being at a point, at a particular pixel in the iconic image – that is how our internal coordinate system works. But what point in a shape can we use to determine its position? What point in the letter W, for example, denotes its position, where it is?

It is impossible to create an algorithm that will select a consistent point in any shape that can be used to represent its position in relation to everything else, so we resolve this problem by adopting the rule that *the pixel that determines a thing's position is the pixel that you are attending*. In Figure 5.2, the datagram you are attending is in a pixel at the centre of the square. The coordinates of this pixel in the overall image are (column 45, row 73), so

those coordinates define the position of the square as a whole within the image. Datagrams in the central pixels of figures normally receive the highest priority so that changes in position can easily be identified.

We will now look at the black square just *after* your attention has gone to the datagram in the central pixel (45,73), the one with a priority of **1000**. You will see from Figure 5.3 that a *Status* section has been added to all the datagrams – the indicator in the *Status* section tells you how this datagram stands in relation to attention The datagram at the top left of Figure 5.3 is the attended datagram in the central pixel (45,73) of the square, so it is given a unique **A**-status. Only one datagram in the entire image is attended at a time, so only one datagram in the entire image ever has this unique **A**-status. The **A**-status says that this is the attended datagram and that it is currently being processed.

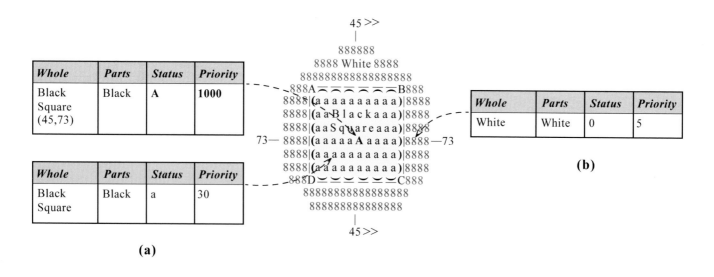

Figure 5.3 The attended black square. *A Status* section has been added to every datagram to indicate how they all stand in relation to attention. The datagram at (45,73) with **A**-status is the only datagram in the image that is being attended; all other datagrams in the black square are given a-status because they are all part of the attended extent. The datagram on the right has 0-status because it is not attended. The pink area denotes the attended region.

The datagram at the bottom left of Figure 5.3 has a-status, as do all the other datagrams in the black square. The a-status tells you that this pixel is part of the extent of the thing that is being attended at **A**, and therefore its datagrams have the same attributes as the attended datagram. When you attend a datagram, you become aware of the full extent of the attended region, so by attending datagram **A** in Figure 5.3, you immediately become aware of the whole of the black square. The

datagram on the right of the figure is in the pixels of the surrounding white region; it is not being attended so it has 0-status in relation to attention. Indeed, the vast majority of datagrams in the iconic image will have 0-status.

All along boundary ABCD of the black square in Figure 5.3 there are two edge datagrams in every pixel. The edge datagrams on the *inside* of ABCD belong to the extent of the attended black square, but instead of being marked with an a-status, they are marked by inward-facing brackets – on edge AD, for example, they are marked by '('. The outward-facing edges along AD belong to the white region; they are marked '|' as they are not part of an attended region so have 0-status. Figure 5.4 shows both of these statuses in the edge datagrams along edge AD.

The edge datagram on the left in Figure 5.4a belongs to the white region that is not being attended, so it has 0-status. The black edge datagram on the right in Figure 5.4b is part of the extent of the attended black square, so it is given an attended ((-status which points to the right, into the black square.

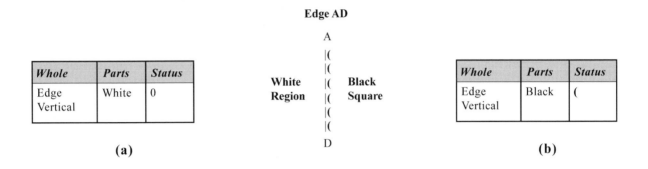

Figure 5.4 This figure shows the status of edge datagrams along edge AD, the left-hand boundary of the black square. (a) Datagrams along edge AD that belong to the surrounding white region; these all have unattended 0-status. (b) Datagrams along edge AD that belong to the black square; these all have attended **(**-status.

Let us now suppose that you have finished processing all the information for the black square. Where do you go to next?

Your attention is still at the centre of the black square, A, but new datagram priorities have been calculated for the next attention transfer. The priorities in the black

square datagrams, on the left of Figure 5.5 have been set to 0 because you have finished processing the black square. The datagram A2, shown on the right of the Figure 5.5, now has a priority of **500** because it would be interesting to know something about the surrounding white region.

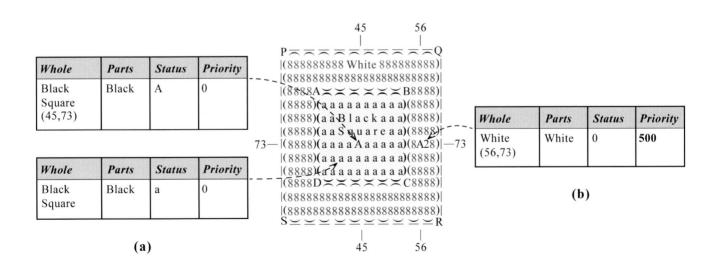

Figure 5.5 Statuses and priority values just before the next attention transfer. (a) These are the datagrams in the black square that have been processed by attention and are therefore no longer a priority. (b) This is a datagram in the surrounding white region that has been given a high priority, **500**, for your attention.

But there is another way of looking at these figures: instead of looking at the white region as a ring around the black square, you could see it as part of a white square that lies *behind* the black square (Figure 5.6). In this case, the white region no longer surrounds the black square, but has been extended *underneath* it to become a complete white square behind the black square; it is in a layer behind it.

The pixels of the white square are now populated with datagrams describing it, and these are allocated priorities for attention in the normal way. The datagram at **A3**, the centre of the white square, has been allocated a priority of **1000** in the datagram shown on the right of Figure 5.6. Because this is 500 more than the priority for the alternative configuration shown in Figure 5.5, your attention has transferred to the centre of the white square

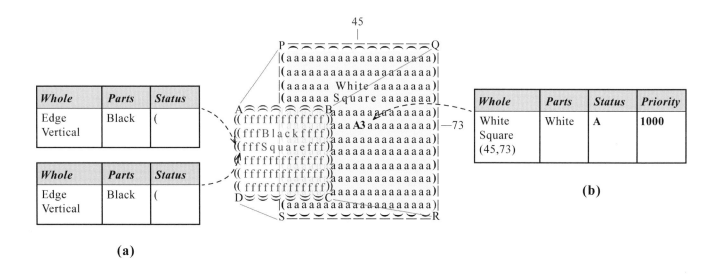

Whole	Parts	Status
Edge Vertical	Black	(

Whole	Parts	Status
Edge Vertical	Black	(

(a)

Whole	Parts	Status	Priority
White Square (45,73)	White	A	1000

(b)

Figure 5.6 The black and white regions have become two squares, one in front of the other, because the edge pairs along ABCD are all turned inwards. (a) The two edge datagrams sharing edge pixels along ABCD have the same inward status ((so they belong to the black square; this allows the white region PQRS to pass underneath and become a white square. (b) This datagram is in the central pixel, **A3**, of the white square. This is being attended because it has the highest priority in the image, **1000**.

at **A3**. This newly attended datagram in **A3** has been given A-status, while all the other datagrams in the white square have been given a-status. The datagrams in the black square will change from a-status to f-status because attention has finished processing the square.

In Figure 5.6, you can see that the boundary of the in-front black square ABCD is marked with pairs of brackets that all face inwards into the black square: for example, the brackets along AD are all ((. The two edge datagrams in each pixel carrying these statuses are shown on the left of Figure 5.6. What has happened here is that the statuses of the outward-facing datagrams on AD belonging to the white region have turned inwards, and as a consequence they no longer belong to the white region; instead both edges now

belong to the 'in-front' black square. It is because there are no 'white' edge datagrams along the boundary ABCD that the white region has been able to pass underneath the black square and form a white square behind it.

What this example shows is that we automatically bring alternative ways of looking at the same data into the process of setting priorities. These alternative configurations are held in separate alternative image layers, and once a particular configuration has been selected, the image layers of the rejected structures are dispensed with. So, in this example, datagrams for the white region that surrounded the black square in Figure 5.5 disappear once you have chosen the white square option.

Edge statuses control how shapes are configured

The boundaries around figures will have one of five edge-pair settings:

|| figure ||	|(figure)|	)(figure)(	((figure))	)) figure ((
(1)	(2)	(3)	(4)	(5)
unattended	on its own	side by side	in front	behind

Each of these gives us a different way of looking at the same thing. Below we show how these five settings, when applied along boundary edge ABCD of the black square, give five different interpretations of the relationship between the black square and the white region.

(1) || White region || Black square || White region ||

In sequence (1), none of the regions is attended, so there is no relationship between them. This is the interpretation showed in Figure 5.2.

(2) || White region |(Black square)| White region ||

In sequence (2), the black square is seen as simply being on its own. The inside black edges of ABCD are facing into the square, but the outside edge sharing the same pixel is uncommitted so there is no relationship between the black square and the white region. This is the interpretation in Figure 5.3.

(3) |(White surround)(Black square)(White surround)|

In sequence (3), the black square is seen as connected to a surrounding white region. The edges of the two regions have the same boundary ABCD, and the reason they are connected is because the edge datagrams of the two regions share the same pixels. This is the interpretation shown in Figure 5.5

(4) |(White square ((Black square)) White square)|

In sequence (4), the black square is in front of the white square. The black square has captured both edges along ABCD, the white region cannot now terminate along ABCD and so it passes underneath and forms white square PQRS. The ((bracketed)) structure is always the in-front one. This is the interpretation shown in Figure 5.6.

(5) ((White surround)) Black hole ((White surround))

In sequence (5), the boundary ABCD indicates a hole in the white region through which you can see a black surface of unknown extent behind it. All the edge pairs along ABCD have been captured by the white region so the black square cannot form; it has no edges. The white surround becomes the in-front region.

At every attention step, you produce all five possible configurations for prioritisation. In almost all cases, there is only one dominant configuration, so we are unaware that we have created and prioritised the alternatives. However, certain configurations can produce two or more plausible outcomes.

(a) Rubin vase

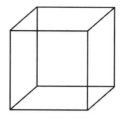

(b) Necker cube

Figure 5.7 The effect of edge statuses on how we see things. (a) The Rubin vase, and (b)The Necker Cube.

The two illusory figures in Figure 5.7 are probably familiar to most people. The image in Figure 5.7a, the Rubin vase illusion, switches from being a white vase to two black faces; with Figure 5.7b, the Necker cube, you see a cube switch the direction it faces depending on which square in the picture you look at. In both cases, the switching is caused by changes in the statuses of their edges in the iconic image. To explain this, we will start with the Rubin vase in Figure 5.7a.

Unattended, the edge pairs separating the black and white shapes will be uncommitted, as shown below:

(1) || Black region || White region || Black region ||

At first your attention goes to the white region, the vase, because its symmetrical shape gives it the top priority in the image. This attention movement produces edge statuses that turn the boundary of the vase inwards, so the unattended || White region || above becomes the attended |(Vase)| below. The result is that the first thing you see is a vase on its own:

(2) || Black region |(Vase)| Black region ||

After processing the vase on its own, the black region surrounding it becomes the priority. However, there are three alternative ways of seeing this depending on how the edges are configured.

(3) |(Black face)(Vase)(Black face)|

In the connected sequence shown above the black faces are connected, attached, to the white vase in one continuous surface. This is an almost impossible scenario in three dimensions, so it is given a very low priority.

(4) |(Black square ((Vase)) Black square)|

In alternative (4), both edges surrounding the white vase have turned inwards into the vase, they both become white, and this allows the black region to pass under the vase and form a square. The black region becomes a square with a white vase in front of it.

(5) ((Black face)) White hole ((Black face))

In the final alternative, (5), both edges surrounding the white vase have turned outwards. They have both become black, and this creates a black region with two black faces. A white region is seen behind the faces through the hole in the black region, and this is usually seen as part of the sheet of paper on which the figure is drawn. This alternative will normally have the highest priority because faces have particular significance for us.

The Necker cube is drawn in such a way that both ends of the cube, the two squares, are visible. The alignment of the cube changes depending on which of these squares you look at; this is because when there is ambiguity, the surface you attend usually becomes the in-front one. Both squares in the Necker cube will have inward-facing edges – ((Square)) – and initially they will have similar priorities. You choose one of the squares and see the view it produces, but your attention soon tires of this view and moves to the other square, which now has a higher priority; you are then presented with a different version of the same figure.

The black squares we have used as examples in the book have all been surrounded by single continuous edges 1 pixel wide, but the boundaries of the squares in the Necker cube are made from lines, not single edges. Although we tend to think of lines as edges, they are not:

lines are continuous regions with two edges, one on either side, like a ring enclosing the figure. So how is it possible for lines to define shapes in much the same way that edges do? Figure 5.8 shows how the edge statuses in a line surrounding a white rectangle produce an overall rectangular-shaped figure in the iconic image.

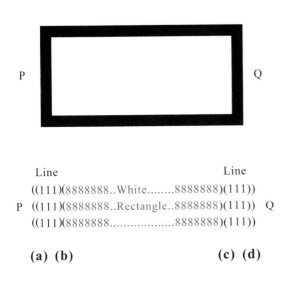

Line   Line
((111)(8888888..White........8888888)(111))
P ((111)(8888888..Rectangle..8888888)(111)) Q
((111)(8888888.................8888888)(111))

(a) (b)   **(c) (d)**

Figure 5.8 How we create shapes from line drawings. The figure shows how edge statuses are able to create whole figure shapes from line drawings. The edge pairs in the vertical parts of the surrounding black boundary are marked with the letters a b and c d. The enclosing black edge datagrams on the *outside* of the black lines (....) produce the rectangular figure as a whole.

Edge statuses in the datagrams in the enclosing black line create an overall rectangular figure as follows:

- The inside-facing black edges at a and b (111) combine to create a black line.

- The inside-facing black edges at c and d (111) combine to create a black line.

- The inside-facing white edges at b and c (88 ... 88) combine to create the inside white rectangle.

- The remaining outside black edge at a and the remaining outside black edge at d combine to create a rectangle whose boundary is the outside edge of the surrounding black line.

The rectangle created by the outside edges of the black line produces a group region that has the white rectangle

and the black ring as its components. The outside black edges at a and d are able to create this overall figure because their vectors pass 'under' the intervening edges, either because those edges have already combined with each other or because they are white.

Why attention is the way it is

Why do living creatures need the processing ability we call attention? The answer, of course, is that they don't. Many creatures operate successfully within their environment without the brain circuits we need for attention. Their long-term memories directly match simple shapes in the iconic image and respond to them with action sequences. Their brains are 'mechanical' systems. As pointed out earlier, clams respond to shadows to remove themselves from danger; it is not suggested that they achieve this using the neural circuits necessary for attention.

Indeed, most of the things that we do are performed unattended: breathing, balancing on a bicycle and avoiding falling over furniture to name but a few – we cover this in Chapter 16. The survival of higher animals, however, ultimately depends on identifying and selectively responding to complex objects, and, given our biological limitations, it is attention that gives us the ability to understand things that are more than just elementary forms.

Why can't two or more attention streams run alongside each other? The reason for this is that priorities can only be set properly if every possible piece of information is presented to a single selection process within a single workspace. If some data have already been captured by another attention stream, they are no longer available and priorities cannot be reliably set. You could of course remove the conflict between two attention streams by simply giving each attention stream its own separate iconic memory, but then they would be separate minds. This is not inconceivable (split brains), but cooperation would be necessary to avoid conflict.

Why, within our single attention stream, can we attend only one thing at a time? To answer this, we need to go back to the definition that things can form datagrams only from parts that have something in common. If we look at two things together and they have something in common, they will create a group datagram to represent themselves together – which is in fact just one thing! If two things do not have anything in common, they cannot form a group datagram and therefore cannot be experienced together; they have to be attended separately.

Why do we attend just one datagram of a thing rather than all its datagrams? Why do we attend just one datagram, which we mark **A**, in the things we attend? Why not attend all a-markers as a group and do away with the **A**-status? We gave the reason for this earlier in the chapter – that the position of a thing has to be registered at a single point in the image, and the point we use to register a thing's position is that of the datagram we are attending. In the case of symmetrical things, like squares, their geometric centres have the highest priority, and therefore we normally use central positions to consistently register their locations. For this reason, most everyday objects are designed to be symmetrical so we can then locate them easily and explain to others where they are.

By attending a datagram, we gain access to its attributes. When we attended the central datagram in the black square, the act of giving it A-status triggered its attribute codes to deliver the sensations that this was a black square; at the same time, we also became aware of the extent of the square's a-status datagrams. So by attending a single datagram in the iconic image, not only do we find out what a thing is, but we also become aware of how far it extends across the image.

How are priorities set? Impersonal priority-setting algorithms ensure that attention makes consistent choices. Many of these fall under the general heading of gestalt psychology; they are a mixture of the rules themselves and the algorithms our brains adopt to implement the rules. But it is our long-term memories that play the dominant role directing attention to find likely matches for the current data and to follow desirable outcomes that improve our personal well-being. In Chapter 17, we discuss in some detail how our personal and impersonal priorities are set.

The status codes that are switched on and off in the *Status* sections of datagrams play an important part in attention-sequencing. We have already mentioned status codes, for example those that mark datagrams as attended A, as part of the attended extent, a, or to show different boundary settings,) or (, but there are many more. For example, if a datagram were a component of an attended parent datagram, it would have a c-status, and if a datagram elsewhere in the image had an attribute that was the same as one in the attended datagram, it could be given primed status – p-status.

Summary

Our attention moves from one datagram to another in the iconic image, processing one thing at a time. This is the method we employ to assemble the parts of things that are complex. The path that attention takes is set by priority values inserted into every datagram.

Datagrams hold statuses to indicate relationships. Datagrams that have not been attended have no status. The statuses – brackets – in edge datagrams describe the relationship that a thing has with its neighbours.

Priorities are inserted into every datagram in the image before the next attention move is made. Priority values are also assigned to datagrams in regions created from alternative edge settings.

6

Deconstructing objects to find out what they are

A picture has logico-pictorial form in common with what it depicts.

(Ludwig Wittgenstein, *Tractatus Logico-Philosophicus, §2.2*)

The things we see often, or that hold a particular significance for us, are catalogued in our long-term memory and given unique class code numbers. If we identify the class code number of something in long-term memory, that class code number is transferred from long-term memory into that something's datagrams in the iconic image as an attribute code, and if we attend that attribute code we experience the sensation of what the thing is – a cat, for example.

The attribute code number in a datagram in the iconic image is the same as its class code number in long-term memory. So why do we give the same number different names? This is because they have different roles. In long-term memory, the number represents a class – the class of all things that are cats, or the class of all things that are a particular shade of green, for example. In iconic memory, however, when attended in a datagram, the same number is an attribute linked to a unique sensation, the unique sensation for a cat or the unique sensation for that particular shade of green.

We identify an object's class code number by using our attention to match its attributes to the class code numbers in long-term memory that select for its identity. It is perhaps easy to understand how this works for simple shapes, squares and triangles for example, but most of the things we see do not have a simple overall shape; instead they are constructed from a variety of parts connected together in a particular way to make a whole. For example, if you look at your hand, you cannot tell immediately that it is a hand because it has no overall shape. It is only when you identify the parts from which it is constructed – fingers, thumb and palm – and see how they are arranged that you are able to tell it is a hand.

In this chapter, we explain how we generate attributes to describe the spatial organisation of components that group together to form objects. (Please note that we are using the word *object* for all physical things that are made from connected parts.) We are talking here about spatial descriptions such as above/below, or in front/behind or left/right.

Take the capital letter **T**, for example. This can be drawn as a horizontal rectangle above a vertical rectangle.

To recognise something as a **T**, it is not enough to know that that it comprises a horizontal rectangle and a vertical rectangle, because these could be arranged in a number of different ways. We need to have an attribute in the horizontal rectangle that says it lies above, and an attribute in the lower rectangle that says it is below. Long-term memory can only match the class code number for a **T** when these structural attributes are coded into the component datagrams of the **T** in the iconic image.

There are two stages to processing an object made from connected parts. In the first stage, its image is copied from the base layer of the iconic image into a segment layer where it is broken down into its component parts. In the second stage, our attention moves around the datagrams in both of these images, and by doing so it generates attributes that fix the relative positions of the object's components.

The black letter **T** produces an image of its shape in the base layer of your visual iconic memory (Figure 6.1a). The datagrams in the iconic image of the **T** in the base layer in Figure 6.1a have no shape attributes because overall the **T** has no recognisable shape – it is just black. To find out what the object is, you must look at its component parts.

In Figure 6.1b, you can see that the object outline in the base layer has been copied into a segment layer that lies underneath the base layer; these two images (a) and (b) have the same coordinates even though they are in different layers. The segment layer partitions the duplicate image into simple convex shapes. In this example, an internal edge has been inserted that splits the overall shape into two components: one rectangle above another. The top rectangle is horizontal, and the bottom one is vertical. The datagrams of these two component rectangles are shown on the right-hand side of Figure 6.1b. The base and segment figures share the same pixel locations because, although they are in different layers, one is directly above the other.

The datagrams in Figure 6.1b describe the two rectangles – the top one as horizontal, and the bottom one as vertical. We can see that the horizontal one is above the vertical

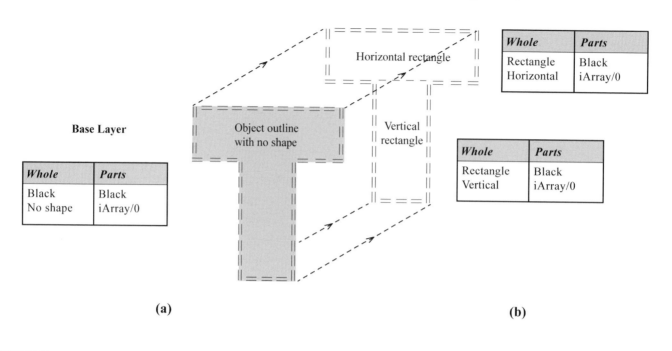

Segment Layer

Base Layer

Whole	*Parts*
Black No shape	Black iArray/0

Whole	*Parts*
Rectangle Horizontal	Black iArray/0

Whole	*Parts*
Rectangle Vertical	Black iArray/0

Horizontal rectangle

Object outline
with no shape

Vertical
rectangle

(a)

(b)

Figure 6.1 The iconic image of a black letter T segmented into its component parts. (a) The iconic image of the **T** in the base layer of iconic memory and the datagram that describes the **T** as a whole. (b) The duplicate image of the **T** in the segment layer where it is divided into its rectangular component segments. The two datagrams describe separately the two rectangles in the segmented **T**.

one, but long-term memory cannot 'see' things; it only understands attributes. For that reason, the positions of the two rectangles must be made explicit by their attributes. To achieve this, your attention goes through a strict sequence of moves that involves datagrams in both the overall group image in the base layer and its two component shapes in the segment layer.

Steps (1)–(4) in Figure 6.2 show the path that attention takes in order to create attributes that will describe the organisation of the components of the **T**:

- Step (1): Your attention starts at datagram **T** in the overall figure in the base layer, to establish it as the thing you wish to identify.

- Step (2): Your attention moves from the parent datagram **T** to component datagram **H** in the upper rectangle of the segmented figure (b).

- Step (3): Your attention then *returns* to parent datagram **T** in the base layer.

- Step (4): Finally, your attention moves to datagram **V** in the lower rectangle in the segmented figure (b).

Step (2) generates an **Above** attribute in the datagrams in the top rectangle, and step (4) generates a **Below** attribute in the datagrams in the bottom rectangle (Figure 6.2b). The combination of datagrams for a horizontal rectangle above a vertical one will produce a match in long-term memory for a **T**, and immediately the attribute code for a **T**, **Tee**, is transferred into all the datagrams of the *parent* group figure in the base layer, as shown in the datagram in Figure 6.2a.

Your attention must always return to the parent figure before moving on to the next component. This is for two reasons: first, because it ensures that all the components visited refer to the right parent; and second, because *it is only parent/component movements that generate position relationship attributes*. The parent/component move from datagram **T** to datagram **H** generated the attribute **Above** in all the component datagrams in the upper rectangle, and the parent/component move from datagram **T** to datagram **V** generated the attribute **Below** in all the component datagrams in the lower rectangle.

You will have noted in the previous paragraph that the **Above** attribute was generated by a movement of attention from the group figure **T** to the top rectangle

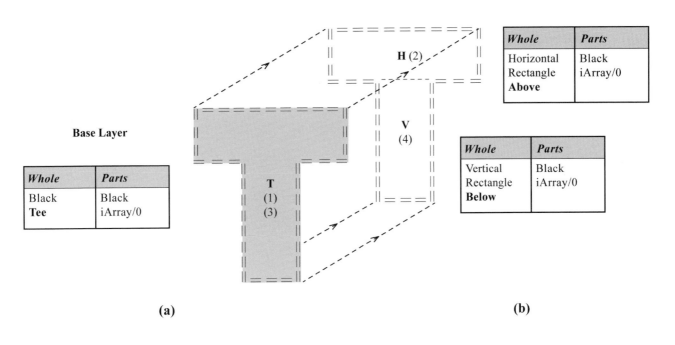

Segment Layer

Base Layer

Whole	Parts
Black **Tee**	Black iArray/0

Whole	Parts
Horizontal Rectangle **Above**	Black iArray/0

Whole	Parts
Vertical Rectangle **Below**	Black iArray/0

(a) **(b)**

Figure 6.2 How attention generates attributes for position by moving step by step between parent and component datagrams. (a) The group parent **T** shape in the base layer. (b) The Horizontal and Vertical component shapes in the segment layer after their datagrams have been coded by attention for their positions in relation to their parent.

H, and *not* by an attention movement from the bottom rectangle **V** to the top one **H**. The **Above** attribute in the horizontal rectangle does *not* tell you that it is above the vertical one; it only tells you that the horizontal rectangle is above the datagram attended in the parent region **T** that combines the two. The reason it *also* happens to be true that the horizontal rectangle is above the vertical one is because your attention selected datagrams at coordinates **H**, **T** and **V** so that they were all in a vertical straight line.

In summary, to locate an object's identity in long-term memory through the organisation of its components, you must first establish a single parent region for the whole thing and then describe its component parts through a sequence of parent/component moves.

The only valid positional relationships are between parent datagrams and their component datagrams. Attention can of course move from any datagram to any other datagram in the image, and attention can clearly move from a component back to its parent, *but none of these movements generates relationships and therefore positional attributes*. The *only* move that delivers a relative position is the move between a parent datagram and one of its component datagrams.

In Chapter 3, we established the binding rule that the *Parts* section of all group datagrams holds the attributes that are common to all its component parts, and that these parent binding attributes are always duplicated in the *Whole* sections of all its component datagrams. However, we will now modify this rule for segmented figures, like our letter **T**. In these circumstances, the binding attributes in the *Parts* section of the parent group datagrams are duplicated in the *Parts* sections of all of its component datagrams, not in their *Whole* sections. In the example in Figure 6.2, you can see that the binding attributes, Black and iArray/0, are in the *Parts* sections of *both* the parent (a) and component (b) datagrams. We go into more detail on the subject of segmentation in the Notes on this chapter.

The relative positions of components that are separate from each other

So, a quick summary of what positional attributes tell you. The attribute **Above** in the datagrams of the upper rectangle of the T tells you that this rectangle is at the top of the parent figure, whereas the attribute **Below** in the datagrams of the lower rectangle of the **T** tells you that this rectangle is at the bottom of the parent figure. These attributes do *not* tell you the positions of the rectangles in relation to each other; in other words, they do *not* tell you that that the horizontal rectangle is above the vertical one, or that the vertical rectangle is below the horizontal one – even though this happens to be true.

This also applies to groups that have components that are separate; their components are not segments. Imagine a lemon and a banana sitting 20 centimetres apart on a dish, the lemon to the left and the banana to the right (Figure 6.3).

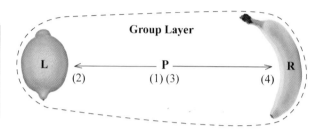

Whole	Parts
Lemon Yellow iPair/20 **Left**	Yellow iArray/0

(b) Base Layer datagram L

Whole	Parts
Banana Yellow iPair/20 **Right**	Yellow iArray/0

(c) Base Layer datagram R

Whole	Parts
	Yellow iPair/20

(a) Group datagram P

Figure 6.3 The relative positions of things in groups is determined by attention. (a) This is the group datagram in the pixels of the group region bounded by the dotted lines that encloses the lemon and the banana. (b) The datagram describing the lemon as a component of a pair. (c) The datagram describing the banana as a component of a pair. The attribute **Left** in the lemon tells you its position in relation to the attended group datagram **P**, not in relation to the banana.

Both fruits are yellow, so together they form a pair relationship and produce a combined group parent (lemon + banana) region in the group layer; their binding attributes are shown as Yellow and iPair/20. To find the positions of the lemon and banana within the group, there are again four steps you will follow:

- Step (1): Your attention starts at the parent datagram **P** in the group layer.

- Step (2): Your attention goes to datagram **L** in the lemon in the base layer, which creates the attribute **Left** in the datagrams of the lemon.

- Step (3): Your attention then returns to the parent datagram **P** in the group layer.

- Step (4): Finally, your attention goes to datagram **R** in the banana in the base layer, and this creates the attribute **Right** in the datagrams of the banana.

The lemon's **Left** attribute tells you that the lemon is on the left of the group region occupied by the two fruit – marked by the dotted boundary – but it does *not* tell you that the lemon is to the left of the banana; similarly, the banana's **Right** attribute tells you it is on the right of the combined region of lemon + banana, but not that it is to the right of the lemon. It is, of course, true that the lemon is to the left of the banana and the banana is to the right of the lemon, but we cannot know this directly.

It is not always enough to know the relative positions of components – we may also need to know how far apart they are. Every component datagram holds a description of the spatial distribution it is positioned within, which includes the interval between it and its fellow components. We can therefore go to the distribution attributes in one of the datagrams in the lemon or the banana and pick up the distance the two are apart: the distribution attributes are iPair/20, which means the interval, the distance between them, is 20.

These positional rules also apply when one object is in front of another. Figure 6.4a shows a red square that is lying 4 centimetres in front of a grey square. Both figures are squares so they form a pair relationship, and together they produce a combined group parent – their binding attributes are Square and iPair/4, as shown in the middle datagram on the right of the figure.

The group parent is a square region in a group layer that is *in between* the red square and the grey square (Figure 6.4b). The parent region has exactly the same dimensions as the grey square because its boundary is the outer boundary of the combined figures.

To work out the relative position of the grey square, your attention must first go to the parent datagram **P**, which is at the centre of the group parent (grey square + red square), and then move back to datagram **G** in the grey square; this generates a **Behind** attribute in the datagrams of the grey square. To identify the position of the red square, your attention must return to the parent datagram **P** and then move forwards to datagram **R** in the red square in front of it. This generates the attribute **In-front** in the datagrams of the red square. The red square is in front of the parent combination of the two squares; the grey square is behind the combination.

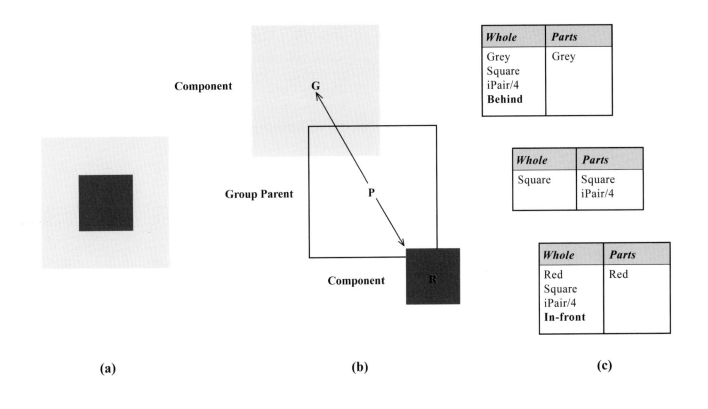

(a)   **(b)**   **(c)**

Figure 6.4 The positioning of a figure against its background. (a) A grey square with a red square positioned 4 centimetres in front of it. (b) The internal image of the two squares. The group parent representing the squares as a pair is positioned in a group layer that lies in between the two. The **In-front** and **Behind** attributes in the component datagrams describe their positions in relation to the group region, not in relation to each other.

This is, however, not really how we think about these relationships. When you look at a house that is on a mountainside, you think that the house is in front of the mountain and the mountain is behind the house; the house is the figure and the mountain the ground. But we cannot know this directly. All we know is that the house

is in front of a parent object (house + mountain) that is *in between* the mountain and the house, and similarly that the mountain is behind this same parent object.

Our iconic image is just the visible portion of a 360 degree visual iconic memory that sits alongside all the other iconic memories in the workspace of the mind, those for sound and taste for example. Each of these iconic memories is enclosed by its own parent group region and together they are all enclosed within a global group region that is the ultimate parent of the whole of iconic memory.

Each iconic memory holds attributes that reflect the prevailing conditions so that distortions in information being received can be corrected. So if for example you tilt your head sideways and look at an object that is vertical, these attributes in your visual iconic memory will adjust the object's skewed orientation so it appears to be positioned vertically.

All this moving around by attention is rather laborious and time-consuming, so how is it that we are able to recognise most objects in under a second? Here are some the factors that make such fast recognition possible:

- To recognise something, we do not have to build a complete internal picture of it; we only have to identify the two or three features needed for a unique match in long-term memory.

- We probably process around 20 attention transfers a second, so this sampling process is not that slow.

- We deliberately surround ourselves with things we can recognise easily. We give familiar things simple shapes and make a few key features stand out so they are easy to identify.

- We live our lives in familiar contexts – home, office, shops, for example – which dramatically limits the number of objects we can expect to see together at any one time.

And, as mentioned earlier, we cheat to compensate for nature's imperfections. We may expect a particular object to be a square, but perfect squares just do not happen in the iconic image. Parts of edges will either be missing or distorted, and many of the datagrams within the 'square' will not say it is a square. However, *some* of the region's datagrams will say it is a square, and because our attention is prioritised to look for good geometry, we will tend to go to a datagram with a square attribute rather than to one with no geometry at all. Attending just one datagram with a square attribute makes that region into a square – even though strictly speaking it may not be!

Summary

We identify what things are from their attributes and from the attributes of their parts. The way a thing's components are arranged is an important identifier, and we use our attention to create positional attributes through a series of parent/component moves.

We use the word 'object' to mean those things that are made up of parts that are all connected together. To identify an object, we first segment it into its component parts, and then our attention makes the parent/component movements that create the positional attributes describing its structure. The binding of parent to component in segmented figures is achieved by the duplication of attributes in the *Parts* sections of their respective datagrams.

The only permitted object-to-object relationship is that of parent/component. Because all valid relationships are between parent and component, and not between components themselves, we cannot use the concept of figure and ground to describe the relative positions of things.

Our iconic image is the visible portion of a 360 degree visual iconic memory that is enclosed, alongside all the other iconic memories, by a global group region. Together they create the single workspace of the mind.

7

Where we have got to so far

For no man can forbid the spark nor tell whence it has come.

(Francis Bacon, *Of Empire*)

Everything ultimately originates from intensity values, and everything we can ever know is ultimately a manipulation of this information source. The smell of a rose, the sound of a flute and Pythagoras's theorem are all ultimately translations of a meaningless jumble of sense data into a form we can understand through the application of a set of simple rules:

- There are only *things*.

- Point values are the only source of information about *things*.

- A *thing* is any entity all of whose component parts share the same characteristic, belong to the same class and are complete.

- Ultimately, all *things* consist of just uniform regions and edges.

- All *things*, experienced or not, are represented by a unit of information, the datagram.

- The extent of a *thing* is the extent of its datagrams.

- Attributes in datagrams are the only descriptions we have of *things*.

- Every *attribute* code is linked to a single unique sensation outside the mind that we experience whenever we attend a datagram.

- *Things*, as components, combine to form groups. The sharing of attributes between group and component datagrams provides the binding that holds them together.

- Space and time are not continuous; they are pixelated.

- There are two types of attribute for space: dimensional attributes describe a *thing's* internal geometry, and distribution attributes describe the structures that surround it.

- A *thing* is experienced through attribute values that describe it as a *Whole*.

- We can only experience *things* by attending them one at a time.

- There is a single attention stream, whose path is set via a system of priorities.

- Relationships and position are only established by attention moving from parent to component.

- Attention can only bind *things* with other things in the relationship parent/component.

These rules are implemented within iconic memory, the workspace of the mind.

Iconic memory is the workspace, the hub. It combines the inputs from our senses with class code numbers from long-term memory and triggers the sensations that give us our experience of being and of the world we live in.

Long-term memory, as well as providing a record of things, also holds the action triggers that deliver our responses.

Short-term memory is essentially an extension of iconic memory.

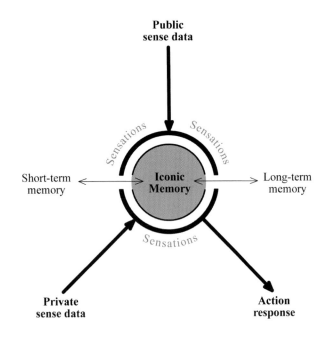

Public sense data

Sensations

Sensations

Short-term memory ← → **Iconic Memory** ← → Long-term memory

Sensations

Private sense data

Action response

Figure 7.1 The three types of memory. This figure shows that both our short-term and long-term memories lie outside the iconic workspace but feed directly into it. The white ring surrounding iconic memory represents the interface linking information in the mind with the biology of the brain that delivers our sensations and produces our responses.

In Figure 7.1, we have shown two types of sense data, one public and one private. Our *public* senses give us our common worldview, so that what I see and hear is essentially what you see and hear. Our *private* senses, on the other hand, produce in us feelings that only we can know about – joy, pain and puzzlement for example. We look at private sense data in detail in Chapters 16 and 17; in the chapters before Chapter 16 we deal exclusively with public sense data.

Iconic memory
Iconic memory is the self-contained information system in the brain that controls our lives. It is the 360 degree workspace where we organise all incoming sense data, access our memories and apply the logic that ultimately produces our experiences and responses. Iconic memory is the mind.

Our external sensory receptors channel signals into separate sense areas in the cortex depending on the type of detector – light, sound, touch or taste, for example. The data in these areas are then segmented into regions and coded with datagrams; the result is an

internal image in the brain that is the source of all sensory information entering iconic memory. Once in iconic memory, these data are matched to class code numbers in long-term memory that are then downloaded into datagrams as attributes to tell us what things are. External sensory inputs include our private experience of our own bodies, for example a muscle stretch or a feeling of nausea, as our bodies too are a part of the outside world.

Similarities in the sense data are not the only basis for forming groups: things that share the same attribute code number will also form groups in iconic memory *even when the things being grouped are not physically similar.* For example, long-term memory will assign the class code number 'ball' to the datagrams in the image of both rugby balls and soccer balls. As a consequence, a rugby ball and a soccer ball seen together will form a pair using the class code number for 'ball' as the binding attribute; the two balls do not look the same, they have different shapes and markings, but they belong to the same class – they are both balls.

So far, we have mainly concerned ourselves with the nature of attention and how it sequences datagrams in the iconic image. But while attended processing is taking place, datagrams in the non-attended parts of the image are also active and communicating directly with long-term memory; we are of course unaware of this because it is not a part of the attention process. The reason we can listen to music and at the same time walk across a room is because datagrams representing the furniture communicate with our unattended long-term memories and trigger muscle sequences that automatically prevent us falling over stuff. We look at unattended actions in some detail in Chapter 16.

Things in the unattended parts of the image are not present in the same detail as the ones we pay attention to. They are the simple representations that come as a direct result of pre-attentive processing. The unattended portion of the image is a jumble of primitive datagrams that contain just enough information to help us carry out simple repetitive tasks. So, for example, an unattended cat is a collection of disconnected datagrams that only come together as a cat when processed by attention; furthermore, these datagrams revert to their *pre-attentive* structure when our attention moves elsewhere, and therefore cease to be an image of a cat.

A simple experiment, originally performed in 1975 and called the 'invisible gorilla test', underlines this. A sequence is filmed that shows a basketball being passed between two groups of players; those watching the sequence are asked to count the number of passes they see. While the players are performing, a large gorilla walks among them, yet very few of those watching the film spot the gorilla. (There is a version of this experiment on YouTube.) This experiment demonstrates not only the focused nature of attention, but also that unattended shapes are not normally given identities. The gorilla was not a gorilla in the minds of those playing – he was a collection of unconnected visual elements – otherwise the gorilla would have been prioritised and caused an interruption.

We take it for granted that a black square is a single entity whether or not we are looking at it. But when unattended, a black square is two separate things: a black thing and a square thing, each with its own separate datagram. In this simple pre-attentive form, datagrams represent alternative ways of looking at the same data, and this is only resolved when our attention selects a single pre-attentive datagram and produces from it an attended datagram that gives us a single coherent view. Most of the thousands of the alternative configurations are irrelevant, but at every step they all have to be evaluated and every datagram prioritised so that a single priority will emerge and our attention can integrate a range of attributes to form a single thing.

We feel that this account accords well with Anne Treisman's feature integration theory, which is an exhaustively researched explanation of the processes involved in early vision. Its key claim is that features (attributes) do not bind together into objects unless a person focuses on them directly; in other words, an object only becomes a single thing when it receives the focus of attention.

We have described how the processing of information in iconic memory is organised in layers, and there are two points to be made here. The first point is that we are talking about layers of *information*, not physical layers of neurons.

The second point is to stress that the iconic image, and therefore each layer of information is essentially a flat surface. When you look at a ball, it produces a two-dimensional circular shape in the iconic image, its curvature being represented by attributes stored in the datagrams of its flat shape. In other words, we do not reproduce three dimensions physically in iconic memory; instead we get the impressions (sensations) of curvature and depth from attributes stored in two dimensions. The world out there is in three dimensions but we can only ever *know* it as a two-dimensional one.

In summary, regions and edges in iconic memory coded by datagrams are the foundation of the mind. To understand any concept, no matter how abstract, it must occupy a coded region in iconic memory and obey the same universal rules that we have applied here to vision. Iconic regions are logical constructs on the lines of Venn diagrams and Carnap's similarity circles.

Short-term memory

When you turn your eyes away from what you are looking at to look at something else, a new iconic image will displace the present one. The previous image, along with all the object identities it contains, is completely lost after a second or so. To avoid this loss of information whenever you attend a datagram, you make a copy of it in short-term memory. Now, when you return to something you looked at earlier, you can reinstate the old attribute code numbers in the new image: you do not have to search for them in long-term memory all over again.

If you could retain old iconic images for a long period of time, there would be no need for a short-term memory. But our brains do not have the biological capacity to do that, so short-term memory compensates for our biological limitations – although it has significant shortcomings. Short-term memory is an extension of the workspace that would not be necessary in the *perfect* mind.

Long-term memory

Long-term memory keeps a record of the things we have encountered throughout our lives. In addition, it holds the information that directs our patterns of behaviour, the triggers that set off actions in response to information coming from iconic memory.

Computers store large volumes of historical data in databases on magnetic media, discs for example. Information on disc is not in the computer's working memory; it must be transferred from the disc into working memory before software in the computer's information system can process it. The same principle applies to our long-term memories. They are held in structures in the brain that lie outside the information system of the mind, so all memories must be downloaded from outside the mind into the iconic workspace before they can be processed and experienced.

However, the *perfect* mind would have an infinite workspace, with every piece of information held and processed in its single iconic memory; the *perfect* mind would have no need of a separate long-term memory.

In Chapter 15, we speculate that long-term memory is a network of class code numbers organised in a class–subclass sequence. It has some of the features of a partially ordered set, a *poset*, and as such it supports some of the equations first introduced by George Boole in his 1854 book *An Investigation of the Laws of Thought*.

This brand of mathematics is commonly referred to as the algebra of sets, and it underpins the design of digital computers and the program logic required to drive them.

It is quite difficult to determine the length of time that each of these three memory systems holds on to the information that is presented to it, but roughly speaking iconic memory retains images for just a few seconds, and the information stored in short-term memory lasts for around 30 seconds. Long-term memory can hold memories of events for a lifetime, but access to old memories can become difficult when later similar events interfere with old access paths.

More about attributes

We have described attributes simply as class code numbers that are transferred into group datagrams from long-term memory when the information in the iconic image matches a particular set of characteristics. Each class/attribute code is a single unique number, so 48 might be the class and attribute number for a square thing and 522 the class and attribute number for a cat thing. Each attribute code number is linked to a unique sensation (sensation code) that is experienced outside iconic memory.

You hold in long-term memory a single class code number for the particular type of thing that is a house, 185 say. This class code number for a house, when downloaded into a datagram as an attribute code number, does not tell you what a house is – it just delivers the single physical sensation that is the idea of a house. However, in long-term memory, there will be class code numbers for rooms, doors and ceilings, and these will be linked to the class code numbers for a house by relationships that are themselves class code numbers.

Some attribute code numbers tell you what a thing is, a cat for example, but others tell you what a thing looks like, say, a black thing. Each sense attribute number that tells you what a thing looks like – an exact shade of grey, for example – is also the individual class code number in long-term memory that represents the group of all things that are that particular shade of grey. The problem here is that every shade of grey has a relationship with every other shade of grey because there is a similarity of experience between adjacent values. This is a significant issue in the field of perception, and how we address this and other matters related to sense attributes is described later in the book, in Chapter 10.

8
Scenes and short-term memory

In a moment Alice was through the glass, and had jumped lightly down into the looking glass room. The very first thing she did was look to see whether there was a fire in the fireplace…

(Lewis Carroll, *Through the Looking Glass, and What Alice Found There*)

To get a complete view of your surroundings, your sitting room or office for example, you have to turn your head and move your eyes. This is because your field of view is restricted to an area that is around 180 degrees wide by around 135 degrees high. You only get to know where things are by turning around and capturing them in a sequence of images. You process each image separately, and yet all the things that surround you appear to be part of a single unit, all of a piece. In the next two chapters, we explain how we achieve this. We show how our short-term memory acts as a bridge, integrating information from different iconic images before presenting it back to us so that we feel we are looking at a single picture.

But first we must revisit the structure of the iconic image itself. When we make eye movements this changes the positions of all the objects in the iconic image. Because we know by how much the image has been displaced we are able to adjust our attention movements and carry on processing the objects in the new image. But this only works well when all the objects we are interested in are present as a self-contained group in every image in the sequence.

Much of the time, knowing where things are in relation to each other is all you need. For example, if you wish to alter the time on your watch, you need only know the position of the watch in relation to your hands and fingers. More often, however, you would like to know where things are in the context of a particular venue – where in your office the coffee maker is located, for example. Once you know the coffee maker's position within your office, you can put this in relation to yourself and go and get a cup of coffee. And if you were out of the office, you could tell someone over the phone where the coffee machine was in relation to the other things in the scene.

Most of the time when you look at things, you see them not in relation to yourself, but in the context of a scene such as your sitting room, office or garden. We will use the word 'scene' to mean the group of *all the things that surround you* at any particular moment in time. All the things in a particular scene are its components; together they make up what the scene is. There is a scene group region in a layer of iconic memory that represents the scene as a whole, all 360 degrees worth. It is the parent of everything in the scene around you, of things you cannot see as well as those you can.

It can be helpful to visualize the scene group region as a layer shaped like the inside surface of a hollow sphere. Below the scene group layer, there is a similarly shaped component layer that holds representations of the things in the scene; the iconic image is the visible portion of the scene component layer. These are of course logical structures, not physical ones.

Every scene is itself a thing, so scenes have class code numbers in long-term memory that tell you that this is your sitting room or garden or office. A scene's identity is established by examining the component objects that make up that scene. Once you have identified a scene's class code number in long-term memory, it is downloaded as an attribute code into all the datagrams of the scene group region. We are always in some scene or other, so the scene group region is always active and always has a scene attribute code in its datagrams that tell you what the scene is.

The 360 degree scene group region provides an internal framework for fixing the location of things in the scene. It positions every object in the scene in relation to a single master scene datagram using a polar coordinate system of longitude and latitude. The master scene datagram is positioned at the point in the 360 degree scene group layer where longitude zero and latitude zero meet – the equivalent of the point on the earth's surface where the Greenwich meridian meets the equator.

In every scene, your long-term memory appoints a single reference object and you calculate the position of everything else in the scene in relation to it. In your sitting room, for example, the reference object could well be the mantlepiece. When you enter a scene, your attention goes to the reference object and this identifies the scene you are in, your sitting room in this example. Your attention then goes to the master scene datagram, at the centre of the front edge of the mantlepiece surface, and this becomes the central point of the scene you are in. However, the master scene datagram is not in the master object itself; it is in the same position but is in the group scene layer lying 'behind' the layer holding the master object. In this way, the master scene datagram in the group layer becomes *the parent of everything in the scene* as well as the zero point of its coordinates.

The position of the master scene datagram is called the scene reference point. Its scene coordinates are zero longitude and zero latitude, and every object in the scene is given an angular position that is left/right of or above/below the pixel that holds the scene reference point. When you enter a familiar scene, you first identify what the scene is, and then your long-term memory directs your attention to the scene reference point datagram. This way, whenever you enter your sitting room the scene coordinates are automatically set up in advance with the scene reference point in the same position every time – at the centre of the top surface of the mantlepiece.

Every pixel in the iconic image and therefore every datagram now has two sets of coordinates, one that tells you its row/column position in the iconic image and another that tells you its position in relation to the reference point of the scene.

You are always moving your eyes around any scene you occupy to keep the things that interest you within your field of view. The problem is that every time you move your eyes, you replace the existing internal image with a completely new one, which destroys the previous iconic image and all the group structures and attribute codes you have so carefully built up. To circumvent this loss whenever you attend a datagram, you automatically make a copy of it in your short-term memory, so when you look at something again you can identify it as the same thing that you saw earlier, and you can reinstate the old attribute codes into the datagrams in the new image. You do not have to reprocess everything from scratch.

I will use my sitting room as an example to illustrate how we use short-term memory to restore lost information in this way. When I walk into my sitting room, I see the fireplace in front of me (Figure 8.1). There is a carriage clock on the mantlepiece, and a mirror on the wall above it. To the left are French windows that open onto the garden, and against the back wall there are a sofa and two easy chairs. When I am standing in my sitting room, I am in a single scene, and all the things around me are parts of that scene. Because the fireplace is unique, I recognise this scene as my sitting room, and my long-term memory will transfer the attribute code number for Sitting room into datagrams in the scene group layer.

The mantlepiece is my scene reference object, and the centre point of its front edge is where the scene reference point is positioned. The pixel position of the reference point is indicated by the <R> at the centre of the mantlepiece in Figure 8.1a. However, the reference point is not held in a datagram in the mantlepiece – because the mantlepiece is a component of the scene – but in a scene group datagram in the same position 'behind' it.

So, the first thing I see on entering the room is the fireplace. I immediately recognise that this is my sitting room, and the attribute code for Sitting room is transferred from my long-term memory into all the datagrams of the scene group region. My long-term memory then identifies the mantlepiece as the reference object, and the datagram at the reference point <R> is given the highest priority in the image.

My attention moves to this datagram that is the centre of the scene coordinate system. At this point, the centre of the iconic image, the centre of the mantlepiece and the centre of the scene – the reference point – all share the same position in the scene, coordinates (0,0), albeit in different layers.

Everything in the room that is to the left of the centre of the mantlepiece, which is also the position of the reference point in the scene group layer, will now be coded as being on the 'left', and everything to the right of the centre of the mantlepiece will be coded as being on the 'right'. The surface of the mantlepiece provides the level for a horizontal line that extends around the room. Anything I see in the room above this line is coded as 'above', and anything below it is coded as 'below'. It is a fundamental rule that every time we attend a datagram in iconic memory, its *Whole* section attributes get copied automatically into our short-term memory. So when my attention moved to the reference point datagram <R>, step (0), the attribute code for **Sitting room** was copied into my short-term memory, where it was given the identity (**s**) – see the top of Figure 8.1b.

Next, suppose priorities tell my attention to go to the carriage clock that is directly above the centre of the mantlepiece. My attention moves from the parent reference point datagram in the scene group layer at position <R> to the highest priority datagram in the carriage clock in the scene component layer – step (1). The position of the clock in relation to the reference point is above, so the attribute Above is inserted into the datagram of the clock. This attended component datagram in the image of the carriage clock is automatically copied into my short-term memory, where it is linked into the scene group datagram (**s**) as datagram (c) (Figure 8.1b). It is important to note that even

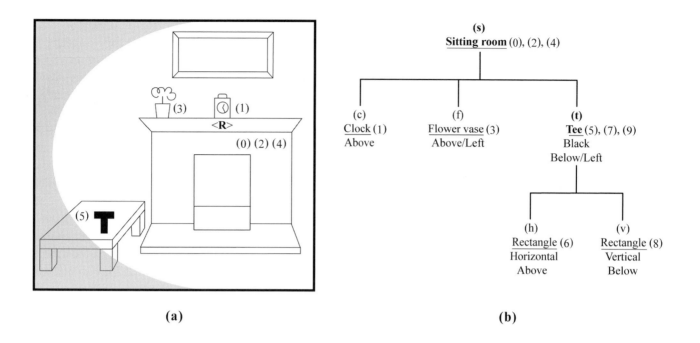

(a)　　　　　　　　　　　　　　　　　　　　　**(b)**

Figure 8.1 How we hold information in short-term memory. (a) An iconic image of my sitting room showing the field of view. The scene reference point <R> is positioned at the centre of the reference object, the mantelpiece. (b) The copy datagrams placed in short-term memory by attention that will help us restore the iconic image if we revisit the scene later.

though my attention has moved to the clock, my eyes have not moved at all; the centre of my retina and iconic image centre are still locked on to the centre of the mantlepiece, which is also the position of the reference point in the scene group layer.

Priorities then switch my attention back to the parent reference point datagram in the scene group layer – step (2) – before being directed to the next high-priority component datagram in the iconic image, which is in the flower vase on the left side of the mantelpiece – step (3). Again, this datagram is copied into short-term memory, along with its position attributes of Above/Left, and this datagram (f) is also linked to the scene group datagram (**s**). Just as before, there is no eye or image movement. And then my attention again returns to the reference point datagram in the scene group layer – step (4).

Next my attention goes from the reference point datagram at <R> in the scene group layer to a black shape (the **T**) that is sitting on a small table to the left of the fireplace – step (5) – and again the attended datagram with its Below/Left position is copied into short-term memory as a black shape with identity (**t**), and it too is linked to the scene datagram (**s**).

But this time my attention does not return to the scene reference point. Instead priorities tell me to go

down and process the segments of the black region (the **T**), so I follow the sequence described in Chapter 6 for recognising the black shape as a **T** – steps (6), (7) and (8). In the process of doing this, the rectangular segments of the black shape, (h) and (v), are linked into their parent shape (**t**), the shape is recognised, and the attribute code for a **T**, **Tee**, is downloaded from long-term memory into the datagrams of the parent black shape in the image.

My attention then goes back to a datagram in the overall image of the **T** – step (9) – and as a result all its attributes, which now include **Tee**, are copied into datagram (**t**) in short-term memory. Figure 8.1b shows the final result after step (9). Again, we assume that there have been no eye movements – all the attention transfers have taken place within one fixed iconic image.

We create just *one* short-term memory datagram for each attended object, and each has its own unique identity – for example, in Figure 8.1b the short-term memory identity of the carriage clock is (c) and that of the **T** shape is (**t**). No matter how many times your attention visits something in a scene, there will only be just one identity for it in short-term memory. No matter how many times I look at the carriage clock, the results from each visit will always be found in a single short-term memory datagram with a short-term memory identity code (c).

Suppose that, after identifying the **T**, I turn around to talk to my wife, who is at the door. The **T** leaves my field of view, and all its datagrams in the image are deleted. When I turn back to look at the **T** again, it is in a new iconic image, and its datagrams in the new iconic image no longer say that it is a **T** – it is just an unidentified 'below/left' region in the scene that is black.

But the datagrams in this black region will be given a high priority because processing was interrupted and datagram (**t**) in short-term memory has a record of its position; so my attention will transfer from the scene reference point at <R> to one of the black region's datagrams in the image – step (11). The new black region datagram automatically creates a new copy datagram in my short-term memory, and it is connected to the scene datagram (**s**) and given a temporary identity (?) (Figure 8.2). However, this new datagram has the same attributes 'black' and 'below/left' as the previous Tee datagram with identity (**t**), so my short-term memory assumes that this is another viewing of the same thing and *gives it the same identity* (**t**).

The act of attaching an existing identity to a new datagram in short-term memory, (**t**) in this example, means that the two are the same thing, so the previously observed attributes stored in short-term memory are automatically inserted into the datagrams of the newly attended region in the iconic image. In this example, the attribute code **Tee** is downloaded from the previous short-term memory datagram (**t**) into all the datagrams in the image of the new black region. And because this is the region being attended, these same attributes are copied back from the new black region in iconic memory into the newly created datagram in short-term memory – step (11).

This matching process also generates the attribute Same in the datagrams of the new iconic image of the **T**, so the attribute Same will be placed in the new datagram that represents the **T** in short-term memory. The processing sequence we have described has not only saved us time, but has also left us with a history of the attributes of the object over time because everything has been recorded against the same short-term memory identity (**t**).

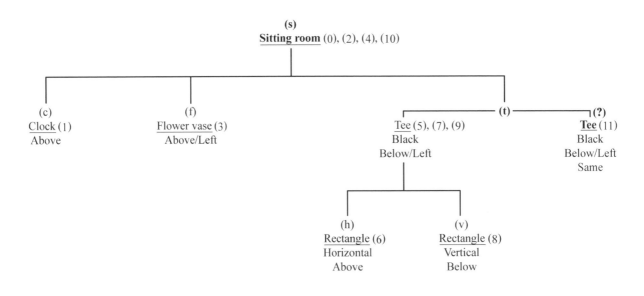

Figure 8.2 Identifying two things as being the same. Every time something is attended in the iconic image, its datagram is copied into short-term memory and given a unique identity. If that thing is attended for a second time, then provided the new attributes match the old ones, the new datagram is given the same identity as the previous one – (**t**) in this example.

This gives us an important new rule. The observation of two things at different times become two observations of the same thing *only when* short-term memory allocates them the same identity and inserts the attribute Same into the attended datagrams. To somebody else, the two things may not be the same, but if *your* short-term memory has assigned a previous identity to what you are attending now, you will experience the sensation Same and the belief that they are the same whether or not they are the same thing, made of the same atoms.

Suppose my daughter, while my head was turned to talk to my wife, had swapped the **T** shape on the table for an identical one, placing the new one in exactly the same position as the old one. When I turned back and looked at the **T** again, I would experience the *same thing* sensation, the belief that this was the same **T** made of the same stuff as the one I had seen seconds before – provided of course I didn't see her make the swap.

But suppose that while I was talking to my wife, my daughter had switched the **T** for another one that was identical in all respects except that the vertical leg of the **T** was slightly tapered so that its shape was a triangle rather than a rectangle. I would probably still register this black region in the 'down/left' location as datagram (**t**) in short-term memory, the same **T**, and provided I did not check out its segments I would believe it was the original **T** and assume that its vertical segment was a rectangle.

But if my attention went to a vertical segment datagram in the new iconic image, step (12) in Figure 8.3, I would find that the lower segment was now triangular and did

not match the rectangle in the original segment datagram (v). Although what I am looking at is still a **T**, it is not the same **T** I saw earlier, so I must create *new* datagrams with new identities (**x** and **z**) in short-term memory to represent it (Figure 8.3).

The datagrams of the two **T**s are similar, but they have completely separate short-term memory identities, (t) and (**x**), so they are different things. They are no longer separate observations of the *same thing*; instead they are observations of two different things that belong to the *same class*, in that they are both **T**s. This is why the (t) and (**x**) connect into the scene datagram (**s**) separately in Figure 8.3. The picture of my sitting room in Figure 8.1 shows the **T** placed vertically on the table to the left of the fireplace. This time, while I am talking to my wife, my daughter picks up the **T** and puts it back on the table, but places it at an angle of 45 degrees to its original position.

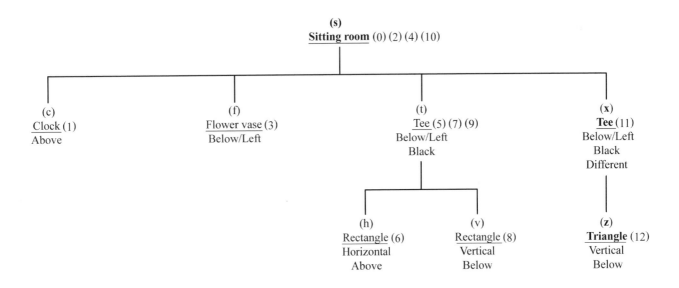

Figure 8.3 Identifying two things as similar but different. In this example, the two **T**s that have been attended are different: the first **T** we look at has a rectangular vertical segment, while the second **T** we look at has a triangular vertical segment. Because their datagrams do not match the two **T**s, they are given separate identities in short-term memory, (t) for the first datagram and (**x**) for the second. They are different things within the same scene.

In this scenario, when I look at the **T** for the second time, step (11), my short-term memory will compare it with the first datagram (t) for the **T**. Although their orientations are different, the rest of their attributes are the same, so my short-term memory decides that this is the 'same' thing and gives them the same identity (**t**) as before (Figure 8.4). The two observations are different views of the same thing. This example also illustrates how we retain datagrams in short-term memory to track changes in the attributes of an object over time.

The same thing sensation tells you that this object has exactly the same characteristics and behaviours as the object seen previously – apart from those attributes you have actually observed to be different – which means that you can treat the new object as if it were actually the old one. It does not, however, tell you that the object persisted in between the two times it was seen. Object persistence is a different concept, provided by a different attribute that depends on more factors than just similarity.

We will now look at how we record the overall scene we occupy. The reference point datagram, which also holds the scene identity, is in the scene group layer, the parent region for everything in the room. Below this are *the scene component layers*, which hold the datagrams that for all the things in the 360 degree scene around you whether or not you can see them. The layers in the iconic image are the visible portion of the scene component layers. The coordinates of things outside your field of view, behind you for example, are retained in long-term and short-term memories and are used to place token datagrams to represent them in the non-visible part of the scene.

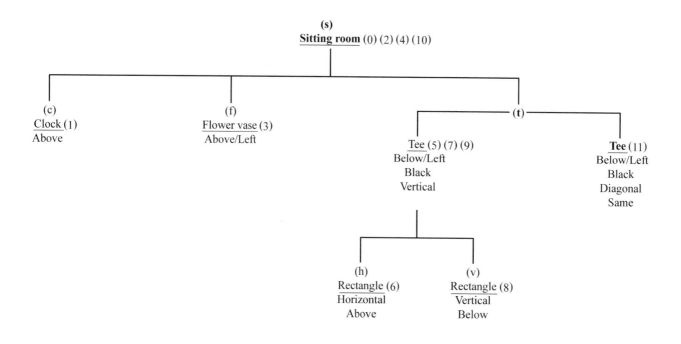

Figure 8.4 How two things can be the same even if their attributes are different. In this example, the same thing produces different attributes for the **T** in short-term memory. This is because the **T** has been rotated through 45 degrees between observations, and its orientation is now diagonal not vertical. However, the two are been treated as observations of the same thing by being given the same identity (**t**).

When you attend something in the iconic image, it may trigger a datagram in short-term or long-term memory for an object that is in the same scene but not in your field of view. For example, while my wife was standing at the door, she might have asked me to tell her the time.

The clock on the mantlepiece is now not in my field of view, but because I hold its scene coordinates in my long-term memory, a token datagram in its invisible location can be prioritised. I can then switch my attention to that token datagram in the scene component layer. My eyes will follow this attention movement, bringing the clock into my iconic image. My attention will go to the real thing in the image, and I will read off the time. Only one token datagram in the scene component layer is set up to represent the clock; it is not an image for a clock, it is a token for a clock.

Scenes are things in the same way that objects are things, and like objects they can come together to form groups. Every room in my house is a scene, but each room can be seen as a component part of the group parent scene that is my house as a whole. The road from my house to Stratford-upon-Avon is a group parent scene constructed from a row of component scenes, each representing a stretch of highway along the way. The reference points in each of these road scenes could be the white lines in the centre of the road.

It is very important to be clear that you cannot directly experience the information held in your short-term memories, or in your long-term memories for that matter; you can only ever experience the information that is held as attributes in datagrams in iconic memory, the workspace. To use information held in short-term or long-term memory, it must first be downloaded into datagrams in one or other of the layers of iconic memory, either as attributes or as tokens.

You too are just another object in the scene you are in at the moment. You are no different from any other object making up the collection of things that comprises the scene you are in. If you get bored reading this book and decide to get up and move around the room, the scene coordinate attributes in the datagrams that describe you will change so that they always reflect your position in the room in relation to the reference point.

In this chapter, we have explained how we use short-term memory to back up our iconic memory; this is necessary because our iconic memory can only retain information for a few seconds. In the next chapter, we explain how our short-term memories bridge the gaps in information flow caused by the eye movements, the saccades, that we make two or three times a second to keep the focus of our attention at the centre of our field of view.

Summary

We see things in the world in terms of *scenes*, a scene being defined as the group of all the things that surround you in a particular context. Every scene has a unique reference object, and at a particular position in the scene reference object is the scene reference point, the centre of the scene coordinate system. The scene reference point is held in the scene group region and is the parent datagram of everything in the scene *whether or not it is in your field of view*.

Short-term memory provides continuity by retaining copies of the datagrams we have attended. As we attend each datagram, we record it in short-term memory, and if it is for something new we give it a unique short-term memory identity so we can recognise it later as something we have already seen. If we attend a datagram with attributes that are the same as for one already recorded in short-term memory, we can attach it to that previous datagram's identity; it is the same thing.

Things that are outside our field of view are positioned as token datagrams in a scene component layer that extends across the full 360 degrees of the scene.

9

The seamless flow of perception

Consciousness, then, does not appear to itself chopped up in bits... In talking of it hereafter let us call it the stream of thought, of consciousness, or of subjective life.

(William James, *The Principles of Psychology*)

We experience the world as a continuous stream of awareness. We switch effortlessly from object to object, from things we see to things we hear, and from topic to topic – and all this despite frequent breaks in the information flow reaching our brains.

We move our eyes to look at the things around us two or three times a second, and in addition we blink some 20 times a minute. While we are in the act of doing these things, the flow of data transmitted from our eyes to our visual cortex is cut off for significant periods; effectively, we live our lives functionally blind for 10–15% of the time. So how do we bridge the gaps in the data so that our perceptions continue to flow smoothly in the way they do?

To answer this question, we are going to describe processes that take fractions of a second to execute. At this level, we measure time in thousandths of a second, and the unit we use is the millisecond (msec), so there are a thousand milliseconds to every second.

Blinks

We blink every few seconds, and when we do so our eyelids block the light entering our eyes for around a fifth of a second – 200 msec. For the period of the blink, we automatically close the information channels that connect our eyes to the visual centres in our brain, and in the meantime we carry on processing the pre-blink image as if it were still a live one. If something occurs that starts and finishes within the time of a blink, we cannot register it.

While we are blinking, we are completely unaware that the image we are processing is not a live one. It is not that a fifth of a second is too short a time to notice a loss of vision – as you can easily prove by switching off a room light for the same time period – but we suppress all new visual information so that it cannot interfere with the processing of the old image (see the Notes for this chapter). (The suppression of information from the eyes actually lasts longer than this – more like a quarter of a second because the visual channels are shut down for an additional 75 msec in advance of the physical blink.)

Eye movements – saccades

We make two or three very fast eye movements, called saccades, every second to keep the things we are looking at in the centre of our visual field. Each of these eye movements takes about 50 msec depending on the size of the rotation of the eyeball. As when we are blinking, the information going through the nerve channels that connect our eyes to the visual centres of our brain is suppressed. Even though our eyes are open, we cannot register anything while they are moving – which is why we cannot see our own eye movements reflected in a mirror – and during the length of the eye rotation, as for blinking, we carry on processing the old image as if it were a 'live' view of the world.

But the interesting thing about saccades is that the visual suppression does not end when the 50 msec of eye rotation ends; instead the suppression of new information continues for another 100 msec or so *after* the movement has been completed. This additional time is needed to convert the new, raw retinal image into the full iconic form complete with regions and edges coded into datagrams. While this image-building is taking place, we continue to sequence the datagrams of objects in the old image, unaware that they could be well out of date.

So the sequence of events is as follows:

We attend things one after the other in a 'live' iconic image that is continuously updated by our eyes. This live period (fixation) lasts around 250 msec, and during it our eyes do not move.

A saccade is triggered to bring the attended object to the centre of the field of view, and immediately all information from our eyes is cut off. While the eye movement is taking place, our attention continues to process datagrams in the 'old' image *unaware that it is frozen*.

Even when the eye movement is complete, we continue to attend datagrams in the old image until the new image is assembled and ready, *as* we still believe the old image to be 'live'.

When the new image is ready, the next attention move is from the current datagram in the old image to the next datagram in the new image. The new image is now 'live' and is continuously updated by our eyes as before – we are again into the fixation period.

Each full cycle lasts around 400 msec, which is made up of 250 msec for processing the 'live' image (fixation), 50 msec for the eye movement and 100 msec for building the new image after the eye movement has been completed. It should be noted that all these times can vary. For instance, the length of the fixation period depends on the type of activity we are involved in, and the time taken for an eye movement depends on how far it travels. The timings we use in this chapter are for illustrative purposes only and are not definitive, although they are, we believe, of the right order of magnitude.

In the previous chapter, we explained how short-term memory restores information to the new images of objects seen earlier. Saccadic eye movements present us with a similar problem. Objects in the new image after an eye movement are not in the same positions that they were in the old one, and their datagrams will no longer have the attribute code numbers, relationships (up, down, etc.) or attention statuses that we so carefully created in the old image. Before our attention can move to the new image, we must work out the new positions of the datagrams we have just been attending so we can transfer across the latest attribute code numbers, relationships and statuses from the old image to the new one.

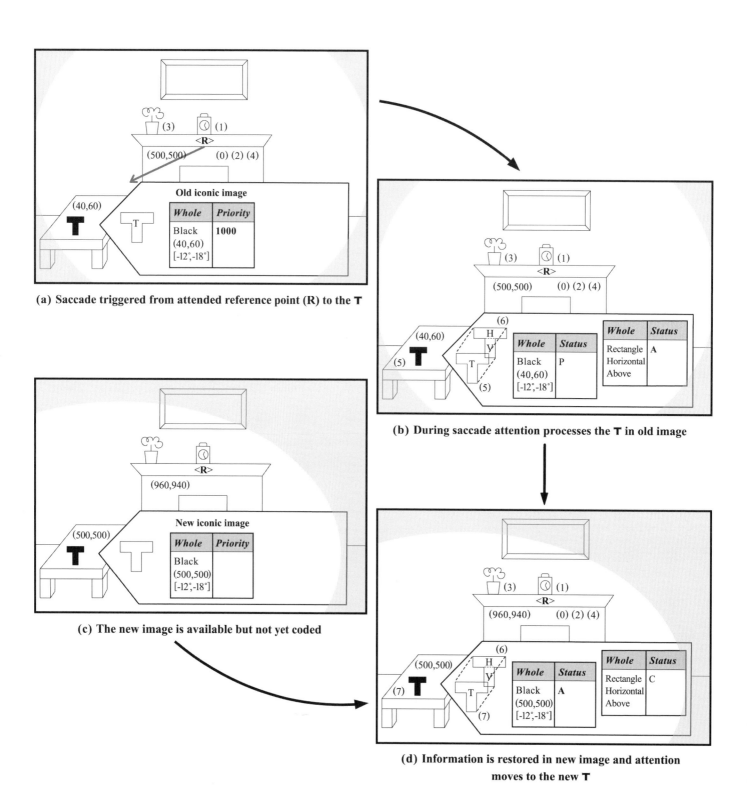

(a) Saccade triggered from attended reference point (R) to the T

(b) During saccade attention processes the T in old image

(c) The new image is available but not yet coded

(d) Information is restored in new image and attention moves to the new T

Figure 9.1 How information in the old image is transferred to the new one. (a) A saccade is triggered from reference point <R> to the **T**. (b) During the saccade, the old image continues to be processed by attention, steps (5) and (6). (c) The new image becomes available, but the information in its datagrams does not reflect the processing that has been taking place during the suppression period. (d) Datagrams in the new image have been brought up to date so our attention can transfer from the old image (b) to the new image (d), step (7), without any break in continuity.

To illustrate how we do this, let's go back to the example of my sitting room. Figure 9.1a shows the internal iconic image I have on entering my sitting room. As soon as I enter the room, my attention is immediately attracted to the mantelpiece, and I make an eye movement that locks the centre of my retina, and therefore the central pixel of my iconic image, onto the reference point <R>. We will assume that the iconic image extends over an area 1000 pixels by 1000 pixels, so the centre of the iconic image at <R> has the image coordinates (row, column) = (500,500). The scene coordinates at <R> are of course [longitude/latitude] = [0°,0°].

As in Chapter 8, my attention goes from the reference point datagram <R> to look at the time on the clock, step (1). When I have completed this, my attention goes back to the reference point parent, step (2), and then to the flowers on the left of the mantlepiece, step (3). Finally, my attention returns to the reference point, step (4). No eye movements have taken place: the centre of my retina is still locked on to the centre of the mantelpiece, which is also the centre of my iconic image (with coordinates of 500,500).

The **T** on the small table to the left of the fireplace is now the top priority for my attention because one of its datagrams, at position (40,60), has been given a priority value of **1000** (Figure 9.1a). However, the **T** is near the edge of my retinal image, where the definition is poor, so an eye movement is automatically triggered to move the image centre from the centre of the mantelpiece to the **T** datagram at (40,60). This will move the **T** to the centre

of my field of view, (500,500), where the definition is good. The arrow in Figure 9.1a indicates the path the eye movement will take. When the eye movement is complete, the coordinates of the **T** become (500,500) – the coordinates of the image centre (as in Figure 9.1c). The scene coordinates of the **T**, its position in relation to the reference point [−12°,−18°], do not change: they are the same in Figure 9.1a and 9.1c because the scene position of the **T** in the scene remains the same regardless of where the **T** is positioned in the image.

Although the eye movement only takes 50 msec or so, the **T** in the new image will not be available for another 150 msec. However, rather than wait, I continue to process the old image – Figure 9.1b – even though it was frozen as soon as the eye movement started. My attention moves from the reference point <R> to a high-priority datagram T in the **T** in the old image, step (5). At the same time, a copy of this datagram is transferred into short-term memory and given the identity (**t**) (Figure 9.2). By attending this group datagram, I segment the **T** into its horizontal H and vertical V component rectangles in the segment layer (see Figure 6.2 and the description in Chapter 6).

Having attended the group datagram T, step (5), the priority for my attention becomes datagram H in the horizontal rectangle in the segment layer and I attend it, step (6) in Figure 9.1b. At the same time, a copy of datagram H is transferred into short-term memory, given the identity (**h**) and attached to its parent datagram (**t**) (Figure 9.2).

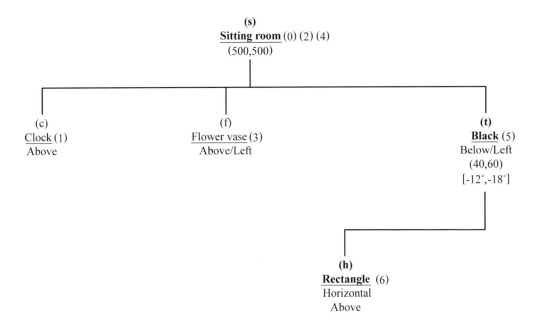

Figure 9.2 The short-term memory datagrams created in the old image awaiting downloading into the new image.

We will now assume that the image-building is complete, and that the new image, Figure 9.1c, is ready to replace the old image in Figure 9.1b. You can see that the objects in the room in the new image are the same as they were in the old image, but they now have different coordinates – the T is now at the centre of the image (500,500) instead of being at bottom left (40,60). However, the datagram for the T in the new image in Figure 9.1c is not segmented in the way it was segmented in the old image, Figure 9.1b. Before we can release the new image, we must recover this information.

When we copy the datagrams of attended objects into short-term memory, we include the coordinates of their positions. If we can convert the old image coordinates into their equivalents in the new image, we will be able to download the old attributes and statuses held in short-term memory into the datagrams of the same objects in their new positions in the new image.

We know the position of the new image centre in both the old and new images – (40,60) and (500,500), respectively – so provided we know an object's position in the old image, we can calculate where it is in the new one simply by adding 460 to its old row number and 440 to its the old column number. Only one datagram for each of the regions T and H will be downloaded from short-term memory into the new iconic image, but these will then be duplicated across the extent of their respective regions.

Once the download of information from short-term memory has taken place, the datagrams in the new image will have become identical to those in the old image in Figure 9.1b. However, my attention is still in the old image, and I need to move it across from the old image to the new one. In this example, the cut over takes place just after I finish attending the upper horizontal rectangle of the T, step (6) in the old image. At this point, the horizontal segment datagram H has attended A-status and the overall parent figure T has P-status.

The next priority for attention is to move from the horizontal segment H in Figure 9.1b back to the parent T, so a parent datagram is given a high priority *in the new image*, Figure 9.1d. The effect is an attention transfer, step (7) from a component datagram in the old image to a parent datagram in the new one, and this attention transfer makes the new image the current one. The parent datagram T in the new image is now given attended A-status and is processed. Because the cut over from old to new image has been done as part of an attention transfer, there is no break in the attention sequence.

Figure 9.1d shows the information in the new image *after* the cut over, step (7). My attention is processing the parent figure so it now has attended A-status, and the horizontal rectangle has been given component C-status.

Although the position of the T in the iconic image has changed from (40,60) to (500,500), the position of the T in the whole scene [−12°,−18°] has remained unchanged. The reason the cut over from one image to another is seamless is because the positions of things in the scene have not changed and the attention sequence is uninterrupted.

The processing sequence for blinks appears to be slightly different. While we are in the act of blinking, we continue to process the old image in the same way we process the old image during saccadic eye movements, which takes about 200 msec. But there is a difference – after a blink has ended, we do not seem to take a further 100 msec or so to process the new image as we do after a saccade, but instead we appear to see things 'live' straight away. The most likely explanation for this is that we do not automatically grab a new image after the blink; instead we identify the changes by comparing images in the subsequent fixation period with the objects in the old pre-blink image. In other words, after a blink we do not see things 'live': we continue to see an old version of the world until we either complete the next saccade or our eyes pick up something so at odds with the old image that a refresh is forced on us. The reason we can persevere at all with the old image is because the retinal displacement caused by a blink is relatively small.

Fixation is what we call the period of time that starts with attending a fresh image and ends with the start of a new saccade; it is the period when we see things 'live'. Fixations last around 250 msec, during which we respond quickly – in around 50 msec – to changes in our environment. However, we do not adjust the image at these very short intervals, even though it feels as if we do. We note the changes and can react to them, but we have to wait for an image from the next saccade before we can again see the complete picture.

There are other types of eye movement too. In smooth pursuit, we follow a moving object with our eyes so that we can fixate on things in a stable image, just like a photographer pans on a moving athlete to get a good picture. Vestibular eye movements compensate for our head movements, again so we can fixate on a stable image. Finally, our eyes track objects moving towards or away from us by rotating in opposite directions.

Summary

In this chapter, we explain how we achieve continuity despite the breaks in information flow caused by saccadic eye movements and blinks. Saccades and blinks produce significant periods of time when information passing from the eyes to the brain is suppressed. During the period of shutdown, we continue to process the old image as if it were live a live one, and while we do so we make copies of the attended datagrams in short-term memory.

We trigger a saccade when attention moves to a datagram that is outside the high-definition area in the iconic image. The physical eye movement transfers the centre of the iconic image to the position of the datagram that triggered the saccade. When the new image is released, we download the data from the old image we stored in short-term memory into datagrams in their new positions in the new image.

When the download has been completed, the next attention move is prioritised in the new image instead of the old one, so attention transfers from the last attended datagram in the old image to the next attended datagram in the new one. The movement from one image to another is seamless because the attributes and relative positions of things are, at this point, the same in the two images.

During a blink, we continue to process the old image just as we do during saccades. However, when the physical blink is complete, we do not go on to process a new image; instead we continue to process the old one until it is refreshed for some other reason.

10

Things that are the same but different – and what they look like

I paint objects as I think them, not as I see them.

(Pablo Picasso)

In this chapter, we will look at groups of things made from parts that are quite small when compared with the size of the group as a whole. The leaves of a tree or the blades of grass in a field are examples of this type of group. Other examples are the pebbles on a beach, the pattern elements in a knitted jumper or a flock of starlings.

The first problem with large groups is that although the things that make up a group are usually pretty similar, they are not exactly the same. The other problem is that groups can be so large that they do not fit into your field of view; instead you have to make a succession of eye movements to take in the whole group.

In the second part of the chapter, we will explain how we search for things within groups and scenes, and finally we will discuss the nature of those attributes that give us a feel for what things look like rather than just what they are.

Building large groups

We have seen how regions in the iconic image will form groups if they share the same attributes. For example, the three black squares we described in Chapter 3 combined to form a row because all the squares were the same shade of black. In practice, however, the three squares would not all have reflected exactly the same intensity values because of differences in surface texture and local variations in lighting. For this reason, the attributes that bind the parts of a group together are often a range of values rather than a single number.

Figure 10.1 shows a row of grey shapes – squares and rectangles – in the iconic image that are all separated from each other by an interval of 6 pixels; each shape is marked with a reflected intensity, a 'grey level', that ranges from 41 to 47 – the lower the number, the darker the grey level.

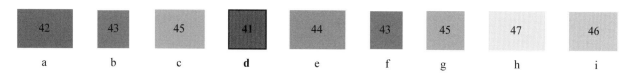

| 42 | 43 | 45 | 41 | 44 | 43 | 45 | 47 | 46 |
| a | b | c | d | e | f | g | h | i |

(a) A row of shapes with similar shades of grey

Whole	Parts
Row Horizontal	41–47 **Av = 44** **iRow/6**

(b) The group datagram for the row

Whole	Parts
Square 41 **Av = 44** **iRow/6**	41 iArray/0

(c) The datagram for square d

Figure 10.1 Things will form groups if they share a narrow range of values. (a) A row of nine grey squares and rectangles, the numbers in the shapes indicating the shades of grey we see in their surfaces. (b) The group datagram for the whole row. Its *Parts* section tells us the range and average of the grey levels in the row. (c) This is the datagram for shape **d** that is the attended component of the row. Its *Whole* section tells us that **d**'s grey level is 41, but it also shows the average of the grey level of the row, **Av = 44**, because, along with **iRow/6**, this is the binding attribute for the row as a whole.

(We will use the term 'grey level' to describe the shades of grey we perceive in a surface, and these will include black and white and all the different greys that we can detect in between those two extremes.)

In Figure 10.1, the variations in intensity, or grey level, between neighbouring shapes in the row are small and reasonably regular, so they will come together as components to form a group, a row. The range of grey levels in the group is 41–47, and the average grey level across the row is 44.

Figure 10.1b shows the group datagram for the row as a whole. Its *Parts* section holds the range of attributes for the row: these are the grey level range of 41–47, plus the shared spatial distribution, **iRow/6**, which tells us that the component shapes are arranged in a row 6 pixels apart from each other. The group *Parts* section also holds the average grey level of the components of the row, **Av = 44**.

Figure 10.1c shows the datagram for component **d**, the shape being attended in the row. You can see from its *Whole* section that shape **d** is square and has a grey level of 41, which is different from the grey levels of its two neighbours, shapes c and e, which have values of 45 and 44, respectively. This presents a problem because the grouping rules say that the components of a group must all hold the same value for the attribute that binds them, and this is clearly not the case here. To resolve this problem, the *average intensity of the row* **Av = 44** in the *Whole* sections of all the component shapes becomes the binding attribute along with the distribution **iRow/6**.

When you look at, attend, shape **d** in isolation and not as part of the group, you will see its grey level as 41. However, if your attention goes to the group (parent) datagram, Figure 10.1b, before going to component **d**, you will see the grey level of shape **d** as the average **44** because this grey level is the basis of the group's existence. If you *then* want to know the level of intensity of shape **d** within the group, you will see it as (**44** – 41 = –3), three shades 'darker' than the average component in the row.

To understand in more detail how we manage groups, we need to understand how we hold information at the entry or *pre-attentive* level of iconic memory. The pre-attentive layer of iconic memory lies in between the internal image (see Chapter 1) and the higher iconic layers of the mind that process the attended datagrams we have been talking about. This iconic entry layer is populated entirely by pre-attentive datagrams that describe not only the regions in the internal image, but also all the different ways they might be organised.

In Figure 10.1a, the *grey* square **d**, as a grey thing, is part of a row of grey things. But grey square **d**, as a *square* thing, is not part of a row because the row is mostly rectangles – instead grey square **d** as a square thing is one of a pair with square g. Clearly, the grey square **d** cannot at the same time be *both* part of a row and one of a pair. To resolve this conflict, we restrict *pre-attentive datagrams to holding just one descriptive attribute and one distribution/interval for that attribute*. So in each pixel of grey square **d**, there will be many different pre-attentive datagrams, each one of which will view the grey square in a different way. Among the pre-attentive datagrams in every pixel of square **d**, there will be one that says this is a grey thing in a row of grey things, and another that says it is a square that is one of a pair of squares. We must choose one or the other of these and decide whether we want to see shape **d** as a grey thing that is in a row or as a square thing that is one of a pair – we cannot see shape **d** as both of these at the same time.

So before you attend a thing, each of its attributes is held in completely separate pre-attentive datagrams, and although they all occupy the same pixels they are not bound together. Pre-attentively, an unattended grey square is not a grey square but two separate things – a grey thing and a square thing; these two unconnected things only become a grey square when you attend one or other of them.

We will now explain how, by selecting a single pre-attentive datagram, we pull together attributes from the other pre-attentive datagrams to create a single attended datagram that holds a complete description of the thing we are looking at. In Figure 10.2, we have added two new rectangular shapes, x and y, to the shapes that appeared in Figure 10.1a. So as well as shape **d** being part of the horizontal row a to i, these new shapes, x and y, can combine in a distribution with shape **d** to form a vertical row because they have similar grey levels, 41, 42, and 43, and they are all 8 pixels apart from each other. This means that shape **d**, as a grey shape, can either be part of a horizontal row of nine shapes, or part of a vertical row of three shapes. But shape **d**, as well as being grey, is also a square, as is shape g, so, as a square, shape **d** is one of a pair as well as belonging to two different rows. Furthermore, you could see shape **d** as just a grey thing on its own or alternatively as just a square thing on its own.

So there are therefore (at least) five alternatives ways you can see shape **d**, and these are represented by the five pre-attentive datagrams, (1) to (5), shown at the bottom of Figure 10.2. All these datagrams are in every pixel of the region of grey square **d** in the iconic image. Let's assume that your attention has chosen pre-attentive datagram (3) with attributes **Av = 42** and **iRow/8**, that describes shape **d** as a part in a vertical row of similarly grey things. This generates an attended level datagram for **d** that holds the attributes of the selected pre-attentive datagram (3) *plus* the attributes of pre-attentive datagrams (1) and (5) that describe the other attributes of shape **d**. In summary, an attended datagram is a combination of the attributes from the selected pre-attentive datagram plus attributes from pre-attentive datagrams that describe the same uniform region.

The attended datagram **d** will generate the group region that overlays the vertical row as a whole as follows. Binding attributes **Av = 42** and **iRow/8** in attended datagram **d** will prime pre-attentive datagrams in shapes x and y because they too have attributes **Av = 42** and **iRow/8**, and together they produce a group region that overlays the shapes **d**, x and y; the datagrams at the group level (Figure 10.2) have the binding attributes **Av = 42** and **iRow/8** in their *Parts* sections. Your attention will now go to a group level datagram and into a parent component sequence that will identify in your long-term memory that this group region is a row and download the attribute Row into all group level datagrams.

Some groups of things are too large to fit into a single glance. When you look at a long hedge, for example, you have to move your eyes and turn your head to take it all in. When you do this, you get the feeling you are seeing a single continuous hedge rather than a number of different hedges one after the other. In other words, it is as if there is a single parent region for the hedge as a whole, extending over a series of iconic images.

To explain how we might achieve this, let us suppose that the row of nine shapes a–i in Figure 10.1 are only the visible section of a longer row a–m, and to see its non-visible section, shapes j, k, l and m, you must move your eyes to the right. To achieve this, you switch your attention from shape **d** to shape i and this moves your eyes so that shapes j, k, l and m enter your iconic image; however, this means you lose shapes a, b and c from the image because you can only see 11 shapes at a time, five on either side of the attended shape. But shapes a, b and c are not lost; they have been moved into the hidden part of the scene component layer where they create token pre-attentive datagrams with the same attributes that they had when they were visible. All shapes a–m are now in a continuous sequence, so the average grey level for the row can be calculated by the pre-attentive datagrams of every shape, and this then becomes the binding attribute that holds the extended row together. A group region follows and becomes the parent that holds together the row of shapes as a single thing.

In these examples, we have shown how our attention produces groups from dissimilar but related things through their pre-attentive datagrams. These procedures, rules, are fundamental and universal because they can be used to pull together data of any sort into a single concept. These are only simple examples because the implementation of this mechanism in the real world is enormously complex. In the Notes for Chapter 10, we look at some of the ways these rules are implemented and the implications that arise.

Developing these structures is an iterative process. Our attention is constantly testing data elements near to groups to see whether they can be incorporated either by extending the range of a defining attribute or because they have a similar distribution. This can involve passing information back through the pre-attentive level into the physical internal image to reset intensity thresholds and filters.

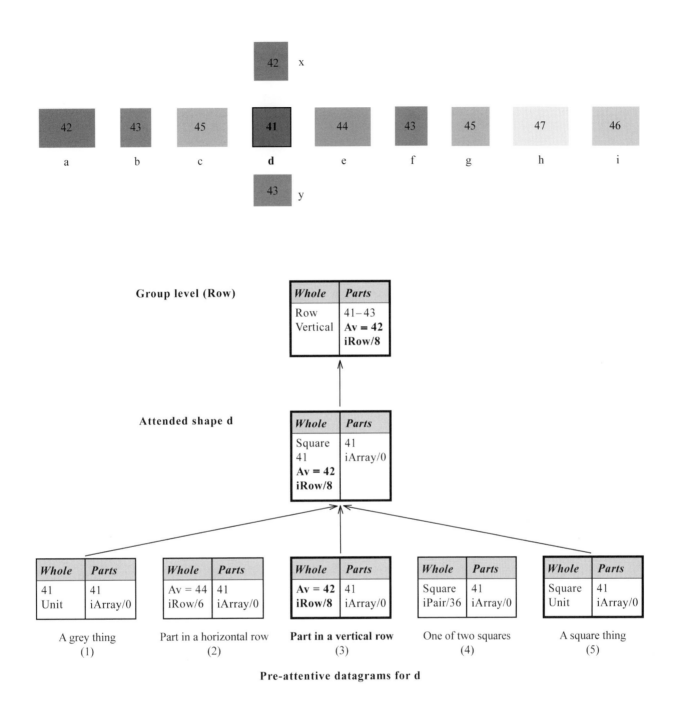

Figure 10.2 Selecting a single pre-attentive view of shape d from the many alternatives. There are many different ways in which we can view things in the iconic image. To illustrate this, we have added two shapes, x and y, to the row shown previously in Figure 10.1a. At the bottom of Figure 10.2, we show five pre-attentive datagrams numbered (1) to (5), each representing a different way of seeing the grey square **d**: (1) as a grey thing on its own; (2) as a grey thing in a horizontal row of similarly grey things; (3) as a grey thing in a vertical row of similarly grey things; (4) as a square in a pair with another square g; and (5) as a square on its own. In this example, our attention has selected pre-attentive datagram (3) that describes **d** as being a part in a vertical row, and has combined it with two pre-attentive datagrams (1) and (5) that tell us that, by itself, **d** has a grey level of 41 and that it is square; together, these three pre-attentive datagrams produce the composite attended datagram for shape **d**.

Whole	Parts
Vertical **Black** **iArray/6**	Black i/Array/0

Whole	Parts
Diagonal (U) **Black** **iArray/6**	Black i/Array/0

Datagram in all vertical black bars

Datagram in target diagonal black bar

(a)

Whole	Parts
White **Vertical** **iArray/6**	White i/Array/0

Whole	Parts
Black (U) **Vertical** **iArray/6**	Black i/Array/0

Datagram in all white bars

Datagram in target black bar

(b)

Figure 10.3 An object in a group 'pops out' if one of the attributes in its datagram is in a Unit (U) distribution; in other words, the object has an attribute that no other object in the group possesses. (a) In this group of black bars, the diagonal bar 'pops out' because its datagram, the one on the right, is the only one with a diagonal attribute, marked (U). (b) When you see this figure as a group of vertical bars the black bar pops out because its datagram is the only one that has a black attribute, marked (U); all the other bars have white attributes. (After Palmer, 1999.)

Spotting the odd one out

We can easily pick out an object from a large group of similar objects if it has a characteristic that the others do not have. For example, if you are asked to pick out a black pebble on a beach where all the other pebbles are white, you will have no trouble in doing so. The object that is different seems to pop out – you don't have to examine lots of pebbles to find the one you are looking for. In addition, the speed with which it pops out does not seem to depend on the size of the group.

So what are the processes that direct us to one particular object? Figure 10.3a shows 21 black bars, each 6 pixels apart in an array. All of these are vertical except for one that is diagonal, and that is the one that pops out. When you see this grouping, your attention will choose a pre-attentive datagram with the group attributes **Black** and **Array/6**. This will bring the bars together as a group of black things and produce the attended datagrams in the vertical and diagonal bars shown in Figure 10.3a.

In Figure 10.3a, we have brought together all the bars as a group of black things with binding attributes **Black** and **iArray/6**. However, the diagonal black bar *as just a diagonal bar* is also in a Unit (U) distribution because

it is the only diagonal bar in the group. Any datagram containing an attribute in a Unit distribution attracts a high priority and 'pops out'.

In Figure 10.3b, we bring the bars together as a group of vertical things with the binding attributes **Vertical** and **iArray/6** in all its datagrams. The distribution for the black attribute in the black bar is Unit because all the other bars in the array are white, it will attract a high priority and 'pop out'.

But there seems to be something unsatisfactory about this last solution because when you first look at the bars, you see them first as a group of white bars, not a group of vertical bars. If this is so, the binding attributes must be White and Array/6, which means that the black bar is not part of this group of bars at all, so it clearly cannot pop out from a group it is not in!

Let's suggest that two things will happen here. Your attention first selects White and Array/6 as the binding attributes, and that is why you see the white array of bars straight away, but then your attention goes back to the pre-attentive level and selects on Vertical and Array/6 instead because this will incorporate the black bar into the array – it produces a bigger group.

This example illustrates again that the building of arrays is an iterative process: priorities drive attention to extend arrays by going backwards and forwards between the pre-attentive and attended layers, incorporating new elements into the array as this goes along. This is only possible because unselected pre-attentive datagrams always remain in place and continue to be prioritised, whereas attended datagrams are automatically deleted when attention moves outside the context of what you are currently looking at.

In summary, 'pop-out' is the method we use to find something in a group without having to inspect every item in turn. We first create a group that includes the thing we are looking for by binding its parts together with a common attribute. If there is one part in the group with an attribute that is not also in all the other parts in the group, it will have a Unit distribution, and it is the presence in an *attended* datagram of an attribute with a Unit distribution that makes that datagram pop out.

The key point about pop-out is that all the computations that lead to a datagram popping out are contained within a single datagram, so cross-references between the datagrams in the group are not needed.

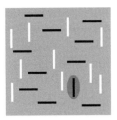

(a)

Whole	Parts
Black Vertical **Rectangle iArray/6**	Black iArray/0

Datagram of target bar
in group of rectangles

(b)

Whole	Parts
Vertical (U) Rectangle **Black iArray/8**	Black iArray/0

Datagram of target bar in
subgroup of black bars

(c)

Figure 10.4 A conjunction search picks out an object if the combination of its features is unique. (a) A group of black and white rectangular bars, some vertical and some horizontal. The target vertical black bar is unique within the group because it is the only bar that is both vertical and black. (b) A datagram in the target bar, its binding attributes telling us that it is in a collection of Rectangles. Neither the Black nor the Vertical attribute in this datagram is in a Unit distribution, so although the bar is unique it fails to pop out. To locate the target bar, we follow this first step by creating a subgroup of just black bars – a segment within the overall group. (c) The target bar datagram as a part in a black subgroup of the overall group of rectangular bars; this places its Vertical attribute in a Unit distribution (U), so the target bar will pop out. (After Palmer, 1999.)

A conjunction search is necessary when you need to identify an object that only becomes unique in a group when you combine two of its features.

When looking for the odd one out in a group, you must first find a feature that lets you define the group as a whole. Figure 10.4 shows an array of black and white bars mixed together. All the white bars are vertical, and all the black bars are horizontal except for one black bar, the target – this is vertical, and this vertical black bar is unique because it is the only one that is vertical *and* black. The attributes that are common across the group are **Rectangle** and **iArray/6**, so we attend a pre-attentive datagram with these binding attributes and this defines the group. However, the datagram in the target bar (Figure 10.4b) does not pop out because this has not put either of its attributes, Vertical and Black, into a Unit distribution – the target bar is still surrounded by both vertical and black bars.

But if our attention now goes to one of the black bars and selects the attribute for black, this will create a subgroup of just black bars, a segment within the overall group of rectangles, and among these is the target we are looking for – its datagram is shown in Figure 10.4c. The group binding attributes in this datagram are **Black** and **iArray/8**, and this time the attribute Vertical has a Unit distribution (U) because it is the only vertical bar in this subgroup of black bars. Because the target bar now has an attribute with a Unit distribution, it will be given a high priority and it will pop out.

Searching for things

We spend a lot of our time looking around for things, trying to separate out a particular object, or objects, from the clutter of information that surrounds us. Here we give a brief description of how we do this. It is important to remember that the search process is not taking place 'out there' in the world, although that is how it seems. What we are trying to do is to locate something in the internal image in our brains.

From work carried out by Ann Treisman, Jeremy Wolfe and others, we suggest that we generally search for things in three different ways, described here.

Parallel search

This is the form of search we described in the previous section: regardless of the number of objects in the array, the object with the unique feature will pop out provided it is the only object in the array with that feature. Your attention simply selects the common attribute for the whole array as the binding attribute, and the 'odd one out' object automatically pops out because its datagrams have an attribute with a Unit distribution.

Scene-based guidance

We see everything within the context of a scene, mostly ones we are familiar with, and we explained in Chapter 8 how we are able to locate things in scenes via the scene reference point. So suppose I am in the kitchen and my wife asks me to pass her coffee cup. I immediately access the description of her coffee cup held in my long-term memory, and download it into my visual iconic memory, where it is inserted *as a token datagram into a scene simulation* iconic memory because this datagram is a token for something that is not yet real. This target datagram does not give a full picture of the real cup but

a list of the cup's attributes: its shape, size and colour, which happens to be purple. The target token datagram is placed in the rough position in the scene simulation where cups in the kitchen are normally to be found. My attention switches to the target token datagram, and this gets copied into my short-term memory.

I then select one key attribute in the token datagram, the colour purple. Doing this gives a high priority to all purple pre-attentive datagrams in that area of the iconic image that hold the attribute purple, including my wife's cup, which happens to be the only purple thing in that part of the room. My attention switches to a datagram in this purple object and creates an attended datagram that is automatically copied into short-term memory. If the real attributes of this datagram match those in the token datagram, the object I am attending is recognised as the same thing, and the attribute for 'same' is transferred into the attended datagram of the cup. I can now reach out, take the purple cup from the cup rack and pass it to my wife. Although this is a very simple example of how we look for things, it covers most of the key features involved in the search process. First, we define the context of the search, which in this example is all the objects in the kitchen. Next, we locate a description of what we are looking for in our long-term memory – the parameters – and then we download this description into a target datagram positioned in the simulation of the scene. *Then*, finally, we use the target datagram's position and attributes to prioritise real datagrams holding those attributes so that our attention is drawn to them.

Serial search

Sometimes we have to attend a series of objects one by one in order to identify a particular feature that tells us that this is the one we are looking for. This is commonly described as serial search, as opposed to pop-out, which is usually referred to as parallel search. Most search sequences are a combination of the two.

Search is a complex area, and we have not covered many important aspects here. The most important rule is that *no search can take place until a parent group region has been defined that contains all the objects that could possibly match the target as a component*. This means that all the objects among which we are searching must have something in common. In this example, my wife's purple cup is among all the things that make up the scene that is the kitchen. That is their common characteristic, that is, the parent group region defining the limits of the search.

It is important to remember that when we are serial searching for something within our visual field, the thing we are looking for is not a complete object, it is in its fragmented pre-attentive form. To find my wife's cup, I must use a single key, purple, to locate a single purple pre-attentive datagram in the scene and hope that it will assemble into her coffee cup – the coffee cup does not become a coffee cup until you find it.

Sense attributes tell you what things look like

In the remainder of this chapter, we will present some ideas on how sense attributes give us the appearance of things and how they are represented as classes in long-term memory.

When your long-term memory recognises a cat, the attribute code for a cat is downloaded into the datagrams of the cat's iconic image, and if attended it will trigger the sensation code for a cat in the physical internal image of the cat. The code number has a dual role: in long-term memory, it represents a class, the class of every cat in the world for example, while the same number in a datagram in iconic memory is an attribute code that triggers the unique physical sensation that tells you this is a cat.

So the attribute code number for a cat does not produce a description of what a cat looks like – it just delivers a sensation that identifies it as a cat. For a description of a cat, you have to look at its parts, its tail, head, ears, eyes and so on. Each of these has its own attribute code number triggering a single sensation code that tells you what this or that component is, but again none of these code numbers helps you find out what a cat actually looks like. Select the attribute code number for 'curly' in a datagram in the cat's tail and you will learn that this is a curly thing, but you will not find out what a curly thing looks like. Only sensation codes in the physical internal image highlighted by sense attribute codes in the iconic image can tell you what a curly tail actually looks like.

Sense attribute code numbers in the iconic image are an abstract representation of the appearance of real things in the outside world. Most types of sense attribute comprise a range of code numbers, with each representing a small part of the range of that attribute – so, for example, the attribute code numbers for orientation might range from 0 to 90 with 0 representing vertical and 90 horizontal; similarly, grey levels might range from 0 to 500, with 0 for the blackest thing you will ever see and 500 for the whitest.

But sense attributes do not work in quite the same way that attributes representing cats do. To understand why, we must be clear about where 'the mind' begins and ends. We use the term 'internal image' up to the point where the raw sense data in the visual cortex have been partitioned into regions and edges but *before* they have been characterised

by datagrams. The raw internal image is a physical, material part of us, whereas the iconic image that overlays the internal image is information in the mind – its datagrams hold pure information so it has no physicality. However, the two types of image share exactly the same spatial organisation because the information image is constructed 'on top of' the material one.

When we attend a datagram in the iconic image, we create an attended extent. That extent is projected on to the pixels of internal image below it and highlights the region in the internal image that contains the physical features that produced the sense attributes codes in the information layer in the first place.

So when we attend the datagram of a thing, what do we actually 'see'? Not the attribute code numbers that stand for its appearance, as these are abstract. What we 'see' are the actual physical features in the internal image of the extent that has been highlighted in the iconic image. In other words, we see things physically, not as information; but what we choose to see is dictated by attention sequences taking place in the information structures of our minds.

To illustrate this, let us suppose you attend a datagram in a pixel in the top edge of a black square. This act will create an extent of datagrams along a ribbon of pixels in your iconic image, and they will highlight the same ribbon of pixels in the internal image that hold the actual top edge of the black square. What you will see is the actual physical edge in the internal image, and the sense attribute code number 90 in all the datagrams along the attended edge will trigger the physical sensation that the edge you are looking at is horizontal.

We need large numbers of values to represent most attribute types because we need to be able to identify small changes in value, but we also need to be able to see certain groups of values as a single class. For example, it would be useful to have a class of all Black things that covered all objects reflecting any value from 0 to 5 on a grey level scale of 500. If you then saw a black cat, the attribute code Black would be downloaded from long-term memory into its datagrams – provided its grey levels fell within the range 0–5. The problem is that if you attend the attribute code for Black in the cat's datagrams, it will not look black – the cat will not look black because the attribute Black only delivers the idea of black and not the very dark shade of grey we expect to see. To see how dark the cat looks, we must attend a sense attribute with a grey level from 0 to 5, in one of the cat's datagrams; only then will we see a cat in the internal image that looks black. But if Black doesn't look black, what then does the sensation of Black deliver? The answer is that the sensation code of Black is 'like' nothing else. Every non-sense attribute code is a meaningless unique number in the mind connected to an equally meaningless unique sensation in the brain. Furthermore, the sensation you feel on seeing Black, or on seeing a cat for that matter, will almost certainly be different from the one I will experience on seeing the same things. This is because new class codes have to be created continuously throughout our lives to provide identities for the new things we come across; whenever we need another one, we are simply allocating the next class/attribute code on the list, along with its particular sensation code. To experience the actual blackness of a black cat, you must attend sense attributes in datagrams in the base layer of the image of the cat so that they can highlight for you the sensation of its blackness in the internal image.

In this chapter, we have just scratched the surface of a number of fundamental issues, in particular the subject of pre-attentive datagrams and their relationship with attended datagrams, as well as where they sit in the boundary between our material and information worlds. We discuss these issues in more detail in the Notes on this chapter at the back of the book.

Summary

Groups are frequently created from parts for which the binding attributes are expressed as a range. In these cases, the binding attribute value must be represented by a single value that is representative of the values in the group, the group average for example. In addition, we use token datagrams in the scene component layer to integrate groups of things that extend outside our field of view into a single entity.

Pre-attentive datagrams hold a value for just one attribute, and for just one of its alternative distributions. So, for example, an unattended black square will have separate unconnected pre-attentive datagrams for it as a square thing and it as a black thing. Only when a pre-attentive datagram is attended will it draw on attributes in other pre-attentive datagrams that share the same region to produce a composite attended datagram that tells us this is a black square.

When an object pops out of a group, it is because one of its attributes does not have the same distribution in the group as the binding attribute. Serial search depends on matching candidates to a target datagram that has been set up in the simulation layer, and the population that contains the target object must be pre-specified as components of a group datagram. The context of every activity we engage in should be pre-specified in a similar way.

Finally, we explained how sense attributes help us to see what things look like, as well as the class they belong to and how we create classes to represent short sequences of sense values.

11

Three dimensions

The marble not yet carved can hold the form of every thought the greatest artist has.

(Michelangelo)

We live in a three-dimensional world, yet our retinas are two-dimensional surfaces. So, like cameras, our visual systems can only register things in two dimensions; we can only produce flat images. Touch is the same: our touch sensors are in a layer under the surface of the skin, and they too can provide only a two-dimensional picture.

In a scene, we convert two dimensions into three by inserting depth attributes, the distance from us, into the datagrams of things we are looking at. Adding depth to two-dimensional images produces what David Marr called a '2½-D view' of our three-dimensional world, not unlike the ones we see in children's pop-up books with their cut-out pictures arranged in depth to give a three-dimensional impression of a scene.

Figure 11.1 We see objects as collections of surfaces positioned at varying distances away from us. This scene from *Alice in Wonderland* is taken from a child's pop-up book, All the figures are printed on two-dimensional surfaces, yet we get the impression that they are three-dimensional. We are only able to record images in two dimensions, but by inserting depth attributes we get the impression we see things in three dimensions. (Original book, Sabada, 2002.)

In Figure 11.1, taken from *Alice in Wonderland*, the Mad Hatter takes the form of a two-dimensional image positioned in a three-dimensional relationship with the other guests at the tea party. We see objects in the world around us in a similar way as they present themselves as collections of surfaces, at varying distances from where we are standing, with some of their surfaces visible and some not.

If I look at the carriage clock in my sitting room from where I am standing, I will see only the clock face and its right-hand side, that is, two of its six surfaces. If I wish to know the time, I need process only the face of the clock, a two-dimensional surface – I have no need to process the clock in three dimensions. Only if I wish to pick up the clock to wind it do I need to have an idea of its volume and overall shape. Virtually all the information we need to know about things comes from their surfaces alone, and depth becomes a factor mainly when we need to physically interact with the thing we are dealing with.

For this reason, we do not normally create accurate internal three-dimensional models of what we see with every nut and bolt specified. Our internal representations need only be coded in enough detail for us to (1) recognise what we are looking at, (2) process the surface information it contains, (3) manipulate it if we wish to do so, and (4) predict how it will behave under certain conditions.

For example, we do not need to create an internal three-dimensional model of a car door to be able to open it – the car door is there physically in front of us, and we only need to be able to locate the handle and execute a general procedure for opening doors.

Surfaces

When you look at an object, you are in fact looking at one of its surfaces. We define a surface as *a region that has a single curvature throughout its entire extent;* any change of curvature in a surface creates an edge that marks the boundary of that surface. Flat surfaces are the simplest as they have zero curvature.

So, for example, the edges around the playing surface of a wooden chessboard define its extent because they are the points at which the top surface of the board joins the vertical surfaces that make up the board's sides. On the surface of a chessboard, there are 64 black and white squares. These are uniform regions of intensity 'in front' of the surface; they are not themselves surfaces because they are not each surrounded by edges of different curvature. The datagrams within each square will hold attributes for zero curvature, but these are secondary attributes of the square and are not binding ones.

We use a variety of clues to work out the curvature of surfaces. The richest sources of information for computing curvature depend on changes in the regularity of surface textures and on the distortion of familiar shapes. Flat surfaces are the simplest to identify because the edges of figures on flat surfaces are normally straight. Changes in the intensity of cast shadows and object movements also provide clues to the nature of surfaces and their edges. Stereoscopic vision provides limited information and is used primarily to compute depth. And of course edge shapes and vertices (where edges meet at a point) provide strong clues, as anyone familiar with wire frame modelling will be aware.

We compute orientation in three dimensions at points across surfaces because these values are particularly important in calculating the way a surface is rotated relative to the person looking at it. Surface rotation is represented by two attributes: the *slant* attribute tells you how far a surface is rotated horizontally, from side to side; and the *tilt* attribute tells you how far it is rotated vertically, from top to bottom.

It is not fully understood exactly how we compute the curvature and orientation of surfaces, but most of us have little difficulty in perceiving curvature and orientation in the objects around us, or indeed in seeing curvature and orientation in the flat images we see on paper and on computer screens every day.

The overall shapes of surfaces, and the shapes of things marked on them, change depending on the angle you view them at. For example, the edges of a rectangle slanted away from you cease to be parallel and, similarly, a slanted circle becomes an oval. To eliminate these distortions, we mentally rotate attended surfaces and turn them into a standard shape, one that our long-term memory can recognise.

The evidence for this mental rotation is striking (see the Notes for this chapter). It mimics the continuous nature of physical rotation and is clever enough not to be confused by symmetry – for example, we do not mistake a left hand for a right hand. Also, interestingly, a small mental rotation takes less time to complete than a long one. The mathematics for calculating the changing values in the surfaces of rotating three-dimensional objects has been around for decades in computer engineering design (CAD) software, and provides the basis for the animation we see in modern feature films.

The top figure in Figure 11.2a shows the internal iconic image of a flat rectangular shape with one end slanted away from the viewer at an angle of 45 degrees. Its straight edges and the markings on its surface tell you that

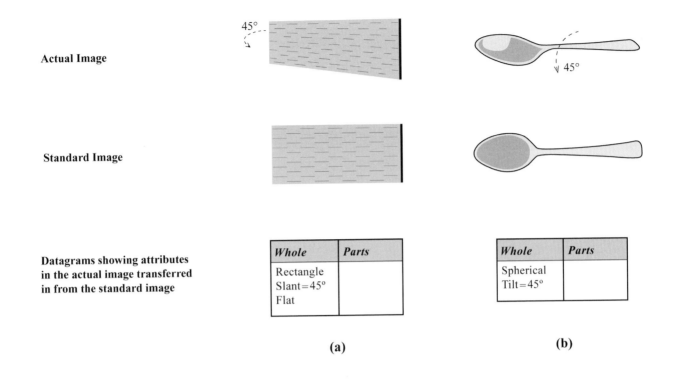

| | Actual Image | | Standard Image | | Datagrams showing attributes in the actual image transferred in from the standard image |

Figure 11.2 We rotate the images of surfaces until they match standard shapes. (a) The top shape is the iconic image of a flat, grey rectangle slanted away from us by 45 degrees. This iconic image is copied and mentally rotated until it gets to the point where it is recognised in long-term memory as a standard shape, a rectangle. Attributes in the datagrams of the actual image show its shape as a Rectangle and its sideways rotation as a Slant = 45°. (b) In the top image of the spoon, you are looking down at it at an angle of 45°. The shape of the bowl is irregular, but when you rotate the spoon towards you by 45 degrees, the bowl takes on a uniform spherical curvature. The attributes in its datagrams show it as having a standard Spherical shape on the basis that you tilt it towards you by 45 degrees.

its curvature is zero, so Flat is recorded in every one of its datagrams. But its top and bottom edges are no longer parallel, so it does not have a regular shape that can be identified in long-term memory.

If you attend the actual image of the rectangle, you will fail to recognise its shape, so you copy its image into a separate iconic layer and rotate it until it reaches a position where its shape is recognised in long-term memory, in this example as a rectangle. The attribute code for Rectangle is transferred from long-term memory into all the datagrams of the *actual image*, along with the degree of rotation, Slant = 45°, that was necessary to produce it (see the datagram in Figure 11.2a). Although the actual projected shape in the image is clearly not a rectangle, it is coded as a rectangle and we will think of it as a rectangle – but as one slanted sideways by 45 degrees.

The same principles apply to surfaces that are curved. Surfaces that are uniformly curved only appear to be so when they are seen from a particular viewpoint – face on.

Therefore, to identify uniform curvature, we again have to duplicate the shape's image and rotate it.

In the top part of Figure 11.2b, you are looking down at a spoon from an angle of 45 degrees, and as a result your internal image of the spoon is rotated by 45 degrees. The bowl of the spoon has a uniformly spherical curvature, like part of the surface of a sphere, but because the spoon is seen at an angle, the rate of curvature recorded in the datagrams will vary across the bowl – it is no longer uniform. The bowl is not recognised as spherical in your long-term memory, so again you copy it into a separate image layer and rotate it until all the curvature values in the pixels of the bowl become the same, that is, spherical. You then transfer the Spherical curvature attribute values into all the datagrams of the actual image of the bowl, and in addition record that it is rotated: Tilt = 45°. It is important to be clear that the actual and rotated figures are both *completely flat*; it is the only the *numbers* in the datagrams of the rotating figure that change – and of course the shape of its outline.

These attributes that have been created and incorporated into the datagrams in the actual image do not replace the attributes that describe the shape as it is – you can still observe the true shape and curvature of the captured image if you so choose.

Some regular shapes can be made into better shapes, and the more symmetrical a shape becomes, the more likely it is to achieve a match in long-term memory. For example, we will rotate an oval to see if it will turn into a circle.

Note that the rotation of shapes to match a single standard image in long-term memory is confined to attended processing. We do match shape attributes in unattended datagrams in long-term memory but use a very different procedure to do this.

Objects

We have established that a surface is any region in the iconic image that has the same curvature throughout. Objects are simply collections of connected surfaces or, to be more precise, *an object is any collection of surfaces all of which are directly or indirectly connected to each other so that they make a whole.* The test is that you must be able to travel from any one surface of an object to any other of that object's surfaces simply by crossing shared boundaries. The binding attribute in the *Parts* sections of connected surfaces therefore always have an interval of 1.

We identify individual objects from both the nature of their surfaces and the way in which those surfaces are organised in three dimensions. Figure 11.3a shows a child's alphabet brick that has the letter A imprinted on its front face. You are looking at the brick from above and from the right, so you can see only its front, top and right-hand surfaces. The datagrams on the cube's surfaces will have attributes for shape, rotation and depth. The brick you are looking at is a three-dimensional object, but inside your visual cortex it is a flat, two-dimensional image coded with three-dimensional attributes.

The visible surfaces of the cube come together to produce a two-dimensional group Parent region that represents them as a single object (see the middle part of Figure 11.3b). The parent region, which is flat, is positioned *in between* the cube's front and back surfaces, and its shape is the area enclosed by the *outside* boundary of all its visible surfaces. This is a similar set-up to the one that represents objects in front of other objects, as described in Figure 6.4.

We process the surfaces of the child's brick in very much the same way that we process scenes. The first thing we must do is establish a reference surface for the object

as a whole. In this example, we will assume that you choose as its reference surface the brick's front surface, the one with the **A** imprinted on it. The attributes for the reference surface of the brick are Slant = 0° and Tilt = 0°, and these are the values held in the datagrams in the reference surface (**A**). The attributes Slant = 15° and Tilt = 15°, the true orientation of the reference surface, are copied into the datagrams of the *parent region* (**P**) to represent the rotation of the brick as a whole *in relation to the viewer*. The parent region **P** is now positioned in the same plane as the front surface of the brick.

As we have said, the cube as a whole is slanted 15 degrees to one side and tilted 15 degrees, and the attributes in the Parent region datagrams, Slant = 15° and Tilt = 15°, now reflect this. Each time attention moves from the group datagram (**P**) to a component surface datagram, it will subtract the parent slant and tilt from those in the component surface so that the attributes of each surface *reflect the orientation and position of that surface relative to the object as a whole* and not relative to the person looking at it.

You now go through a parent/component attention sequence to identify this figure as a cube. Your attention starts at a central datagram (**P**) in the group parent region and then goes, in turn, to datagrams in each of the three visible surfaces (**A**), (**T**), and (**S**). Although the directions of the lines joining the parent and component datagrams (PA, PT and PS) are in two dimensions, we can compute the three-dimensional position of each surface by using the depth attributes held in their datagrams.

You can see the results in the datagrams in Figure 11.3c. This shows that the attributes In-front, Up and Right have been inserted into the datagrams of the front, top and side surfaces, respectively, by the movement of attention. It also shows that the top surface of the brick is tilted back 90 degrees from the front surface, and that the side surface is slanted by 90 degrees in relation to the front surface. No matter how the cube is rotated, the attributes that describe its component surfaces do not change: they always locate each of its surfaces in its correct position relative to the reference surface.

Of course, most objects are more complicated than a child's brick. We usually identify a car by what it looks like from the front, its standard view being a head-on one. The surface of the windshield is a good reference surface because all cars have a windshield that faces the front, although this is tilted away from us when ideally we would like the standard surface to be vertical, thus having zero rotation. We can get around this by putting a non-zero tilt in the reference object instead of a zero one.

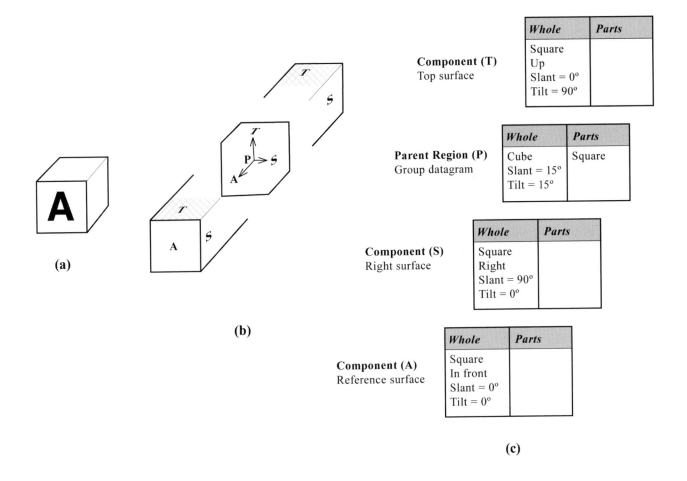

Whole	Parts
Square Up Slant = 0° Tilt = 90°	

Component (T)
Top surface

Whole	Parts
Cube Slant = 15° Tilt = 15°	Square

Parent Region (P)
Group datagram

Whole	Parts
Square Right Slant = 90° Tilt = 0°	

Component (S)
Right surface

Whole	Parts
Square In front Slant = 0° Tilt = 0°	

Component (A)
Reference surface

(a)

(b)

(c)

Figure 11.3 How we identify objects from their surfaces. (a) This shows a child's alphabet brick slanted 15 degrees and tilted 15 degrees so that its side and top, **S** and **T**, become visible. (b) A two-dimensional parent region **P** representing the brick as a whole has been inserted between its front and back surfaces. The boundary of the parent region is the combined outer edges of the brick. (c) The datagrams for the brick, for Parent region (**P**), and for each of the three component surfaces of the brick that are visible, (**A**), (**S**) and (**T**).

Scenes

The position of any object within a three-dimensional scene depends on (1) how far it is to the left or right of the scene reference point, (2) how far it is above or below the scene reference point, and (3) where it is located within the body of the scene.

When you look at an object, the slightly different views you receive from each eye are used to calculate how far away that object is from where you are. But there is a problem. Unlike the other two scene coordinates (vertical and horizontal), the distance attribute only tells you the distance between you and the object; it does not tell you the position of the object in the scene. If I move around my sitting room while looking at the clock on the mantlepiece, the distance from me to the clock will change continuously even though the clock's position in the scene has not changed.

To solve this problem, we need to establish an unchanging position for any object in a scene *regardless of where we are in the scene ourselves*. We do this by creating a *standard viewpoint* so that the positions of all the objects within a scene are always the distance they are from the same fixed point in the scene. Only by standardising the viewing position will the coordinates for the position of an object be the same every time, and only then can our long-term memories tell us whether or not that object has moved. This means we now have both a reference point and a viewpoint for every familiar scene stored in long-term memory so that we have the basis for locating any object in the body of any scene in three dimensions.

In theory, it does not matter exactly where the standard viewpoint for a scene is located, although once set its position never changes. The standard viewpoint is usually positioned at a point near the centre of a scene facing the reference object. For example, in my sitting room it would be a point near the centre of the room facing the fireplace. There is a line joining the scene reference point to the standard viewpoint, which is called the reference line, and the distance between these is held in the reference point datagram. It makes sense for the reference line to be at right angles to the reference object. When we enter a scene, the first thing we do is look for the reference object so we can use it to fix the reference point. But how do we locate the standard viewpoint, as it is not attached to anything but is just somewhere in the three-dimensional void in the middle of the scene?

When we enter a scene, we look at familiar objects and compare their distance and size attributes against our record of them in long-term memory. We then use the differences between the actual and the stored attribute values to compute where the standard viewpoint is. In other words, the position of the standard viewpoint is automatically calculated for us from the objects in the scene, so we do not need to know where the viewpoint is. It is not necessary for us to go to the standard viewpoint physically – we only need keep track of our displacement from it and adjust the position attributes of the things we see by that difference. As I move around my sitting room, these displacement factors are continuously recalculated, so although the positions of objects change in my iconic image, they do not appear to change at all. The positions of objects in a scene no longer depend on where I am.

It would make sense for the scene reference point datagram to hold the factors that locate the viewpoint and track our changing position in a scene; this way, a single position can act as the group parent in three dimensions.

But we don't always want to observe things as part of a scene. Often we wish to look at objects just in relation to ourselves. You can achieve this by transferring your attention to a personal reference point in the iconic image that produces coordinates in datagrams so that the positions of the objects you are looking at become relative to you, the viewer. So, for example, if I want to go to the carriage clock on my mantlepiece to advance its hands because it is running slow, I want to see its position relative to myself when I pick it up, and not relative to where it is in the scene. I first locate the clock from its scene coordinates, but then I switch to my personal reference point datagram as parent, so I see the clock in relation to myself and not to the overall scene. We expand on the role of our personal reference point in chapter 16.

Your body, like any other object, creates datagrams in the iconic image, so it too has a position relative to the viewpoint. You are simply another object in the room, a thing like any other. If you move from the door to the fireplace, your position in the image will change, and the attributes in your datagrams in the image that give your scene position will adjust to reflect your new position in the room. The datagrams of you in the image will also hold your own unique attribute code number, supplied courtesy of your long-term memory, and if you choose to attend one of them, you will experience the unique sensation that this is you.

The area an object takes up in the iconic image is a reflection not simply of its size, but also of how far away it is. So that we can have a consistent size value for an object regardless of how far away it is, we adjust the recorded size attributes, the area it is occupying in the image, to the size attributes that would be recorded if the object were at a standard distance from us, 1 metre away for instance.

We can use this size-scaling procedure in reverse. If we recognise an object that is some distance away from us and we know its size at 1 metre, we can compute how far away it is. Similarly, if we see an unknown object in the vicinity of a known object, we can calculate how far away they both are from the size of the known object, and use this information to compute the standard size of the unknown object.

The three sets of space attributes

Three systems are used for describing space. These systems each use different attributes, but because they all operate within the same framework and use the same unit of measurement, the pixel, they are consistent with each other. The three are as follows:

- *Distribution attributes*. As we described in Chapter 3, these tell you the position of a thing in relation to other things that belong to the same class. Distribution attributes are automatically generated in pre-attentive datagrams, and they describe the type of distribution and the interval between its elements.

- *Dimensional attributes*. These describe the internal characteristics of the extent of a thing – its height, area and curvature, for example. Like distribution attributes, dimensional attributes are generated automatically in pre-attentive datagrams.

- *Context attributes*. These tell you the positions, coordinates, of things in relation to a parent, the context. They can be within the context of a self-contained group of things, within the context of a scene, or within the personal context of you the viewer. The context is chosen by attention, and context attributes are generated by attention moving from parent to component within the chosen structure. Image coordinates, including depth, are also assigned to pre-attentive datagrams because image coordinates are necessary for priority-setting and for the control of unattended behaviour.

It is important to emphasise again that only those things we are attending are in a form we would recognise. Everything else in the image is in the pre-attentive form of disconnected alternatives. If a bird is flying overhead and is within your field of view but you do not attend it, then its body, in your internal image, is not connected to its wings, and its beak is not connected to its head; the part of the image where the bird is flying is an incoherent collection of primitive unconnected shapes, pre-attentive or proto-objects. If one of these disconnected shapes now catches your attention, you

will assemble those disconnected shapes into a bird, and it will be populated with attended datagrams that tell you what it is and what it looks like. You cannot know what something looks like if you have not attended it because its elements are dispersed. Exactly how one pre-attentive datagram will combine with another pre-attentive datagram cannot be known until your attention makes a choice.

The continuous switching of information between the pre-attentive and attended forms affects how you see things in scenes. When you enter your garden, you identify some of its features, and as a result your long-term memory recognises it as your garden and downloads its class code number. You will then attend this in a scene datagram, and you will know this is your garden and that its extent covers the entire image. But the attributes in the scene datagram do not tell you what is in your garden; to find that out, you have to go to datagrams in the scene component layer, which at this point is still a collection of incoherent pre-attentive datagrams.

To see the things in your garden, you must convert these pre-attentive datagrams into a bed of roses, a lawn and a child's swing by attending them. Because all this switching happens quickly and in the same context, you feel that you are seeing these things together in a moment in time, a composite, when you are in fact experiencing a sequence of impressions rather than a single picture. The reason that you get this impression is that all the things in the garden have become time components of a group time region, a space/time extent that overlays them. The group time datagrams hold the elapsed time taken to look around the scene and a single 'average' time – the midpoint value of the elapsed time, say – and these are downloaded into the datagrams of all the things in the garden. So, although each thing in the garden is recorded at a different point in time, we see everything as having the same average time or *present time*. These are the same principles that we proposed, when earlier in Chapter 10, we assembled a sequence of grey shapes into a row.

One of the reasons you can process information so quickly is that when your attention leaves a datagram to go to another one, the one you have just left does not always revert to its pre-attentive form. This means that when you revisit a previously attended region at the parent-region level, you do not have to reconstruct it *provided* you have not moved outside the context that brought your attention to that datagram in the first place. The context is partly defined by long-term memory and partly by the position of the attended region within the active datagram hierarchies in the layers of iconic memory. The positions and roles of datagrams in the active hierarchy are determined by their status codes that were introduced in Chapter 5.

Attributes in pre-attentive datagrams can control unattended action sequences provided the context has in advance been set up in long-term memory by attention. For example, I can walk around my sitting room avoiding the furniture without paying attention to what I am doing. I can do this because I have trained my long-term memory to recognise each obstacle by a single pre-attentive datagram. If I automatically avoid walking into the coffee table, it is not because I have recognised it as a coffee table but because some particular feature, its brass edges (say), have triggered an automatic 'if this, then that' reaction in long-term memory. The subject of unattended processes is dealt with in Chapter 16 in more detail.

A final general comment on the subject of three dimensions. Throughout the book, we deal entirely with two-dimensional images because two-dimensional extents are the only ones our senses can produce directly from the raw data. We use attributes for depth and curvature to extend two dimensions into '2½'- dimensions but accept that this can only produce an approximation of a real world of three-dimensional objects.

Yet this might be putting things the wrong way around. We can only ever experience the extent of *things* directly in two dimensions of space and one of time, so we can only ever *know* two space dimensions. We use a third dimension to help us understand how things change and move over time, but we cannot *know* that three space dimensions are a direct reflection of the outside reality.

Summary

The iconic image is a two-dimensional representation of what we are looking at. By adding an attribute for depth, the distance to an object, we obtain a '2½-D' impression of the world. We define a surface as a region that has the same curvature throughout its extent; an object is a thing made from surfaces all of which are connected directly or indirectly to each other. Curvature is described by attributes stored in datagrams in a two-dimensional image of the surface.

In long-term memory, we hold a standard view of the things we are familiar with. We mentally rotate objects until they present a standard view that we can recognise, and we insert the attributes that describe these manipulations into the datagrams of the original image, along with its identity.

So we can locate exactly where things are within the body of a scene, we establish a standard viewpoint, and when the distances from this viewpoint are combined with reference point coordinates, we get a three-dimensional fix for the positions of everything in a scene. In this way, the position attributes of things in a scene are not affected by where we are standing at the time we see them.

As a result, we now have three sets of attributes for describing the positions of things. Distribution attributes describe the position of a thing relative to other things that belong to the same class; dimensional attributes describe the nature of the extent of a thing; and context attributes describe the position of a thing relative to a parent of our choosing.

12

The way things move

People call me a painter of dancers, but I really wish to capture movement itself.

(Edgar Degas)

Specialised groups of nerve cells detect when things are moving across our retinas and generate attributes in the datagrams of the iconic image that tell us how fast something is moving and in what direction.

Figure 12.1a shows a black cat running across my sitting room in front of the fireplace. My internal image of the cat does not actually move – it is a static snapshot of the cat taken at the moment in time that the image was captured. In other words, I cannot see the cat *in the act of moving*; I only know that the cat is moving because the movement attributes in the datagrams of his 'still' figure give me the sensation that this is something moving in relation to its background. (As an aside, you are able to capture a stable image of a moving object by following it with your eyes, in smooth pursuit, but your visual system cannot then tell you how fast and in what direction it is going.)

You think that you see the state of the world as it is now. But what you really see is the state of the world as it was some time ago. This is because after each eye movement, as we explained in Chapter 9, it takes a further 100 msec to set up the datagrams in the new image. So by the time I get to see the cat running across my sitting room, the data are already 100 msec old, and the cat's position in the room is out of date by the distance he has moved in that time. But what I really need to know is of course where the cat is *now*, not where he was at the time I captured the image.

We all have an internal clock that tells us the time an image was captured, and there are attributes in datagrams that tell us how things are moving. Using this internal information, I can calculate the cat's position in the image at any time in the future – provided of course that he does not change the way he moves in the meantime.

However, simply updating the positional attributes in the datagrams of the captured cat figure does not give the full picture because my internal figure of the cat is still in the wrong place in the image. I need to move the figure of the cat across the image so I can see his true position as he runs across in front of the fireplace. But how do I do this?

In advance of releasing each new iconic image, I need to compute the future positions in the scene of *every* object in the image and insert token datagrams into the image that predict their future paths. These predicted object positions are held in time layers that overlay the real image. Tokens switch on and off in successive layers as their predicted time becomes the time it is *now* – the effect is a bit like the way the bulbs in a chain of Christmas lights switch on and off in sequence to give the impression of a light moving in the dark.

The full internal image of the cat, together with all the datagrams that describe him, remains unchanged in the position where it was originally captured. The token datagrams that mark the cat's future positions do not hold a full description; instead they only hold its 'cat' identity plus its movement attributes and a status code that, when active, indicates that this is the token for where the cat is *now*. If I transfer my attention to an active token, I will become aware of where the cat is *now* and also aware of the sensation of 'being in the present'. This is because token datagrams have an attribute 'now' that becomes active when the datagrams' *now* status becomes active. So when I attend the cat's token for *now* and then transfer my attention to the full image captured some time earlier, I will see the 'old cat' in his new position in the 'present'.

To illustrate all this, let's assume that the cat runs across the room in front of the fireplace at 10 metres per second (this is a very fast cat!) (Figure 12.1a).

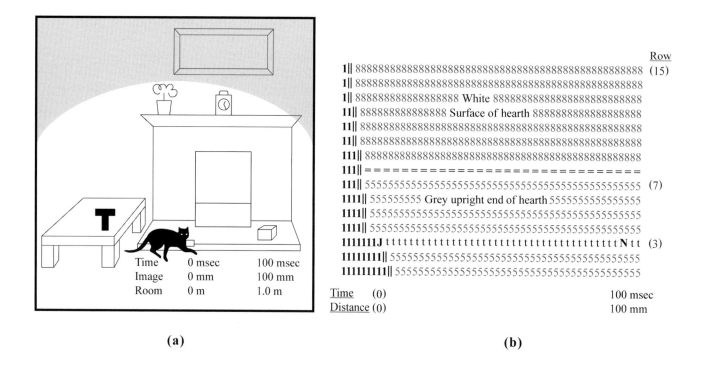

The figure (b) shows rows of datagrams:

```
                                                                    Row
1‖ 8888888888888888888888888888888888888888888888888888  (15)
1‖ 8888888888888888888888888888888888888888888888888888
1‖ 88888888888888888 White 8888888888888888888888888888
11‖ 88888888888888 Surface of hearth 888888888888888888
11‖ 8888888888888888888888888888888888888888888888888888
11‖ 8888888888888888888888888888888888888888888888888888
111‖ 8888888888888888888888888888888888888888888888888888
111‖ ==============================
111‖ 5555555555555555555555555555555555555555555555555555  (7)
1111‖ 555555555 Grey upright end of hearth 5555555555555555
1111‖ 5555555555555555555555555555555555555555555555555555
1111‖ 5555555555555555555555555555555555555555555555555555
1111111J ttttttttttttttttttttttttttttttttttttttttttttNtt  (3)
11111111‖ 5555555555555555555555555555555555555555555555555555
111111111‖ 5555555555555555555555555555555555555555555555555555

Time     (0)                                    100 msec
Distance (0)                                    100 mm
```

In figure (a):

Time   0 msec   100 msec
Image   0 mm   100 mm
Room   0 m   1.0 m

(a)   **(b)**

Figure 12.1 Tracking the path of a cat as it runs across the room. We can only capture three images of the cat every second, which is not enough to track his progress across the room, so to compensate for this we create tokens that predict where the cat will be at intervals of a few milliseconds in the future. (a) The detailed iconic image of the scene at the time it was captured (0 ms). (b) Token datagrams (**t**) are shown on line (3) marking the predicted position, at 2.5 msec intervals, of a point on the cat's leading edge (**J**) as he crosses the room; each **t** is in a different time layer. The **N** token on the path at 100 msec is the point where the cat is now, the time our internal clock tells us is the present moment.

The cat, coming from my left, catches my attention, and I execute a saccade to him, producing the internal iconic image shown in Figure 12.1a. The cat is captured just as he passes the left-hand side of the fireplace. The attributes in the cat's datagrams give me a description of the cat at the instant the image was captured, time (0). They tell me how fast he is moving across the image (1 mm per msec) and in what direction (across the front of the fireplace). From this information, I automatically create a sequence of token datagrams (**t**) that are spread across the new image in time layers predicting the future positions of the cat in the scene (Figure 12.1b). In this example, tokens have been created to predict the cat's position at 2.5 msec intervals as he runs across the room. All this information is inserted in the iconic image before it is released.

After 100 msec, the image and datagrams of the cat that describe the instant of capture are released. The full internal description of the cat never changes, but in the 100 msec that have elapsed since the image was captured, he has moved across the room. To see the cat where he is *now* in the image, my attention must go to the token datagram in the time layer that predicts where the cat should be after 100 msec. The token **N** at 100 mm in the row of **t** symbols marks the position in the image where the cat is *now*, 100 msec after I captured him visually. But while the cat moves at 1 mm per msec, that is, 1 metre per second, in the image, he moves across the room 10 times faster than this – at 10 metres per second. So after 100 msec, while the cat has only moved 100 mm across the image, he has in real life moved 1.0 metres across the fireplace – because in this example 1 mm per msec in the iconic image equates to 10 metres per second in the room itself.

To see the cat's features in detail, my attention must go to the datagrams in the static cat figure at time (0). They tell me what the cat looked like 100 msec ago, but I will believe that this is how the cat looks *now*. We can never see anything 'live'; what we see is a strange combination of how things looked a short while ago plus an estimate of where they are now. We can never see anything as it really is because of the time needed to convert raw data into a form that we can understand.

After 100 msec, when the cat has travelled 1.0 metre across the room, he passes in front of a small box that sits on the hearth, and as a consequence the box is hidden from view by the cat's body. To reflect this, the token datagrams for the box in the time layer position 100 mm will be given a status that makes them 'disappear' when the time for *now* moves to 100 msec. In other words, static objects are sequenced through time in successive time layers in exactly the same way that moving ones are; it is just that their positions do not change.

So by the time the new image has been released, the future paths of all objects, moving or not, attended or otherwise, have been pre-programmed step by step into time layers so that we can identify the future positions of any object at any point in time. Although we are normally concerned with attending tokens that give the position of things for *now*, we can also attend tokens that are backwards or forwards in time; in this way, we can find out where an object has been in the past or where it will be in the future.

For example, after 100 msec, rather than looking at where the cat is now, my attention could go back in time to see the cat when he was at position (0), or alternatively I could move my attention forwards 700 msec into the future and anticipate that the cat is going to run into a chair because the tokens of the two objects in the future coincide. Whether we choose to look at the present, past or future depends on the priority values set in the token datagrams as well as those set in the datagrams in the full image.

So what information do we hold in these tokens? To answer this, we need to go back to how we detect movement in the first place, and the answer is quite surprising, because we cannot identify directly that a thing is moving as a whole – we can only detect moving edges. Moreover, we can only accurately measure the movement of edge junctions, the points where two edges meet. What each token sequence shows us is simply the path an edge junction takes as it crosses the image, starting at the position of that junction in the full captured image, its position at time (0).

In the small section of the iconic image shown in Figure 12.1b, the grey levels 8, 5 and 1 describe the different surfaces. The 8s represent the horizontal white surface of the hearth, and the 5s the vertical surface at the front of the hearth where it ends, with the horizontal row of = = = marking the edge separating these two surfaces. The **111**‖s are the front of the cat, with the upper vertical edge being his leading shoulder and the lower edge being the top of his leg; these two edge runs meet at junction **J**.

The **t**s are a row of tokens that predict the future position of junction **J** at 2.5 msec intervals as the cat moves across the image. Each of these tokens will become active (and then inactive) in turn as the *now* time moves along the row. There will be many junctions in the structure of our cat, not only in his boundary edges, and each of these junctions will have its own token path and starting position that originates in the static figure of the cat.

If the cat produces many different tokens and therefore many token paths, how do I decide exactly where the cat is at a particular point in time? As we have said before, objects do not have one particular position, and the position of an object is, by definition, the position of the pixel that holds the datagram you choose to attend. So if I attend the token datagram **J** at time *now*, after 100 msec, that part of the cat is where the cat as a whole is now.

Tokens create groups in time layers that provide crude representations of their extents. Where two extents share the same position in the same time layer, we use their depth attributes to predict which one is in front and which is behind. The datagrams of the 'behind' object are then given a status indicating that it is not visible. This is how we were able to make the box on the hearth disappear behind the cat after 100 msec.

On average, we create fewer than three iconic images a second. Each of these images is a 'still': it remains unaltered for somewhere around 400 msec before it is completely replaced by the next one. Yet we are able to respond to changes in our visual field in less than 100 msec. How can this be?

For a third of a second, the iconic image is frozen, and if a moving object suddenly changes its direction or speed, its future positions, as predicted by token datagrams, will be incorrect. To deal with this during the fixation period, we continuously compare predicted positions with actual positions from the outside world. We automatically capture a limited iconic image every 50 msec or so, and produce datagrams for just edges, junctions and simple data groups *at the pre-attentive level only*. These 'real' datagrams crudely represent where things *actually* are. By comparing the positions of 'real' datagrams with their token equivalents, we can check that things are where they should be, whether the cat is in the position we predicted – or not.

The same verification process is applied to objects that are not moving, so that if an object suddenly appears or disappears, this will be detected. A traffic light switching from red to green, or an object disappearing because something has passed in front of it, is an example of a failure to predict.

All objects in the iconic image are subject to this verification process whether or not they are attended. When an object's token fails the verification test, its token datagrams are marked as inactive and its future predictions are disabled – but *no changes are made to the visual content* of the full iconic image; it remains fixed until it is completely replaced. The priority-setting system takes into account token mismatches and if necessary directs attention to unverified token datagrams, and if it does so, it will generate an interrupt in the current attention sequence. Interrupts almost always trigger saccades to the object that created the mismatch so that the old image is immediately replaced with current data.

It is likely that we retain predictions from images prior to the current one, and in this way we are able to look back at where things were in the past, seconds ago rather than just milliseconds ago. Here we are looking at old predictions as if they were actual records of events, but because the verification deletes inaccuracies, these old tokens can become reliable memories. The verification process is completely separate and different from the full image-building cycle. It is only when we capture and attend things in the full image that we get a new picture of how things look.

Finally, as we pointed out earlier in this chapter, we can never see things as they are *now* because it takes time to process the images we receive into a form we can understand.

The things we see are a composite of how they were at some time in the past combined with a prediction of where they should be now.

Summary

When we capture a moving object following an eye movement, we interpret the information in two ways. First, we record the object in full detail in the iconic image as a snapshot at a point in time and include in its datagrams attributes that describe the way it is moving. In addition, we insert token datagrams into successive time layers across the image, thus producing a pathway that tells us where the object will be in the future. When we attend a moving object, we see its detailed image not in the position in which that image was captured, but in the position it should be in *now*.

Token datagrams become active when the time of their predicted position becomes the time it is *now*, and an active token becomes inactive as soon as the time for *now* switches to the next time token. Tokens create crude extents that enable us to predict when one object will pass another or when two objects might collide. We regularly check the predicted positions of things against real data from the retina during the fixation period.

It takes time to create both the still image and its tokens, so by the time we get to see an object, the information about it is at least 100 msec old. We can never see something as it really is, nor can we see it in its true position at the present time.

Evidence for a split in the processing of moving things is supported by the case of a patient admitted to hospital with a complete inability to perceive motion. She could only see moving things as a series of snapshots, stills. A paper describing the case is (Zihl, J., Von Cramon, D., & Mai, N. (1983). Selective disturbance of movement vision after bilateral brain damage. Brain, 106, 313-340). The case is summarised in Chapter 10 of S. Palmer's *Vision Science.*

13

The attributes of time

Every instant of time is a pinprick of eternity.

(Marcus Aurelius)

The internal image is a two-dimensional collection of pixels. Each pixel receives values from the outside world, and we use this information to create datagrams in the iconic image that help us to understand what we are seeing. The information in the image's pixels provides a spatial description of the way things are at a particular point in time.

But things in the world do not stay the same way for ever. They constantly change, and unless we introduce a representation for time, we will be unable to track events, plan the future and exert control over our lives. In the iconic image, we count along rows of pixels to get the sizes of things and the intervals between things. We now introduce rows of pixels in time that we can count to measure how long things last and how things relate to each other over time.

Pixels are fundamental units. Every pixel is 1 space unit, the smallest any thing can be – *this is a rule*. In the visual cortex, each space pixel has an actual size, and for the purposes of illustration we will assume that every space pixel is a miniature square 1 mm by 1 mm.

In the same way that the space pixel is the fundamental unit of space, so there is a time pixel that is the fundamental unit of time – 1 time unit. Again, for the purposes of illustration, we will assume that the each time pixel lasts 1 msec, or one thousandth of a second. These two types of pixel – space and time – combine so that every pixel in the iconic image becomes a tiny three-dimensional cube, a combination of 1 space pixel with 1 time pixel at right angles to it. These three-dimensional pixels are the smallest units that exist, and we will refer to them as Pixels with a capital P (Figure 13.1b).

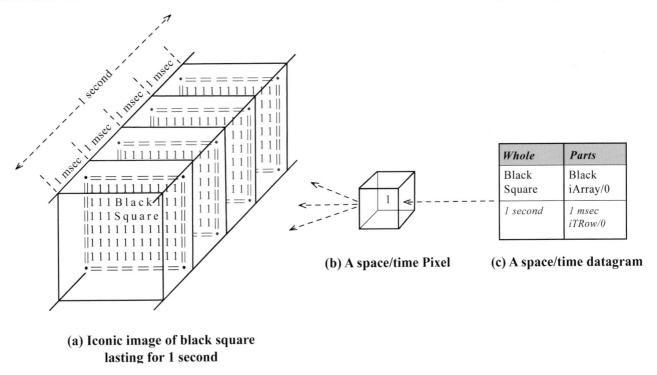

(a) Iconic image of black square lasting for 1 second

(b) A space/time Pixel

(c) A space/time datagram

Whole	Parts
Black Square	Black iArray/0
1 second	*1 msec iTRow/0*

Figure 13.1 The representation of things in space and time. A black square is flashed on a white screen for 1 second.
a) The time-row of the black square in the iconic image. (b) A Pixel in the time-row holding a datagram describing the black square in space and over time. (c) The space/time datagram in every Pixel describing the 1 second exposure of a black square.

When you look at a black square flashed on a white screen for a second, you create a three-dimensional space/time region of black Pixels in iconic memory (Figure 13.1a). Each space pixel in the image of the black square is extended into three dimensions by 1 time pixel; together, they produce a single *instance* of the black square that lasts 1 time unit, that is, 1 *msec* in our example. Successive instances of the black square, each lasting 1 time pixel, become a *time-row* that extends for as long as the square lasts. In this example the square lasts for *1 second*.

A single Pixel cube is shown in Figure 13.1b; its dimensions are 1 mm × 1 mm × 1 msec. The datagram describing the life of the black square (Figure 13.1c) is stored at the centre of each three-dimensional Pixel (Figure 13.1b). In the datagram, the top two lines of attributes describe the region's spatial characteristics, indicating that, as a whole, the region is black and square and made from an array of black pixels at zero intervals.

The bottom two lines in the same datagram hold the time attributes that describe the region's time characteristics; they tell us that the black square lasts for *1 second* and is made from a time-row of instances at zero intervals from each other. Time attributes are always shown in italics, and they mirror a datagram's spatial attributes. Each instance of the black square lasts for just 1 time pixel – 1 msec – and the next instance starts immediately the last one has finished because the Pixels of the black square are continuous in time; therefore the time attributes in the *Parts* section of the black square are *1 msec* and *iTRow/0*, with *iTRow* telling us that the squares are instances in the time-row at zero time intervals from each other.

In the next example, we again have a white screen onto which we project a black square. After 100 msec, the black square is switched off and we then see the white screen again for 150 msec; this is followed by the black square for another 100 msec, after which we see only the white screen. So what we have effectively seen is a black square flash twice for 100 msec each time, with a white 'interval' of 150 msec in between the flashes. The way we present this in the iconic image is shown in Figure 13.2a.

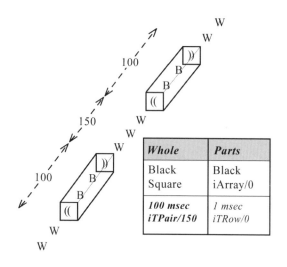

(a) Black square flashing twice

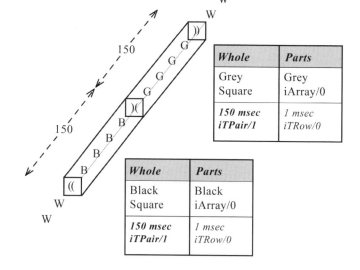

(b) Square changing from black to grey

Figure 13.2 How we describe the way things change over time. (a) A black square has been flashed twice on the screen with an interval of 150 msec in between the flashes. The figure shows a time-row lasting 350 msec; this comprises two component black square time-rows of 100 msec with an interval between them of 150 msec. The datagram describes the component black squares making up the 350 msec sequence; they are bound into the time-row by the attributes **100 msec** and **iTPair/150** in their *Whole* sections. (b) A black square flashed on the screen becomes a grey square after 150 msec. The figure shows a time-row lasting 300 msec that comprises a component black square lasting 150 msec followed immediately by a component grey square also lasting 150 msec. The attributes **150 msec** and **iTPair/1** in the *Whole* sections of their datagrams bind them into the 300 msec time-row.

Figure 13.2a shows the time-row of a single Pixel in a black square that is projected twice onto a white screen for 100 msec with a gap of 150 msec in between the projections. When the black square is projected onto the screen for the first time, the Pixel for each space/time position becomes black, and as each millisecond passes the next 99 Pixels in the time-row also become black because the black square lasts 100 msec. The screen then goes white, so the next 150 Pixels in the time-row turn white. After this, the black square is again projected for 100 msec, so the next 100 Pixels go black in turn. Finally, the Pixels revert to white again.

The two time-rows of black Pixels in Figure 13.2a are terminated where they start and finish by time edges. One pair of edges, ((, is placed in the time pixel where the time-row starts, and the other pair,)), is placed in the time pixel where the time-row finishes. These brackets are the time equivalents of the edges) and (we described in Chapter 5 that mark the limits of things in space.

The datagram in Figure 13.2a shows that the black squares are made from arrays of black pixels at zero intervals from each other, iArray/0. The time attributes of the black squares are shown separately, in italics. Each of the two black squares in the sequence lasts for *100 msec* and each is made from rows of time pixels *1 msec* long at zero intervals from each other – shown as distribution attributes *iTRow/0*. As a whole, each of the black squares is a component in a pair relationship with another black square separated by a time interval of 150 msec, as shown by the binding attributes *100 msec* and *iTPair/150* in the *Whole* section of the datagram.

Figure 13.2b shows the time-row that is created when a black square projected on to a white screen changes to grey after 150 msec without any time in between the two phases. The black square time-row starts with a time edge ((and lasts for 150 msec. However, when it ends, it is not terminated by time edge)) as you might expect, but by the time edge)(. This 'sharing' time edge indicates that the time-rows on either side of the edge are connected to each other – that the black and grey time-rows are beside each other in time.

The black and grey squares each last for 150 msec, so *150 msec* is placed as a time attribute in the *Whole* sections of the black and grey datagrams. The two squares are components in a pair relationship in time and this is represented by the binding attributes *150 msec* and *iTPair/1* placed in the *Whole* sections of their datagrams. These are the binding attributes in time that equate to the binding attributes Square and iPair/1 for two squares side by side in space, which were described in Chapter 3.

But it is not enough just to see the datagrams that represent the individual parts of a time-row; we also need to see the attributes of the row as a whole, as a group. The flashing black squares in Figure 13.2a will form a parent space/time region populated by the group datagram in Figure 13.3a; the row as a whole lasts 350 msec (100 + 150 + 100 msec) and comprises a *pair* of components each lasting 100 msec with an interval between them of 150 msec, shown as *100 msec* and *iTPair/150* in Figure 13.3a. The group datagram for the square that changes from black to grey in Figure 13.2b is shown in Figure 13.3b: the row as a whole lasts 300 msec and is made from a pair of components, each lasting 150 msec side by side in time, shown as *300 msec* and *iTPair/1*.

Whole	Parts
350 msec	*100 msec* *iTPair/150*

(a) Group datagram for flashing black squares

Whole	Parts
300 msec	*150 msec* *iTPair/1*

(b) Group datagram for black to grey squares

Figure 13.3 Things taking place across time form groups just as they do across space. (a) The group datagram for the flashing black square that was shown in Figure 13.2a. The group time-row lasts for 350 msec. Its group *Parts* attributes are duplicated in the *Whole* sections of its components in Figure 13.2a. (b) The group datagram for the black square changing to grey that was shown in Figure 13.2b. This group time-row lasts for 300 msec. Its group *Parts* attributes are duplicated in the *Whole* sections of its components in Figure 13.2b.

In the example shown in Figure 13.2a, it is only *after* the two black squares have flashed on to the screen that we are able to observe them as a pair. To do this, we go back in time to a datagram in a Pixel in the middle of the group space/time-row, as the parent, and then go further back in time to a datagram in a Pixel in the first component black square; we then return to the parent Pixel and go forwards in time to a datagram in a pixel in the time-row of the second black square. The act of attending the first component square will put the attribute 'Earlier' into its datagrams because it is earlier in time than the Pixel

in the middle of the parent row, and similarly the act of attending the second square will put the attribute 'Later' in its datagrams because it is seen as later in time than its parent datagram.

Of course, most things in the world just sit there, they do not keep flashing on and off, and they persist more or less indefinitely –therefore most of the objects we deal with do not have length-of-time attributes in their *Whole* sections. In order to show how we deal with persistent objects, we have reproduced in Figure 13.4 the side-by-side grey and black squares we discussed in Figure 3.5.

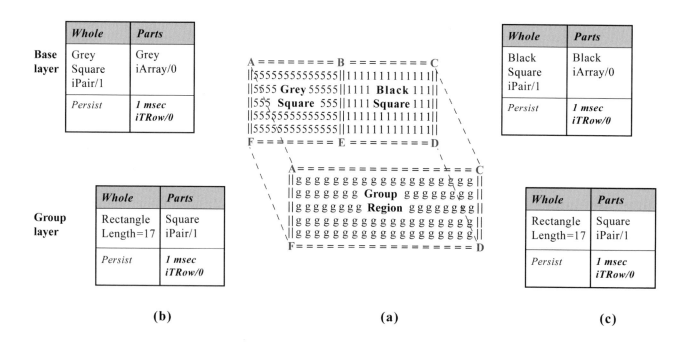

Base layer	**Whole**	**Parts**
	Grey Square iPair/1	Grey iArray/0
	Persist	*1 msec iTRow/0*

Group layer	**Whole**	**Parts**
	Rectangle Length=17	Square iPair/1
	Persist	*1 msec iTRow/0*

	Whole	**Parts**
	Black Square iPair/1	Black iArray/0
	Persist	*1 msec iTRow/0*

	Whole	**Parts**
	Rectangle Length=17	Square iPair/1
	Persist	*1 msec iTRow/0*

(b)   **(a)**   **(c)**

Figure 13.4 Objects that persist indefinitely are treated as time segments. We have added time attributes to the datagrams of the grey and black squares we saw in Figure 3.5. The attribute *Persist* has been added to group and component datagrams to show that they continue indefinitely, side by side in time, both as squares and as a pair. The binding attributes are *1 msec* and *iTRow/0*, but they are duplicated *Part* to *Part* rather than *Whole* to *Part* because they are two segments of the same time.

The grey and black squares shown in Figure 13.4 will individually last indefinitely, and together as a pair of squares they will last also indefinitely; therefore the attribute *Persist* is placed is placed in the *Whole* sections of both component and group datagrams. The *Parts* time attributes of the two component squares are *1 msec* and *iTRow/0* because they are continuous in time. But the *Parts* attributes of the pair of squares as a group must also be *1 msec* and *iTRow/0* because together as a pair they are continuous in time for as long as their component squares are. So *1 msec* and *iTRow/0* are the binding that holds

the pair of squares together over time, and the squares are time segments of the group time region because the binding attributes are *Part* to *Part* rather than *Whole* to *Part*. This mirrors the way that the rectangles of a **T** in Chapter 6 were bound together *Part* to *Part* by the attributes Black and iArray/0.

There is a clear parallel here between the edge configurations that mark the limits of things in space and the edge configurations that mark the limits of things over time. Pre-attentively, all edges in space and time are set to || (see Chapter 5) because, if they are unattended, there is no commitment in space or time as to whether a region is a thing or an interval between things. The different possible outcomes arising from alternative time/edge configurations are represented by pre-attentive datagrams in every time layer of the iconic image and are prioritised before the next attention step. The choice of pre-attentive datagram that attention then makes decides the path we take through time in the future.

We explained towards the end of Chapter 11 that we use three different sets of attributes to describe space. *Dimensional* attributes describe a thing's internal dimensions, *distribution* attributes describe the spatial relationships between things, and *context* attributes describe where things are within the context of a parent structure. Time attributes are organised in the same way. The length of time a thing lasts is a *dimensional* attribute, the length of time between two similar things happening is a *distribution* attribute, and *context* attributes describe how a thing is positioned in time within the context of a parent structure.

Dimensional and distribution attributes are a simple measure of length in space and time. These lengths have no direction so, for example, a square is the same width whether you measure it from left to right or right to left, and similarly a flashing square lasts the same time whether you measure it forwards from the time it started or backwards from the time it finished.

Context attributes, however, are not like that. To fix the positions of things in space or time, we have to know the direction of the measurement within the overall context. Chapter 6 used the example of a lemon and a banana to show how parent/component attention movements position things in space, which fruit is on the left and which is on the right. And in the same way as *context* attributes 'left' and 'right' relating to position in space were inserted in Figure 6.3, so, the *context* attributes 'earlier' and 'later' are inserted into component datagram sequences to provide direction in time.

There are two parent contexts that dominate the way we fix the positions of things in *space*. The first, the *personal* context, is viewer-centred and operates through a coordinate system that has its origin at a personal reference point in the iconic image that positions things in relation to the central point of a line joining the centres of your two eyes. The personal context is fundamental because in it we see everything positioned in relation to ourselves.

The other dominant spatial context is the scene. This coordinate system operates in the same way, but instead of being centred on the viewer, its reference point is based on an object in the scene, combined with a viewpoint. We will call this the *public* context because the positions of things do not depend on our personal viewpoint but on objects in the scene itself. This helps us communicate where things are with others, which is why we call it the public context.

There are also two parent contexts that dominate the way we fix the positions of things in *time*. In the *public* context, we use synchronised clocks and a reference point that is a single point in time, 12 am midnight, together with a shared calendar. This provides us with a shared framework, a parent, for calculating the positions of things in time.

The *personal* context for time provides us with a framework for measuring the positions of things in time as they happen. We propose that the time *now*, the present moment, is our personal reference point for positioning the things that we attend in time as they happen and as we remember them. The time *now* and my personal reference point are therefore the two fundamental parent reference points that anchor my personal understanding of how the world around me is organised in time and space.

Personal context attributes are the basis for public ones. Our personal view is the basis for the public scene view we share with others, and our personal experience of a time centred on *now* is the basis for the public clock time shared by the world from Copenhagen to Canberra.

Context attributes may only appear in attended datagrams because they have been created by parent/component relationships. Pre-attentive datagrams do not have relationships with each other so they do not have context attributes, only dimensional and distribution ones. They therefore have no need for attributes that describe the direction of time. The implication here is that things in the world we pay no attention to do not have a direction in time, a past and a future, in the same way as the things we attend directly have.

We explained in Chapter 12 that when a time layer in the iconic image matches the time now in our internal daytime clock, a *now* marker, **N**-status, is switched on in all datagrams in that time layer for 1 time unit (see Figure 12.1). After 1 time unit, all those **N**'s are immediately switched off and **N**'s are switched on in all the datagrams in the next time layer – and so on. The same principle is applied to the personal reference point datagram, the one that positions everything in relation to the viewer. Personal reference point datagrams, like everything else, have time attributes, and they are in a personal reference point time-row: their *now*, **N**-status, will also be switched on and off as time passes layer by layer.

The personal reference point datagram that is *now*, N-status, is therefore the master personal reference point for space and time combined. This personal datagram is the fixed reference that ultimately anchors all our personal experiences. The time reference point **N** separates our future from our past very precisely because its present moment, *now*, lasts only for an instance, 1 time unit. But what does this *now* time represent? Is it the instant something happens out there in the world or is it the instant that we become aware of that something happening? This is important because there is a gap of milliseconds between something happening and us becoming aware of it – and the length of time varies from sense to sense.

We propose that there is only one *now*, and this is the time (the millisecond) when things actually happen in the outside world. But we can never know what is happening in the outside world now because it takes us many milliseconds to process the data that will tell us – by which time it is no longer now. So instead what we do is predict what will happen in every future now based on past data. The result is that what we believe is actually happening is not really happening now; it is a prediction of what we expect to be happening now.

The position-in-time attribute of the time layer we attend is recorded in long-term memory, and when we recall something, we experience the length of time since it happened as the difference between the position in time *now* and the *now* position in time recorded against that past experience. As our experiences move further and further into the past, they become less and less relevant to our present-day lives so are less likely to be prioritised for our attention. Logically, we cannot forget or lose a memory just because it is old, but our brains lose memories with age as a form of archiving because they have limited capacity – unlike *perfect* minds that would age the data but would never delete anything.

We have discussed here the representation of time in terms of things we see; the question is, do the other senses handle time in a similar way? To answer this, we need to point out that the mind is a single workspace representing everything in a single space and time that integrates all the senses including sound and touch; vision is just another sense that has its datagrams represented in this single space – although it is the dominant one.

Summary

The extent of the lives of things is described by datagrams held in time-rows. The fundamental unit of information is the Pixel, which is an instant of 1 space pixel that lasts 1 time pixel. There are attributes for space and time in every datagram. The *Whole* sections of datagrams have time attributes that describe how long a thing lasts, its extent in time, and the *Parts* sections hold the extent and distribution in time of the thing's components.

Time edges mark where things are terminated in time. They are in pairs and are similar to those that mark the end of uniform edges in space; pre-attentively, they provide for alternative paths through time. Regularities in space and time create group regions that are populated by group datagrams. The duplicated parent/component attributes that bind a parent to its components in time mirror those that bind a parent to its components in space.

To describe the sequence of things over time, attention moves from parent to component datagrams and fixes their positions in time as earlier or later. Our personal reference point for positioning things in time is the time that things are actually happening *now*, which is the time equivalent of the centre of our body iconic image that is our personal reference point in space.

Time is an attribute of things in the same way that space is an attribute of things. Time, therefore, is not a thing – an overall continuum in which events take place – it is an attribute of the objects we see around us. However space and time are not attributes in the same way that black and square are attributes, they are instead 'the form into which our mind fits our sensations.'

14

Tracking movement, change and causation

We must take the current when it serves, Or lose all our ventures.

(William Shakespeare, *Julius Caesar*)

In the previous chapter, we looked at how we describe things over time that are static, and in this chapter we explain how we describe things that are moving. If an object is not moving, its datagrams stay in the same spatial position in successive time layers; effectively, its datagrams are copied into the same position from one time layer to the next. But when an object moves across the iconic image, the datagrams in its time-row disappear from their spatial positions in one time layer and reappear in different positions in the next time layer.

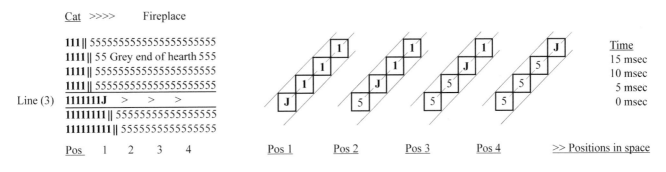

(a) Cat in position 1, time = 0   **(b) How the Pixels in positions 1-4 change over time**

Figure 14.1 The changing positions of the cat as he runs across the room at 1 mm per msec. (a) This shows part of the leading edge of the cat running across the room in Figure 12.1. The edge junction **J** is where the cat's leg meets his shoulder. This point travels across the image on line 3 starting at position 1, time = 0, in the image. (In this figure each interval is 1 msec.) (b) The position of junction **J** at 5 msec intervals, starting at position 1, time = 0, and reaching position 2, 3 and 4 after 5, 10 and 15 msec. The first Pixel in each of the four time layers tells you what is in the Pixel in that position at time = 0; the following three Pixels tell you what is in the Pixels in those positions after 5, 10 and 15 msec.

To show how this works (Figure 14.1a), we will return to the black cat that is running across the internal image of my sitting room at 1 mm per msec. The cat runs across the room from left to right in front of the fireplace, starting at position 1. In Figure 14.1a, we see the cat in the form in which he is captured in the iconic image. His leading edge is a string of ||, and his black body is represented by rows of **111**.... The position along his leading edge where his leg meets his shoulder is marked by a token, **J**, and this is the Pixel we will track on line 3 as the cat moves across the room. The hearth in the background is represented by rows of 555....

Figure 14.1b shows four Pixels 5 mm apart on line 3. At the start, time = 0 msec, the cat's token datagram **J** is in the Pixel at position 1, and the Pixels in positions 2,

3 and 4 show the hearth, which has a grey level of 5. At this point, there will be nothing in the four Pixels in time layers 5, 10 and 15 msec because they represent the future and we do not know what the future holds.

Over the next 5 msec, the cat moves 5 mm, so the **J** moves from position 1 to position 2, where it is recorded in the 5 msec time layer. The **J** we recorded in position 1 in time layer zero is not deleted because that is a record of where the **J** was 5 msec ago. The Pixel in position 1 in the 5 msec time layer now registers as **1** because the cat's black body (grey level 1) is passing that position. The Pixels in positions 3 and 4 in the 5 msec time layer continue to record the hearth (grey level 5) because the cat has not reached those positions yet.

After a further 10 msec, the cat's token **J** reaches position 4, and this is recorded in the 15 msec time layer. Figure 14.1b as a whole shows how Pixels in the image have changed over time as a consequence of the cat crossing in front of the fireplace. The sequence of datagrams occupying these **J** pixels represent the time-row the cat creates as he moves across the room.

Whole	*Parts*
Cat Black	Black iArray/0
1 mm/msec	*iTRow/0* *iSRow/0*

Figure 14.2 Datagram describing how the cat is moving across the room. The overall speed the cat is travelling at, *1 mm/msec*, is in the *Whole* section of the datagram. The datagram's *Parts* attributes show that he is moving continuously.

The datagram occupying each of the four **J** Pixels is shown in Figure 14.2. The cat's physical attributes are shown in the top half of the datagram, and his time-related attributes are in italics in the bottom half. The cat is present continuously in time so he is represented by *iTRow/0* in his *Parts* section. The cat is also in a succession of positions along a line in space, a space-row, at intervals of zero, and this is represented by *iSRow/0* in his *Parts* section. The cat in time and space is moving across the image, so its speed, *1 mm/msec*, is placed in the *Whole* sections of each datagram. This datagram is typical of a single object in motion.

We explained earlier that iconic memory is constructed on the principle that the space/time Pixels in our iconic memory are fundamental units: they have an exact size and are the smallest units of information our minds can directly represent. For the purposes of illustration, we will assume, as we did earlier, that a space pixel's dimensions are exactly 1 mm × 1 mm, and that a time pixel lasts for exactly 1 msec.

In the example in Figure 14.1, the cat was running across the pixels of the iconic image at a speed of 1 mm per msec; from where I am standing in the room, this is the equivalent of 10 metres per second. We can now represent the cat's movement in the simplified form shown in Figure 14.3a.

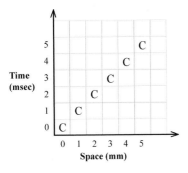

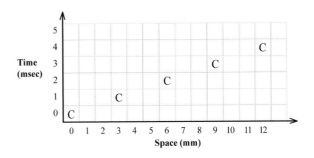

(a) Cat moving at 1 mm/msec

(b) Cat moving at 3 mm/msec

Figure 14.3 Diagrams showing why there is a limit to the speed that we can represent a cat moving at. (a) A simple representation of the tokens of the cat moving at 1 mm per msec in the iconic image, and (b) how we have to represent the cat moving at 3 mm per msec even though the cat is not continuous in space and time.

Figure 14.3a shows the cat, C, moving continuously across the 5 mm separating position 1 and position 2, and taking 5 msec to do so. Between the two positions, the cat C has followed a continuous path through both space and time, creating an unbroken chain of Pixels with zero intervals between them.

But what if, under the same conditions, the cat runs at 30 metres per second instead of 10 metres per second? Remembering that the image scale is 1:10, this will translate to C moving across my iconic image at 3 mm per msec. An object travelling faster than the fundamental space/time units ceases to be a single continuous object because it cannot be represented by a row of Pixels at zero intervals in both space and time. Instead it becomes a row of stationary objects switching on and off in sequence.

Our attention converts this row of stationary objects into a single moving object by creating a group time-row that overlays them. The lengths and times of the intervals in the time-row produce a movement attribute, *3mm/msec*, in the *Parts* sections of the time-row's group datagrams and this generates a row of token datagrams along the movement path, see Figure 14.3b. The movement attribute, *3mm/msec*, then downloads as an 'average' from the group level datagrams into the *Whole* sections of every one of its component datagrams, see Figure 14.4. If we attend one of these token datagrams we will experience the cat moving at 3mm per msec. This is a similar process to the one we described in Chapter 10 where we transferred the average grey level of a row into every one of the row's component datagrams.

So we can perceive movement in two ways, either by attending movement attributes that have been created pre-attentively from the raw data or by attending movement attributes that we have created by manipulating information where we believe motion to be present. Attributes created by the second of these methods produce the apparent motion we experience when we watch a motion picture or TV.

Whole	Parts
Cat Black	Black iArray/0
Av=3 mm/msec	iTRow/0 iSRow/0

Figure 14.4 Datagram of a cat moving faster than the limit. The movement attribute *3 mm/msec* does not come from the base data but is the result of the attention manipulations described in the text.

Next we will look at how objects move at speeds below the maximum, in our case at speeds below 1 mm per msec. In the first example, Figure 14.5a, our cat is running across the room at 5 metres per second rather than 10 metres per second, which translates into an image speed of 0.5 mm per msec.

The problem with the cat moving 0.5 mm per msec, is that nothing can move half a pixel at a time because a pixel is the smallest unit of space. Our cat solves this problem *by moving 1 mm every alternate millisecond.* He moves during 1 time unit and then pauses during the next one, so in other words he moves 1 mm in 1 msec and stays still for the next 1 msec – as illustrated in Figure 14.5a above. The cat remains the same thing over time because his parts, pixels, are always in a continuous distribution in both time and space. His *Parts* attributes are still *iTRow/0* and *iSRow/0* whether he has paused for a millisecond or is moving to the next adjacent Pixel.

This stop/start way of explaining motion looks very strange, but over the cat's path as a whole the arithmetic works – the cat in Figure 14.5a is moving at 1 mm every 2 msec across the image, representing a speed of 5 metres per second in the outside world even though he is standing still for half that time!

But now things get even stranger. What if our cat were running slightly slower than this? What if the cat were taking 2.2 msec rather than 2 msec to move 1 mm? To make the arithmetic work, the cat needs to wait in the same place for an additional millisecond after every 10 msec. The extra millisecond can be inserted at any point along each 10 second run; we illustrate this in Figure 14.5b, where we show the extra millisecond inserted after 6 msec. So instead of moving to the next pixel the cat, **C**, remains in the same place, delaying the move until the seventh millisecond – this slows the cat's movement across the room from 1 mm per 2 msec to 1 mm per 2.2 msec.

Adopting this approach, we can depict very small variations in speed between 0 and c_{max}. But there is a price to pay: we can never know the exact speed something is moving at at any point, or Pixel, on its path because its speed can only be calculated from the accumulation of its position over many Pixels in a time-row. The reverse is also true: if we know the speed of something overall, we cannot know exactly where it is, which pixel it is in, because its position could be anywhere depending on where the delays have been inserted.

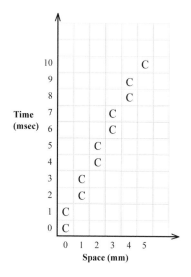

(a) Cat moves 1 mm every 2 msec

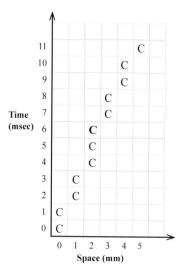

(b) Cat moves 1 mm every 2.2 msec

Figure 14.5 How we represent objects moving at speeds slower than the limiting value. (a) The cat moving at 1 mm every 2 msec makes a movement every alternate millisecond, while during the other millisecond he stays still. (b) The cat moving at 1 mm every 2.2 msec moves exactly like the cat moving at 1 mm every 2 msec except that he stays still for an extra millisecond after ever 10th millisecond.

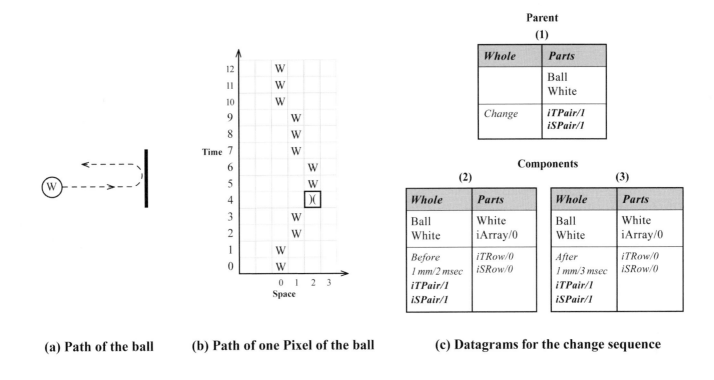

(a) Path of the ball   **(b) Path of one Pixel of the ball**   **(c) Datagrams for the change sequence**

Figure 14.6 The datagrams created by a billiard ball that crosses a table hits a cushion and returns along the same path. (a) The path of the ball. (b) The path of 1 Pixel at the right-hand edge of the ball is represented by two time-rows in the iconic image. (c) The datagrams in the ball for the sequence of movements: datagram (1) is the parent of the two paths combined; datagram (2) is the path of the ball before it hits the cushion; and datagram (3) is the path of the ball after hitting the cushion.

Changes in movement, cause and effect

We can now tackle how we represent changes in the way things move and the more complex sequences that result when changes in movement are caused by the impact of one object on another. Figure 14.6a below shows the path of a white ball, W, travelling across a billiard table from left to right; after 4 msec, it hits a cushion at right angles, recoils and travels back along its original path.

Figure 14.6a shows how, as it moves across the table, the billiard ball hits a cushion and returns along its previous path. Figure 14.6b shows the path in the image of the right-hand edge of the billiard ball as it moves across the image. It moves from left to right for 4 msec, hits the cushion at the 4 msec point, and then from 5 msec onwards moves in the reverse direction at a reduced speed. The change point is marked by an time-edge pair)(placed in the Pixel where the change took place – in this example after 4 msec and 2 mm. The time-edge pair marks a *change* in the motion characteristics of the ball.

This is not, however, how the sequence is presented to us pre-attentively. The before and after paths start out as separate stand-alone sequences without any connection between them; the terminating time edges in the Pixel where they meet are ∥ and not)(; the two paths, pre-attentively, are not connected. We could simply look at each leg on its own and ignore the other one, but to connect them together as a composite change sequence, we have to use our attention to join the two legs together as a pair and form a single space/time group region with a parent datagram that holds the sequence together as a whole (see datagram (1) in Figure 14.6c).

Once we have a group region, our attention can sequence datagrams in the two legs as components and generate the *Before* and *After* attributes in their datagrams, as shown in component datagrams (2) and (3) in Figure 14.6c. Note that the structure has generated a *Change* attribute in the group datagram (1) to say that a change has taken place. The *binding* attributes that hold the two legs together are ***iTPair/1*** and ***iSPair/1*** in the *Parts* section of the group parent datagram (1), and these are duplicated in the *Whole* sections of its two component datagrams, (2) and (3).

When the change points of two objects meet in the same Pixel, we interpret this as a causation – because the coming-together changes the way they both move. In the example in Figure 14.7, a white ball, W, moves from left to right across the table and hits a stationary black ball B, which causes the black ball to move straight across the table to the right. After the impact, the white ball recoils from the black ball and travels back to the left on its original path.

From Figure 14.7a and b, you can see that the white ball moves from left to right until, at 4 msec, it hits the black ball, reverses direction and moves to the left – it follows the same pathway as the white ball in Figure 14.6. The black ball is static until 4 msec, when the white ball hits it, and then the black ball starts moving to the right.

The two balls both change the way they move at the moment in space and time that they meet in the Pixel marked **X** in Figure 14.7b. This single Pixel therefore *should contain two pairs of time edges*, one for the change in the path of the white ball and the other for the change in the path of the black ball, because this is where they are together in the same space and time at (4 msec, 2 mm). However, *it is a rule that a Pixel can only ever hold one time-edge pair*, so just one)(must do for whatever time sequences pass through a Pixel.

Datagrams in change edges)(have attributes that describe the nature of the things in the pre-change and post-change sequences on either side of the change point; this is how the sequences become connected. The problem here is that we have two change sequences occurring in a Pixel. We would like to have two sets of edge datagrams but are only allowed one, so how do we know which pre-sequence to connect to which post sequence when we cannot hold all four descriptions? The answer is that we do not – no information is held in the shared Pixel except the direction in time of the causal sequence.

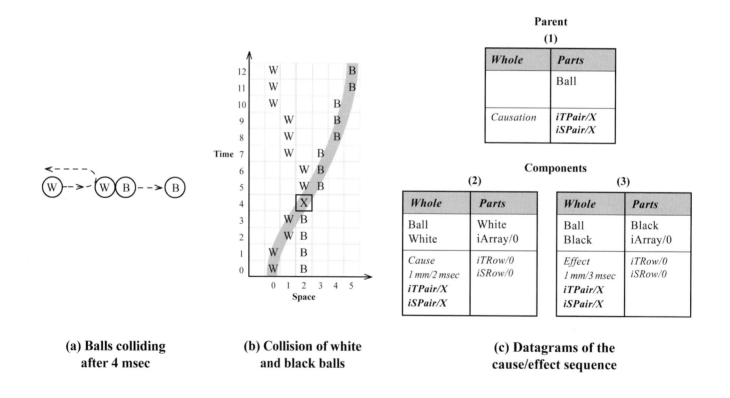

(a) Balls colliding after 4 msec

(b) Collision of white and black balls

(c) Datagrams of the cause/effect sequence

Figure 14.7 A white ball moving from left to right across the table collides with a static black ball after 4 msec. (a) The paths of the two balls before and after the collision. (b) The intersecting change sequences. The path of the white ball in the image is identical to that in Figure 14.6 where it recoiled after hitting the cushion; the black ball is static until hit by the white ball, the impact then causing it to move to the right. (c) Datagrams showing the sequence of the white ball hitting the black ball.

Our attention therefore has to look at the four possible ways in which the pre and post-sequences in a causation can be connected and choose one as follows. The alternatives in our example in Figure 14.7, which we will call (p), (q), (r) and (s), are as follows:

(p) The pre-change white ball connects to the post-change white ball. The configuration is seen simply as a change in direction and speed of the white ball – as in Figure 14.6 – and the black ball is not involved.

(q) The pre-change black ball connects to the post-change black ball. The configuration is seen simply as a change in direction and speed of the black ball, and the white ball is not involved.

(r) The pre-change white ball connects to the post-change black ball. The white ball is seen as causing the black ball to move.

(s) The pre-change black ball connects to the post-change white ball. The black ball is seen as changing the direction of the white ball.

The manner in which attention processes a causal sequence is similar to that for tracking change (see Figure 14.6c). In alternative (r) above, where the white ball is seen as causing the black ball to move, our attention goes first to the parent group region overlaying their pre and post sequences. Attention then moves to a component datagram in the pre-change white ball sequence, returns to the parent and finally moves to a component datagram in the post-change black ball sequence. These pre and post legs are marked as continuous in Figure 14.7b, and the datagrams that this creates are shown in Figure 14.7c.

The interval attribute for a causal sequence is represented by an **X**, so the binding attributes in a causal sequence are *iTPair/X* and *iSPair/X*. The parent/component attention movements generate the attribute *Cause* in the pre-change sequence datagrams, and the attribute *Effect* in the post-change datagrams. The attribute *Causation* is generated in the *Whole* section of the group datagram.

However, we have a problem. It is a fundamental rule of the mind that we can only form a group from things that share common characteristic, so in Figure 3.5 the grey and black squares could combine because they were both squares, and in Figure 13.2b the black square and the grey square it changed to could combine because they both last 150 msec. But the two legs in these Change and Causation figures do not appear to have time characteristics in common so how can we claim that they will combine into a single sequence?

The answer is that regions in space or time connected by a shared boundary (interval = 1) *do not have to have a common characteristic other than the boundary they share*. So in Figure 3.5 the shapes did not need to be square, and in Figure 13.2b the black square and grey squares did not need to both last 150 msec for them to form groups; the fact that they shared a common boundary was sufficient. In our Change and Causation examples, the contact Pixels where the billiard balls change direction are the shared boundaries that allow the four component time-rows to combine into four alternative parent sequences.

This representation of change and cause supports the principle that causal sequences arise only when change sequences coincide in the same place in space and time. Bertrand Russell described causation more precisely and elegantly in *Mysticism and Logic* as a 'sameness of differential equations'.

Summary

Things move across time layers at intervals of zero in space and time. In other words, whenever something moves, the information in each of its Pixels transfers to another Pixel that is adjacent to it in both space and time. Nothing can travel faster than 1 space pixel in 1 time pixel – faster than that and it ceases to be the same thing. To accommodate slower rates of movement, the transition from Pixel to Pixel is converted to a stop/start sequence that over time produces the average speeds that we observe. These average speeds are continuous numbers, they are not multiples of the fundamental units for movement that describe what is actually happening.

We mark a change in movement by inserting a change time edge)(into the Pixel that joins the before and after legs; this produces attributes that bind the two legs into a change sequence. A causal sequence is where the change points of two change sequences share the same point, Pixel, in space and time. The pairing by attention of the pre-change leg of one change sequence with the post-change leg of the other sequence is what produces the causal sequence.

In Chapter 3 we made the point that space is an attribute of things and not an all-encompassing thing out there in which all objects lie. Similarly in Chapter 13 we made the point that time is an attribute of things and not a single continuum in which all events take place. Yet in our Figures we have located space and time in pixels that appear to be part of the fabric of an all-encompassing space and time. So what are these pixels? The answer is that pixels are a device we use to help us explain, picture, how space and time relationships work. Pixels are a fiction, there is no space or time lying in between things, attribute values in datagrams alone tell us all we need to know.

15

The way long-term memory is organised

We cannot develop and print a memory.

(Henri Cartier-Bresson, cited in *Creative Camera*)

Our long-term memories are responsible for the storage and retrieval of the masses of data we accumulate throughout our lives. Essentially, they perform two tasks. First, they supply iconic memory with the attribute code numbers that tell us what things are (recognition) and what their past associations are (recall). Second, they hold the triggers that produce our physical responses, not only those we are conscious of, but also those we perform unattended.

Commercial databases on disc hold large volumes of data both locally and in mass storage facilities, on iCloud for example. These data are outside the information systems that use them and can only be processed when downloaded into a computer's working memory.

Similarly, our long-term memories are held in structures in the brain that are outside the mind, and we only gain access to this information when it is downloaded into the workspace of the mind. So our long-term memories are strikingly similar to commercial databases, and in fact there is nothing much that our long-term memories can do that a commercial database couldn't do equally well – if not better. The interesting question is not 'what do our long-term memories do?' but rather 'how do our long-term memories do it?'

Our long-term memories are outside the mind, and therefore outside its rules, so why do we not treat it as a 'black box' and just pass on to Chapter 16 where we consider how we use the information our long-term memory produces? After all, in Chapters 1–3 we felt able to ignore the processes outside the mind that create uniform regions because outside the mind meant outside the rules, and this is a book about the rules.

The reason we look at how our long-term memories might work arises from our belief that the rules of the mind are the same whether implemented in an animal mind, a human mind or a *perfect* mind. So although the long-term memories of human beings are held outside the iconic workspace, they must appear to be stored internally in the limitless workspace of the *perfect* mind, and to achieve this, the rules controlling our external long-term memory must be consistent with the rules governing a mass memory held entirely within the workspace.

So in this chapter, we propose an organisation for a long-term memory that lies outside the mind but possesses a structure and rules that are consistent with a long-term memory operating within the mind. The relational structure we have chosen comes mainly from working with large engineering and manufacturing databases. This structure seems to function well as a long-term memory, but we have no hard evidence that this is in fact the way information is structured in the brain. There may well be a logical data organisation that matches our long-term memory better than the one we propose here.

This is the area of our discussion that presents us with the most difficulty – not surprising when you consider its complexity. This chapter and the two that follow it are a work in progress; we accept that there are logical flaws that need addressing, and there are gaps – for example, we do not describe in detail how we integrate new information into the existing data record. This whole area is very much open to debate. Nevertheless, we believe that our approach offers plausible solutions.

We all have a fair idea how the memory of an electronic computer works. As I type the words for this page on to my computer screen, the computer's software converts them into an internal string of letters in its working memory, creating an electronic copy of what I see on the screen. When, at the end of the page, I click on the 'save' icon, the letters on the page are copied onto the computer's hard disc, its long-term memory.

But our long-term memories do not appear to work like this. They appear to hold items of information linked together in a network with each node in the network representing a type of thing (class) *just once*. So there is a single node for cats, and when you see a cat this unique node/class number for a cat is matched, the class code number for a cat is inserted into your iconic image as an attribute and, if you attend it, you get the sensation that 'this is a cat'. The single 'cat' node with its unique class code number stands for every cat that there is now or ever will be. It is all ginger cats, tabby cats, dead cats and china cats. You cannot think of a cat unless you can somehow trigger its unique 'cat' class node in long-term memory.

The word 'computer' is repeated on the page on my screen (say) 10 times. When I click on the 'save' button, the word 'computer' will be copied to disc 10 times, once for every time it occurs on the page. But when I *read* this page, every time I see the word 'computer', I will locate the single node for a 'computer' in my long-term memory. No matter on how times the word 'computer' is used in this book, there is only one node in my long-term memory for the word 'computer'. It is the links from the single 'computer' node to other nodes that provide the various meanings I experience every time I use the word.

What if Word documents on disc were organised in exactly the same way? The computer would have a master dictionary that contained each word in the English language *just once*. As you typed in each word, the single dictionary entry for that word would be located, and the document number and the position of the word in the document would be stored against that entry in the dictionary. For example Doc XYZ, page 90, line 6, word 12 would be stored against the dictionary entry for 'computer' to register that the word 'computer' occurs in Doc XYZ on page 90, line 6, word 12. If the word 'computer' occurred 10 times in the document, the dictionary entry for 'computer' would have 10 document/page/line/word entries against it.

To reproduce the full document, it would then just be a matter of keying in the Document number, XYZ, and letting the computer take over. The print program would first search the dictionary and locate the word that had 'Doc XYZ/page 1/line 1/word 1' stored alongside it, and it would then put that word as the first word in the page in working memory. The computer would then find the word at position 'Doc XYZ/page 1/line 1/word 2' and place it as the second word on the page in working memory, and so on. When there were no more words for page 1, the computer would print the page and start to build page 2.

But if computers operated in this way, they would be seriously inefficient because they are built to process information serially using just a handful of very fast processors. Our brains, on the other hand, are constructed from billions of processors – neurons – that handle information in parallel, so they are ideal for processing data held in this relational fashion. It is for this reason that we propose that our long-term memories are collections of nodes, each representing a particular class of things, all connected together within a single relational network.

The structure of long-term memory – things, classes and subclasses

Before we start this section, we need to be clear on the meanings of certain words. A *thing* is something you can physically experience, like that book you have just picked up or the sound of the radio in the next room. A *class* is a concept, an idea; it is a list of things, not the things themselves. You can pick up a thing but you cannot pick up a class. 'A book' is a class that means any book; 'a Bible' is a class also, but *my* Bible is a *thing* that is both '*a* book' and '*a* Bible'. Every *thing* is a member of some class or other. Many people are understandably wary (as we are) when it comes to talking about classes, but here we only need to understand two things about them:

- A *class* is simply a collection of *things* that share a particular characteristic. Long-term memory is simply a network of classes; it contains nothing else but classes.

- A *subclass* is a collection of *things* that belong to two classes at the same time. In other words, every thing in a subclass has the defining characteristics of both *parent* classes. All subclasses are themselves classes, and most classes are also subclasses of some other class. Every class has two parent classes, but a class can have any number of subclasses.

To illustrate this, the class of flowers is a collection that contains all the flowers in the world. The class of things in my sitting room is every object in my sitting room. The flowers in the vase on the mantelpiece in my sitting room are the combination of some of the flowers in the world and some of the objects in my sitting room. So they are both a subclass of the flowers in the world and a subclass of the things in my sitting room. Every individual thing in that vase is both a flower and in the room. In Figure 15.1, we show how we represent this relationship in a network of classes – every 'node' on the long-term memory network is either a class or a subclass.

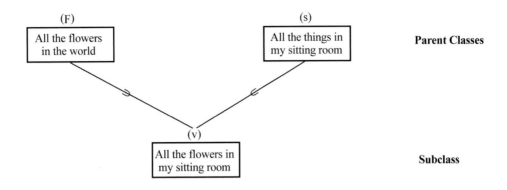

Figure 15.1 A simple network of classes and subclasses. Node (v) represents *both* 'that subclass of all the flowers in the world that are in my sitting room' *and* 'that subclass of all the things in my sitting room that are also flowers'. The U-shape on the two lines connecting the nodes is an 'arrow' indicating the direction class/subclass.

Figure 15.1 shows how the class of all the flowers in the world and the class of all the things in my sitting room join together to create a subclass – the flowers in my sitting room. In our model, a subclass can only ever have two parent classes, and these are of equal weight. So the flowers in my sitting room can be seen as either that particular group of all the flowers in the world which are in my sitting room, or as a particular group of things in my sitting room which are also flowers. The links between nodes represent the relationship class/subclass, and *this is the only relationship permitted*. Although *each class node has only two parents*, it can have any number of subclass links. For example, the 'all the flowers in the world' node will also have subclass links to nodes for all the different types of flower that exist.

Every node in the network has a unique class code number; in Figure 15.1, these codes are (F), (s) and (v). You will have noticed that the class code number (F) for 'All the flowers…' is in capitals and the other two class code numbers, s and v, are lower case. A class code number in capital letters signifies that this class is a *key*

class. If a region in the iconic image is matched to a node that has a *key* class code number, that class code number will be transferred into the datagrams in that region as an attribute code, and will, if attended, trigger a unique sensation. In this example, if the node with class code number (F) is matched, it will be downloaded into iconic memory and trigger the sensation that this is a flower – but only if it is attended. It is a rule that *at least one of the two parents of a key class must itself be a key class*.

The other nodes shown in Figure 15.1, (s) and (v), have lower case class code numbers, and we call these supplementary classes. If a *supplementary* class is matched, its class code number is not downloaded so it does not produce sensations.

Long-term memory is a single network of connected nodes sequenced downwards in class/subclass order from a single node: the **Class of Everything**. Connected directly to the Class of Everything is a row of sense class nodes that stand for all the sensations we receive from the outside world. These are all key classes.

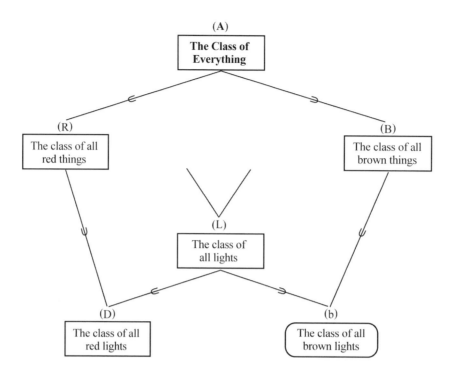

Figure 15.2 The basic sensory classes, (R) and (B), are key subclasses of the Class of Everything; they have no other parent. All classes in long-term memory are, ultimately, subclasses of the Class of Everything. In this and future figures in this chapter, we show key classes as squares or rectangles and non-key subclasses as lozenges.

The class of all red things, (R), and the class of all brown things, (B), in Figure 15.2 are key classes, and hence they have class code numbers in capitals. The class of all lights, (L), is not a basic class but it is a key class, because lights as a group are felt to be important things; when this node is matched, its class code number is downloaded into datagrams as an attribute code that triggers the sensation that tells us this is a light.

The class for all red lights, (D), has also been given a key class code number because red lights can be a warning for danger. Brown lights, on the other hand, do not have any special significance, so the class of all brown lights has a supplementary class code number (b). If we attend the attributes in a brown light's datagrams, we will not experience a particular sensation – other than that this thing is a light and it is brown. In the figures in this chapter, we distinguish between key classes and supplementary classes by showing key classes as squares or rectangles, and supplementary classes as lozenges. Long-term memory is only able to hold descriptions of classes, not of things, but if a class has only one member, it is obviously referring to only one thing.

Suppose that only one of the flowers in the vase in my sitting room is red. If attended, it will match both the class of all red things (R), and all the flowers in my sitting room (v), and this will produce a subclass that is the class of all red flowers in the room. As this is a class with only one member, it will identify just one thing – the red flower in the vase on the mantelpiece.

And that essentially is it. In summary, long-term memory is a network of classes, each with its own class code number, held together by the relationship class/subclass. At the top of the network is the Class of Everything; this node is connected, as parent, to a row of basic classes each of which represents a particular sense attribute from our environment – shape, shade, colour, area or movement, for example. Every other node in long-term memory is connected, directly or indirectly, to one of these basic nodes.

This long-term memory network is like an inverted tree with the Class of Everything that ever existed at the top. The tree goes down subclass by subclass from the Class of Everything, and at the end of every subclass branch is a unit class with only one thing in it, the equivalent of a single leaf or bud or fruit. All the basic classes, those that emerge directly from the sense data, have as their other parent the Class of Everything. This means that, ultimately, everything is a subclass of the Class of Everything.

Class/subclass hierarchies in long-term memory are not bound by the top/down parent/component hierarchies we see in iconic memory. Iconic memory is sequenced like an engineering parts list, starting with a complete unit at the top that is then broken down, level by level, into its component parts. The top-down order in long-term memory owes more to the relative significance of things and the relationships between them.

For example, if you saw a flock of starlings in the shape of a circle, you would create a circular group region in iconic memory with the attribute code for a circle, and a lot of small regions for the birds in the level below it, each having the attribute code for a starling. The group parent is a circle, and its components are starlings. But in long-term memory, this order can be reversed. Depending on the attention sequence you could see the circular flock of starlings as either the subclass of all circles that are constructed from starlings, or the subclass of all starlings that are in groups that are circular – in much the same way that, earlier, we could see the flowers in my sitting room as either just those flowers in the world that are in my sitting room or just those things in my sitting room that are flowers.

How we create matches in long-term memory

Long-term memory performs two functions. First, it holds the class code numbers that, when matched, are downloaded into datagrams to become the attribute codes that tell us what things are, and second, it sequences our physical responses (see Chapter 16). In this section, we describe how we search through million of connections for a single node to tell us what a particular things is.

When you first attend a datagram for a region, this creates a match to the top node in long-term memory, the Class of Everything. So, for example, the moment you attend a datagram in a black square, the Class of Everything is matched and that class code number is downloaded into the attended datagram as an attribute to give you the sensation that you are looking at 'something' – although at this stage you do not know what it is.

The next thing that happens is that the sense attributes in the attended region's datagrams 'black' and 'square', for example, will match the basic class nodes that have the Class of Everything as their other parent. And the basic class nodes will in turn prime all their subclass nodes wherever they occur in long-term memory. So, for example, the basic class node for 'all black things' will prime the class nodes for all black squares, black cats and black shoe polish.

These primed class nodes in long-term memory are a major factor in setting the priority values that tell our attention which datagram to go to next. Priorities in this context are set on the relative probability of a primed node being a feature of the attended object. It is important to appreciate that all these long-term memory processes are driven by attention as it moves around iconic memory from one datagram to the next.

Before we go any further, we must be clear what we mean when we use the words *match* and *prime* in relation to our long-term memories. A node is given *matched* status when both of its parent nodes have been matched and all of its parents' parents have been matched all the way back to the Class of Everything.

Whenever we *match* a node, we automatically *prime* the nodes of every one of that node's subclasses and their subclasses' subclasses and so on. For a node to receive primed status, it only needs one primed parent. So, for example, when we attend a red thing, all the classes of all the red things we have ever seen are immediately given primed status – all red lights, red socks, Father Christmases and so on.

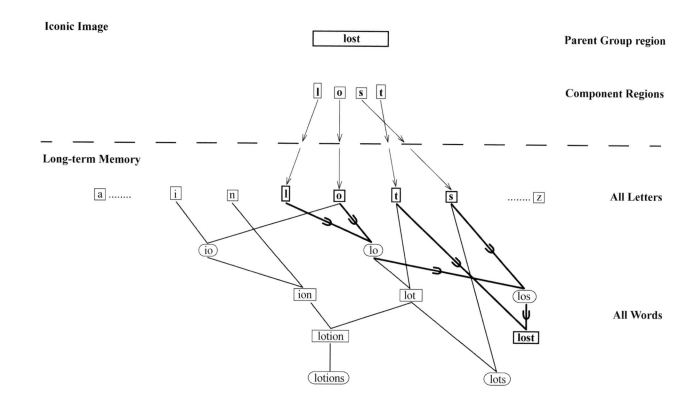

Figure 15.3 How we find a unique match for the word 'lost' in long-term memory.

In the lower half of Figure 15.3, we show part of a section of long-term memory that holds class code numbers for the letters of the alphabet and for some English words. This part of the network will help us to recognise the class code numbers for the words 'lot', 'lots', 'lotion', 'lotions' and 'lost' when their letters are presented to us in the iconic image, the upper part of Figure 15.3.

In this example, the letters **l**, **o**, **s** and **t** are presented to us in the iconic image as components, and we must use our attention to match them to their letter classes in long-term memory so that, ultimately, the class code number for the complete word **lost** is matched and is downloaded into the datagrams of the parent region that overlays the component letters **l o s t**.

The row of nodes a... i, n, l, o, t, s... z are the 26 nodes in long-term memory that represent each and every letter in the alphabet. Each node has a unique class code number whose ultimate parent is the Class of Everything. As we said above, square or rectangular nodes represent key classes, and lozenge-shaped nodes represent supplementary ones.

The first thing we do is go to a datagram in the parent group region that overlays all the letters for the word

lost as a whole. Using this group region as parent, we attend each of the component letters **l o s t** in turn, always returning to a parent datagram after each letter until the word is complete and we have found a match to the class code number for **lost** in long-term memory. At that point, the class code number for **lost** is downloaded, as an attribute code, into the datagrams of the group region.

The first component letter we attend in the image is **l**, and this matches the class code number **l** in long-term memory. This then primes all the nodes in the network that are subclasses of **l** – for example, 'lo', 'lot', 'lots', 'los', 'lotion', 'lotions' and '**lost**'. Our attention then returns to the group parent.

Next the letter **o** is attended and matches class code number for **o**. This produces a match in primed node 'lo' because it is the joint subclass of **l** and **o**. This match confirms the priming of 'lot', 'lots' 'los', 'lotion', 'lotions' and '**lost**'. The third letter **s** matches the primed node 'los' and confirms the priming of **lost**, but it has the effect of deleting the priming of 'lot', 'lots', 'lotion' and 'lotions' because these expect the third letter to be a **t** not an **s**.

The class code for **lost** is now the *only* node from our example list above that is primed, but we cannot assume that this is a match without attending the last letter **t**; we have to *complete* the sequence by attending every letter covered by the parent region. The need for 'completion' is a fundamental rule as you cannot identify any thing with certainty unless all its iconic elements either support a match, or at least do not exclude one.

The next example we look at is the word 'lotion'. As before, the first two letters match the node 'lo' and prime the nodes 'lot', 'lots', 'los', 'lotion', 'lotions' and **lost**. But the third letter '**t**' conflicts with the '**s**' in '**lost**' so the class code number '**lost**' is excluded; the '**t**' creates a match to class code 'lot', but there are more letters to come so the match is not complete; 'lotion' and 'lots' remain primed. The next letter is 'i'. This appears to exclude 'lot' as a match, but by priming 'io' and 'ion' it keeps 'lotion' primed as a potential match so 'lot' is not excluded but 'lots' is. The next two letters, '**o**' and '**n**', complete a match with class code 'ion', and this then combines with 'lot' to give the unique match 'lotion'. There is no '**s**' to follow, but 'lotions' is a supplementary node anyway and does not have to be satisfied for the match to be complete or for the class code number for 'lotion' to transfer into the datagrams of its group parent – where it becomes the attribute code that tells us that this is a lotion.

This last example illustrates an important point. A match sequence that has been built up is not automatically deleted if the next thing that is attended does not combine with the last node in the sequence to make a further match, *provided* the thing attended makes a match that primes the last node in the sequence. This is why the node 'lot' was kept alive here: even though the next attended letter '**i**' did not make a match with 'lot', it was able to prime a node that that would ultimately do so.

The search to match something in iconic memory to a unique class code number in long-term memory always starts with a match with the Class of Everything. The search terminates with a match that is 'complete' – in the sense that it satisfies all the features presented. However, there can be more than one completion in the matching sequence. So, for example, if you opened a tube of tennis balls and to your surprise out fell a daffodil, you would probably exclaim 'What is that flower doing there?' rather than 'What is that daffodil doing there?' Both of these matched class code numbers are correct, but as a rule we normally select the simplest class that differentiates a thing from its context.

The special classes that help us organise long-term memory

The network structure in Figure 15.3 above is in fact not strictly correct. In the network, we have assumed that parent nodes combine to produce subclasses in the sequence that they take in the word. For example, we have assumed that the parent classes 'l' and 'o' always combine as 'lo' never as 'ol'. But in long-term memory, there is no priority of parenthood: *the subclass of parents 'l' and 'o' is a single node that represents both 'lo' and 'ol'* – in the same way that the single subclass of the flowers in my room is both the subclass of all flowers that are things in my room, and the subclass of all the things in my room that are flowers.

The links between nodes in long-term memory only give you a class/subclass relationship – they cannot directly produce ordered sequences. To represent a sequence, we have to add an extra step that incorporates two special classes that we hold in our long-term memory: one is the class of all things in the world that are *always first* in a sequence, and the other is the class of all things in the world that are *always second* in a sequence.

In this example, the letter, 'l' must first combine with the '*always first*' class node giving that subclass of all 'l's' that always precede in a sequence, and the letter 'o' must combine with the '*always second*' class node giving that subclass of 'o's' that always follow in sequence. These two subclasses then combine as parents to give the subclass class of all 'l's' and 'o's' that are in the sequence of an 'l' followed by an 'o'.

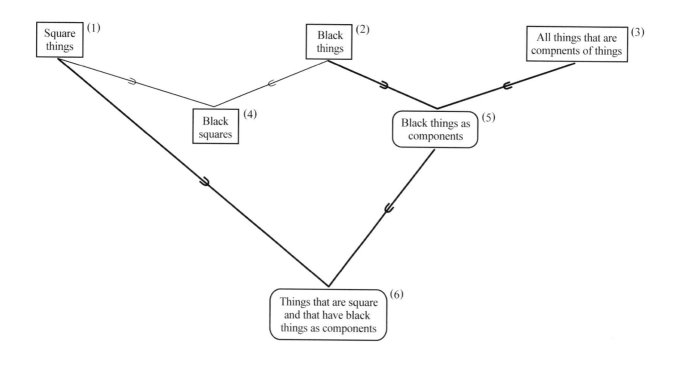

Figure 15.4 How we create classes from things made from other things. There is a special class that represents all those things that are components of things. This helps us distinguish between when something is a part of something else rather than something on its own, by itself.

The next special class we look at is the relationship between a thing and the component parts from which it is made. To describe a black square in long-term memory, we join the class of all squares with the class of all black things, and produce a subclass node which is the class of all things that are both square and black – see nodes (1), (2) and (4) in Figure 15.4. But what if a square is created from a pattern of black dots arranged so that they form a square? This is still a square, but this time it is not a black square but a square made from black things.

To solve this problem, we have in our long-term memories another special class – the class of *all those things that are components of things*. Whenever our attention moves from a parent datagram to a component datagram, it automatically creates an as a component attribute in the component datagram that matches, in long-term memory, *the class of all things that are components of things*, node (3) in Figure 15.4.

So if we attend the group datagram for a square made of black dots, it will match node (1) in long-term memory for all square things, but it will not match node (2) for all black things because the square is not completely black. When we then move down from the group datagram to a datagram in one of its component black dots, this will create an as a component attribute in the attended datagram. The black dot will match two nodes in long-term memory – node (2) for all black things, and node (3) for things that are components. Together, they combine to create a subclass in node (5) – the class of all black things that are also components. This node (5) will now join with node (1), and together they create a unique match in node (6) that represents the class of all square things that are made from black components.

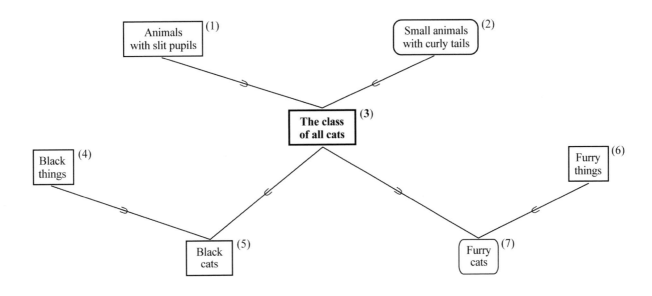

Figure 15.5 An example of a key class and its subclasses.

Key classes

Our long-term memories revolve around key classes, which provide identities for the things we see and hear, cats for example. Every one of these key classes is defined uniquely by its two parent classes, and, as mentioned earlier, at least one of those two parents must itself be a key class. Although key classes have only two parents, those parents have usually been derived from complex pair combinations higher up in long-term memory.

As an example, the key class for all cats is shown in Figure 15.5. If I look at a small animal that has slit pupils and a curly tail, my long-term memory in Figure 15.5 will uniquely make a match to the key class for all cats, node (3). Class nodes (1) and (2) are the parent classes that tell me this is a cat. If the animal is a black cat, node (3), the

class of all cats, will combine with the class node for all black things (4) and produce a match to subclass node (5) for all black cats.

Class node (5) is the class for all black cats, but it does not tell me whether all cats are black or just some cats are black. Similarly, class node (7) only tells me there are furry cats but not that, in my experience, all cats are furry.

What we need is a way to distinguish whether a subclass applies in *all* circumstances or whether in just *some*. We solve the problem by creating yet another special class in long-term memory. This is *the class of all classes whose subclasses have the same members as their parents*. In other words, its parent class and its subclasses will always contain the same things! This special class is node 20 in Figure 15.6.

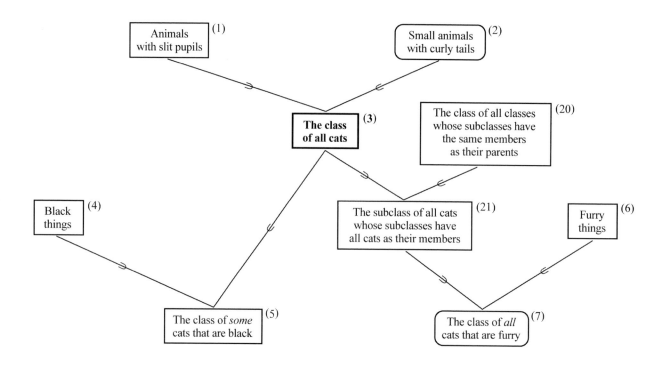

Figure 15.6 Distinguishing between the *some* and *all* subclasses of a cat. We use a special class (20) to identify when a characteristic applies to all members of a class rather than to just some of them.

Class node (5) is the joint subclass of all cats and all black things, but it does not tell us that all cats are black or that all black things are cats – because that is not true; it simply tells us that *some* cats are black. Class node (7) is now a subclass of all cats that contains all cats in it, and it is also the subclass of furry things, node (6), so in effect node (7) is saying that all cats are furry. The special node (20) allows us to express a universal characteristic of something as a subclass. Once I have established that this is a cat, node (3), I can immediately know that it is also a furry thing by going via nodes (21) and (7) to node (6).

This special *all* class is an important ingredient in a range of processes. For instance, it enables us to match a key class even when only one of its parent classes is primed *provided* we can identify a characteristic that is in one of its *all* subclasses. Suppose my cat is in a chair fast asleep; I can see his curly tail but I cannot see his eyes. His curly tail (2) will prime node (3) for cats in my long-term memory, but his eyes (node 1) are not visible so I cannot complete the match to node (3). However, my sleeping cat will match the class of all furry things, node (6), and this will prime node (7), which will, via the *all* class node (21), prime node (3) and so complete the match that this is a cat.

This combining of top-down priming with bottom-up *all* priming to produce a match is vitally important for object recognition because, more often than not, the top-down parent class/subclass sequence alone does not hold sufficient detail for a unique match to take place.

Bottom-up priming can also block a top-down match. Let us suppose a wide-awake, coiled snake was sitting in the chair instead of my cat. Its eyes (1) and coiled/curly tail (2) will meet the top-down criteria for the class of all cats and create a match to node (3). This match will prime node (21) and then node (7) for 'all cats are furry'. But the other parent of node (7), node (6), is not primed because the snake is covered in scales not fur. So node (7) will fail to prime node (3), preventing me from mistaking a snake for my cat.

There is just one more question before we leave the *all* classes: how do we know that all cats have curly tails? We can only experience the sensations of what a cat looks like once we know it is a cat because it is the downloading of a thing's subclasses into iconic memory that tell us what a thing is like. The two defining characteristics we have used here to recognise a cat – slit eyes (1) and curly tails (2) – are *parent classes* that are experienced before we know what they refer to, so we cannot use them to tell us what sort of eyes or tail a cat has. To make these characteristics accessible, our long-term memories combine nodes (1) and (2) with the *all* cat class node (21), to turn them into subclasses of all cats. One subclass node would be the class of *all* cats that have slit pupils, and the other the class of *all* cats that have curly tails. Because key classes are structured in this way, we can never know which two characteristics of a cat are its parent classes. In any case, this is irrelevant because although all key classes are unique, only rarely can they be identified uniquely by their parents alone; mostly it is a thing's *all* subclasses that tell us what a thing is.

Whenever we match a key class node in long-term memory, its class code number is automatically downloaded, as an attribute, into the datagrams of the attended region so that we can know what it is. At the same time, the *attributes corresponding to its 'all' subclasses* are also downloaded into the attended datagrams, because they describe the nature of the thing you have just recognised. So when you recognise a cat, not only is the attribute code number that tells you it is a cat downloaded into its datagrams, but so also is the attribute code number that tells you that this is a furry thing.

Language contributes to our understanding of the world more than almost anything else, largely by assigning names to things so we can retrieve their descriptions without the need to observe them directly. For example, we use the spoken word 'kæt' to represent the class of all cats, so that whenever we hear the word 'kæt', it brings into our mind a cat's characteristics. The sound 'kæt' is of course a thing just like everything else.

We recognise a cat when its features match the nodes leading uniquely to the class of all cats – node (3) in Figure 15.7. When we make this match, we automatically match the *all* subclass node (21), and this primes node (9), 'all cats are called kæt'. The other parent of 'all cats are called "kæt"' is node (8), the class of all sounds resembling 'kæt'; this node has no other subclasses because only cats are called 'kæt'. Because cats and 'kæt' have this one-to-one, *all*, relationship, the *attribute code for 'kæt' is transferred into a datagram in auditory iconic memory*. The act of recognising a cat has produced an internal simulation of the sensation of the spoken word for a cat.

The process also works the other way around. If I hear someone say the word for a cat, the sound will match node (8) for 'kæt', which creates a match in node (9) for 'all cats are called "kæt"', and this, through node (21), the *all* class, produces a match in node (3) for 'the class of all cats'. The result is that the class code number for a cat, node (3), is downloaded into a 'token' datagram in the simulation iconic image.

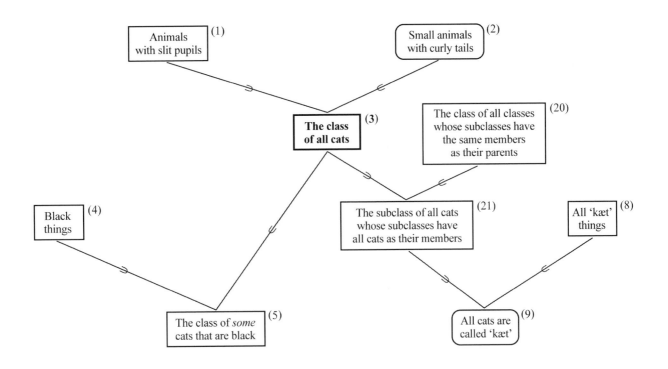

Figure 15.7 How the name of a cat brings to mind a cat and its features.

But it doesn't stop there. By attending the attribute code for a cat in the simulation layer, I trigger a match with the other *all* characteristics of cats, and these matched nodes will transfer their attribute codes into the cat's token datagrams in the simulation iconic image. This shows how hearing a word can bring to mind the appearance of something that is not in front of us.

All these sequences are possible only because we are allowed to prime up the long-term memory network from subclass to parent class when the parent classes and subclasses contain the same members.

Objects are mostly complicated, and it is not easy to recognise them from their characteristics alone. But most objects are found in familiar surroundings, and we can use this knowledge to identify their class code numbers in long-term memory more easily. When I enter a scene, my sitting room for example, my long-term memory immediately identifies its scene class code and uses it to prime the class codes in long-term memory of the things to be found in that scene. As long as I remain in my sitting room, the scene datagram will remain active in iconic memory as the ultimate parent, and the scene class code number will continuously prime, in long-term memory, the classes of all the things to be found there.

This continuous priming of long-term memory helps us to recognise things easily. To recognise a carriage clock out of context, we would need to first identify it as a clock and then, from its brass case, identify it as a carriage clock. But in the context of my sitting room, where the carriage clock is the only brass object, I only need move my attention to its case and straight away its brass colour, combined with its being in my sitting room, will produce a match to the class code number for a carriage clock. Again, this only works because the carriage clock is a permanent feature in my sitting room and is therefore a permanent *all* subclass in long-term memory of the scene class code number.

We create layers in iconic memory
to help us process complex information
We manage complex datasets by holding them in content-specified layers in iconic memory. Uniform regions in these layers operate in concert with their associated classes in the long-term memory hierarchy. To illustrate this, let's suppose that you are reading a magazine article about poetry, and on the page a single verse is presented as follows (with apologies for 'It is' and not the original ''Tis'):

> I hold it true, whate'er befall;
> I feel it when I sorrow most;

> It is better to have loved and lost
> Than never to have loved at all.

Let's assume that you have come across this verse before, or at least the last two lines of it, and that you know it is taken from a poem called *In Memoriam A.A.H.*

When you encounter the verse on the page, it is just a jumble of letters in the base layer of the iconic image. From the individual letter regions, you create a word layer with separate regions for each word, a line layer with four regions – one for each line of the verse – and a verse layer that is a single region for the verse as a whole. All these layers are one on top of the other in the iconic image, and the regions in the higher layers are the parents of the regions directly below them. This organisation is shown in Figure 15.8.

Your long-term memory will recognise that this is a verse from its structure and download from long-term memory the attribute code for a verse into the datagrams of the verse region, the attribute code for a line into the datagrams of each of the four line regions in the line layer, and the attribute code for a word into all the word regions in the word layer.

The only thing you know at this stage is that this is a verse comprising lines and words; there is no content. Your attention will now, starting from a datagram in the parent verse region, perform a series of attention steps that are designed to match the letter sequences in the basic layer to word class codes in your long-term memory. When the letters of a word are matched to a node in long-term memory, the class/attribute code of that word is transferred into the region directly above it in the word layer. When a line of words in the word layer is complete and has been matched to the single class code for that string of words, that class/attribute code is transferred from long-term memory into the line region above it in the line layer; and when the class/attribute code in long-term memory for the identity of the poem is matched, it will be transferred into the all the datagrams of the verse region in the verse layer.

Figure 15.8 shows the attribute codes that populate the regions of your iconic image at the moment you recognise the poem from line 3. The two words 'In Memoriam' stand for the attribute code that gives you the unique sensation that this is the poem *In Memoriam*; it is not the poem itself and it is not the name of the poem – it is the unique attribute code that stands for everything this poem is. Similarly, the word 'better' in the word layer is the attribute code for the sensation you get when you recognise the word better – it is not what the word 'better' looks like or sounds like.

Iconic Image

In Memoriam	**Verse Layer** **1 region**

	Line Layer **4 regions**
'Tis better to have loved and lost	

it	is	better	to	have	loved	and	lost	**Word Layer** **8 regions (line 3)**

i t   i s   b e t t e r   t o   h a v e   l o v e d   a n d   l o s t   **Letter Layer**
28 regions (line 3)

Figure 15.8 How we organise the iconic image for a verse of a poem. Our attention uses four levels of detail when reading this verse. In the verse layer, at the top of the hierarchy, a single region represents the verse as a whole – this is the parent of each of the four line regions in the line layer that are directly below it. Each line region in the line layer is the parent of all the word regions in the word layer that are directly below it, and similarly each word region in the word layer is the parent of all the letters directly below it in the base layer. Then, starting with the letters in the base layer, our attention creates matches in long-term memory that produce attribute codes that build up the layers until the verse is complete.

We will now explain how your long-term memory processes the information in these image layers, and provides the attribute codes in iconic memory that enable you to appreciate what you are reading.

Figure 15.9 shows a network of class nodes in long-term memory. The part of the network on the right of the figure is dedicated to recognising letters and words and then processing them into word sequences – sentences or the lines of poems, for example. At the top of this network are 26 class codes, one for each letter of the alphabet. Below them, but connected to them by a network of subclasses, are the class code numbers for every word you know, which is probably around 50,000.

We will now outline the steps you take reading line 3 in Figure 15.8. Your attention goes down from the region for line 3 in the line layer to the region in the word layer that overlays the first two letters **i** and **t** in the letter layer. You then go down to the letter **i** in the letter layer, and the letter **i** is transmitted into long-term memory, where it is found to match the class code for the letter **i** (Figure 15.9). You next go back to the parent region in the word layer and repeat this parent/component sequence for the second letter **t** so that the letter **t** is transmitted into long-term memory and matches the class code number for the letter **t**. The class codes **i** followed by **t** match class code (1) for the word 'it', and the attribute code for 'it' is downloaded from long-term memory into the first region in the word layer, the one that overlays the letters **i** followed by **t** in the letter layer.

You then go back up to the line layer and down to the next word in the word layer, and then down again to the first letter **i** of the second word 'is' and so on. This process is repeated for all the letters in the letter layer up to and including the last word, 'lost'. The eight regions in the word layer now hold individual attribute codes for each word in line 3.

As each word is recognised in the word layer, it matches a sequence of subclass nodes, (1) to (8) in long-term memory (Figure 15.9). When the line has been completed by the last word 'lost', the uniqueness of the word sequence in the line is recognised and the class code (8) downloads the attribute code (8) for the whole line into the datagrams of line 3 in the line layer in Figure 15.8. At the same time, in long-term memory, class code (8) for the line, triggers class code (9) that in turn matches class code (10) for the poem *In Memoriam* – because *all* versions of this poem contain this particular word sequence. The matched class code (10) downloads the poem's attribute code into the datagrams of the verse layer of the image and, when attended, it will tell you this is *In Memoriam*.

An important general point to note is that the moment your attention moves outside an iconic region, all the primings and matches you have created in long-term memory in order to establish what its class code number is are lost. So before you leave a parent region of, for example, a word, you must be sure that you have first identified its class code in long-term memory from its component letters. This is why, when you are interrupted during a task, you can find it difficult to pick it up later where you left off; often you have to go back to the beginning and start again.

The very top layer of your iconic memory holds a single group region. It is the ultimate group parent, it extends over everything else that you are processing, and it covers all the senses: vision, sound, touch and so on. All the datagrams in this top region hold one important attribute code – the iconic memory equivalent of the class code for the Class of Everything that is the top node of your entire long-term memory network. This top group region in iconic memory has permanent attended status because it is the source of your single continuous attention stream.

Recording new information while maintaining integrity and efficiency

Although we rarely encounter entirely new things, many of the things we see on a daily basis have features that do not find a good match in our long-term memories, so we need to record them. We record new information as

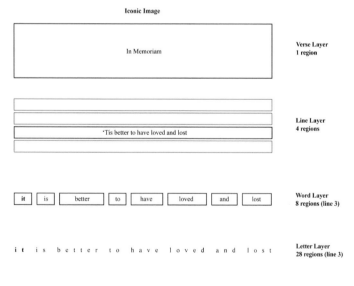

Figure 15.8 How we organise the iconic image for a verse of a poem. Repeated from page 99 in order to assist the reader in following the information transfers between iconic and long-term memories.

Long-term memory

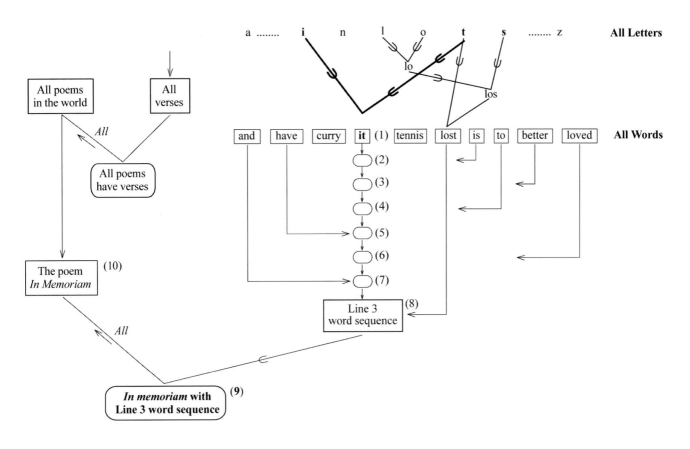

Figure 15.9 The long-term memory classes that help you to recognise the poem. The letters a......z at the top right are the 26 key classes that stand for each letter of the alphabet, and below them are the classes that represent all the words we know. Letters attended in the iconic image accumulate to match words in the long-term memory network above. When a word is matched to its class code, its attribute code equivalent is downloaded into that word region in the iconic image in Figure 15.8. In this way, the line of the poem is constructed and eventually recognised.

a supplementary subclass of an existing key class, but we only record new information in long-term memory if we have attended it. Normally, we will be focused on a particular new characteristic associated with a particular key class and attach the new characteristic to it as a subclass. Attributes of the attended datagram that are not the focus of attention form temporary subclasses that are deleted after a short space of time *unless* they prime significant consequences – in which case they will create priorities for attention.

The unattended activities we perform are driven by long-term memory but do not alter its structure in any significant way. Unattended activity may alter the record of the frequency with which we record seeing things, and so influence memory retrieval, but no new information can be recorded unless our attention is involved.

We suggest that the integrity of our long-term memories is maintained through a process of *normalisation* similar to that used in commercial relational databases. This removes redundancies, streamlines access paths and ensures that classes are not duplicated. The key principle applied here is that we retain a clearly defined population of key classes each with its own single class code number and that we do not mistake an existing class for a new one and create a new class code number for it.

When we see something strange or a change in something familiar, we normally incorporate it into our long-term memories as a subclass of the key classes we already have.

We later consolidate this new information at the right logical level so that the overall consistency of the network is maintained. Sometimes newly acquired information conflicts with existing class connections, and these contradictions need to be either eliminated or highlighted.

New experiences are, however, not always incorporated in long-term memory as subclasses of existing class nodes. Suppose you went to a new country and saw a green cat for the first time; you would automatically record it as a type of cat (subclass) using your existing key class codes for 'cat' and 'green'. But if you later saw that these green cats had webbed feet, caught fish in the sea and laid eggs, your long-term memory might decide that this is not really a cat at all but something entirely new that needed a new key class with a new class code number with its own unique sensation. The next time you saw one of these creatures, you would not see it as a cat – you would see it as something entirely new. In pseudo-Darwinian terms, it has become a new species of thing.

But the key classes that dominate our lives are those we give to the people we know. We assign a key class code to every person we recognise as an individual and then attach to this key class code everything we know about them. They are of course all unit classes.

Summary

We are proposing that long-term memory is a single network of nodes, each node representing a unique class of things. All classes in the network have just two parent classes but can have any number of subclasses. There are two types of class – key classes and supplementary classes – and one parent of every key class must also be a key class. Key classes are those that are of particular significance.

The only permitted relationship between classes in long-term memory is that of class/subclass. However, because we need to recognise other forms of relationship, we use a group of special classes as links to achieve this.

Only classes and not things are represented in long-term memory, but a class can have just one member. A unit class will therefore have a one-to-one relationship with the thing that is its only member.

Our attention sequences datagrams in a way that will produce unique matches in long-term memory. When a unique match to a key class is achieved, its class code number is downloaded as an attribute code into datagrams that, if attended, trigger the physical sensation in the brain of what the thing is.

In advance of processing complex data structures, our attention organises datagrams in layers in iconic memory that equate to the logical class structures that represent that data in long-term memory; this has the effect of synchronising the activities of the two memories.

Only when new information is attended can it be incorporated into our long-term memories. The class structure of long-term memory is under continuous review in order to maintain its logical integrity, efficiency and relevance.

16

How and why we respond to things

No man steps into the same river twice.

(Heraclitus)

And finally, at last, how do we respond to all this the information; how do we act our part in the world – for better or for worse?

First, we need to understand how we represent the sensations we receive from the different parts of our bodies. Our nervous systems generate uniform regions and datagrams in two separate iconic images, one public and the other private.

Attributes in public datagrams tell you what an object is like, for example whether it is round or square, rough or smooth, hot or cold. Datagrams in the public image do not tell you anything about your body's reaction to what you see and touch – they simply describe the things you see or touch. We call these public sensations because we expect two people seeing or touching the same object to have similar experiences.

A completely different set of attributes, located in datagrams in your body iconic image, describe your body's *private* reactions to what you touch. The *private attributes* in these datagrams tell you how you feel about the contact you are making. If, for example, you press a needle against your finger, you will detect that it has a sharp narrow point, a public perception, but you will also feel a piercing sensation in your finger created by your body's reaction to the pressure from a sharp point. The receptors under your skin are feeding into two separate iconic images: the public one provides a picture of the thing you are touching, and the private one delivers sensations that describe your body's personal reaction to it.

Whenever you touch something, the receptors under your skin create a region in your touch iconic image that represents the area of the object surface that is in contact with the surface of your skin. This is similar to the way that objects projected onto the retina produce regions for the things you see in the visual iconic image. Public datagrams populate the region representing the extent of the contact area, and their attributes describe the object's nature – rough or smooth, hot or cold, for example.

The things in your touch iconic image are positioned in public space and time in exactly the same way as the things are in your visual iconic image. In other words, the separate uniform regions of vision and touch are integrated in the same public space even though their datagrams are in different iconic images; it is as if vision and touch are in separate layers of a single global 360 degree iconic image. In this way, you are able to get a *public* description of what a thing both looks like *and* feels like. Your own body as a whole is *not* represented in this unified public image – unless of course you see it or touch it!

Your *private iconic image*, on the other hand, contains a permanent representation of your body *and nothing else*. All the parts of your body are uniquely represented and occupy permanent regions within the private iconic image, and together they make a single figure that is rather like the one shown in Figure 16.1.

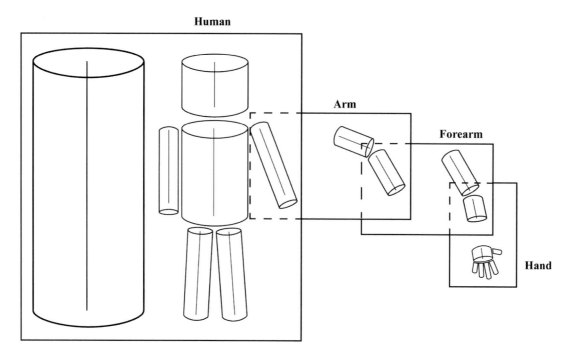

The logical way in which our bodies are represented in our body iconic image

Figure 16.1 The organisation of body structures held in your body iconic image. The logical way in which are bodies are represented in our body iconic image. Each segment of the body is populated with datagrams that describe that particular part, its shape and size, how it feels and its position both relative to the body as a whole and in relation to the outside world. (After Marr and Nishihara, 1978.)

Figure 16.1 shows the logical structure of your body in your private body iconic image. This is constructed from regions representing each of your body parts organised into layers. In the top layer is a single group region that has the overall shape of your body, and in the bottom layer are the smallest of the parts, the top segment of your right index finger, for example.

Your body iconic image has the type of parent/segment structure we introduced in Chapter 6, so the layer below your overall body region has the same overall shape, and we will assume for the purposes of illustration that it is segmented into six regions, each representing one of your major body parts – your head, trunk, two arms and two legs. In the layer below that, your right arm region is segmented into three regions that represent your upper arm, your forearm and your hand as a whole. In the layer below that there will be segmented regions that include your palm and each of your fingers, and finally, in the lowest layer, there are the segments for each jointed region of each finger.

The datagrams making up your right-hand region in your private body iconic image describe the

characteristics of your hand and hold the attribute code that tells you that this is your right hand; the attributes in the datagrams in the region of your right index finger describe the characteristics of your right index finger and identify it as your right index finger – and so on. Datagrams in each of the parts of the body in your body iconic image give you their position in relation to their parent segment and therefore ultimately to your body as a whole.

There are two categories of private attribute in the segment datagrams of your body iconic image, the first of which describes the processes taking place inside your body. A good example of these of attributes is the sensation of a muscle stretch that you feel when you move some part of your body. If you raise your right index finger, the attribute for the sensation of a muscle stretch will be inserted into the datagrams of the segment representing your right index finger in your private body image, and if you attend one of these while your finger is moving, you will receive the private sensation that the muscles in your finger are stretching. You will experience this sensation in a physical internal body image in the brain that shares the same pixels as your body iconic image.

You do not usually bother to attend this attribute because the movement and the sensation go together, but if your finger were restrained so it could not move, the muscle stretch attribute would not be delivered into your index finger as expected. In this case, a priority interrupt would call your attention to the failure of your finger to execute the planned move.

The private attributes that you are most often aware of are those that describe the impact of an external object on one of your body parts – the sensation when you prick your finger with a sharp needle, for example. These attributes are the feeling partner of the public sensation of touch that describes the thing you are touching, and they are held in the datagrams of your body iconic image. You feel the sensation in the body part involved, and not in relation to the public space around you. Contact with your body usually affects only a small area of the body part involved, so for example the pricking of your index finger will only affect an area of skin (say) 1 mm² in the region of your index finger's top segment. The impacted region is itself a segment component of the top of your index finger, making its datagrams integral to that body part.

We need to locate the parts of our bodies in terms of the world around us so we can know their positions in relation to other things. To achieve this, we use the shared *public* coordinate system that we use for vision and all the other senses. In other words, the datagrams in each of our body parts in our private body image also have positional attributes that reflect the present position of each body part in the public world around us; you have only to attend a public positional attribute in the private iconic image of your right big toe to know where it is in the space around you.

Of course, this means that whenever you make a movement, you have to 'articulate' the attributes of your body parts in your private body image so that you can track them relative to all the objects in the world around you – not only where they are now, but also in terms of where they will be in the future. We need to project these spatial relationships forwards in time in the same way that we projected my cat's future positions as he moved across the hearth in Chapter 12.

This presents us with a mammoth processing problem, and to solve it we employ two iconic structures to represent our bodies in the private image just as we had two iconic structures to represent my cat.

The first iconic structure is the detailed private one that contains the regions and datagrams that give us all the private sensations we have been talking about – the prick of a pin or the feeling that our muscles are stretching, for example. This is the body structure depicted in Figure 16.1. It represents the parts of our bodies in complex detail, and carries the datagrams that give us the sensations we feel in our bodies.

But the datagrams in this body representation provide no information about our body's position in relation to other objects in the world around us, or about how different parts of our body are moving in relation to each other. We have a separate simple body model that moves through public time and space in the same way my cat did, and it holds the attributes in token datagrams for body location and movement in both the real and simulation layers of public space and time. We can imagine its form as an articulated stick figure that has exactly the same segmentation and dimensions as the full body representation described in Figure 16.1.

Regions in this articulated figure have the same public coordinates as the things you see, so your visual hand in the public image and the feel of your hand in the private image can now become one and the same thing, and they can share the unique class code number that tells you this is your hand. It is through the integration of these private and public images that we are able to move our bodies accurately in space and time. *What you have done is identify things in the public domain that are parts of you.* You now know what you can control directly because it is a part of you, and what things are not part of you and therefore cannot be directly controlled.

So the way we experience our bodies is a composite of two private representations. Of course, neither of these views of ourselves actually moves around physically inside our heads – we track the positions of things in the world by comparing their space and time attributes, and not by comparing their physical positions. It was the same for my cat in Chapter 12: it never moved inside my head, but the spatial coordinates in my internal representation of it still told me where it was in relation to the other things in the sitting room.

So our view of the world is divided between private experiences that only we know of and public experiences we share with everybody. Attributes in datagrams in the *public* iconic image tells us what is going on out there and what we are doing, while attributes in datagrams in our private iconic image generate sensations in our internal body image that tell us how we feel about things. However, our private attributes also tell us who we are and provide us with our sense of self, feelings that seem very different from the public 'out there-ness' of the world we all occupy. The question is how do we reconcile, connect, the two?

We are able to combine our private and public views because our private and public iconic spaces have the same pixel structure and because our personal reference point is positioned in the same place in the two body representations, at the centre point of a horizontal line that joins one eye to the other.

So each datagram in the public iconic image has three sets of coordinates: a column and a row number that locates its position within the image, polar coordinates that locate its position in relation to a point in the surrounding scene and personal coordinates that locate its position in relation to our head position. In addition we now have personal coordinates in private datagrams that locate them in both private and public space.

Integration of the senses

To get a complete picture of the world, we must integrate all the information we receive from our different senses into a single picture. Even though the information we receive from each of our senses is stored in separate parts of our brains, we integrate that information as layers in a single iconic image.

Every sense layer presents its information in the form of an iconic image, because every piece of information is presented to us as a region in a space and time that is shared by all. This shared public space is not visual space, although it feels like it because vision is so dominant; vision is just another sense in its own sense layer sharing the global space/time structure. Space/time is the medium through which all the data from the different senses are integrated. Even sounds must be located in space – although sounds are usually integrated with other senses through sharing a common time rather than space. Integration of the senses takes place at the base sense level. There are three fundamental rules here: (1) you can only integrate data coming from different senses if you have established that they are attributes of the same thing – of the same region; (2) the integrated representation is held in an integration layer; and (3) the composite datagrams of a thing in the integration layer hold copies of all the attributes in all its contributing sense regions. We are not creating a group datagram here, as this all takes place in the base layer; instead we are fusing together datagrams from separate senses into a single datagram that represents all aspects of the thing we are observing.

Take, for example, the way the datagrams of a black square with a rough surface combine into a single description:

- The rough surface region in the touch layer overlays the black square region in the visual iconic layer so they share the same space and time. They are therefore two views of the *same thing*.

- This creates a datagram in the integration layer that will integrate the two descriptions.

- The attributes for the square as a whole – Black, Square and Rough – are copied into the *Whole* section of the integrated datagram, and Black, Rough and iArray/0 are copied into its *Parts* section.

It is important to re-emphasise that we are not creating parent/component relationships here. Instead we are simply merging datagrams in the base layer so that descriptions from different senses will become descriptions of the same thing rather than of different things.

All the sense layers are extended in time layers organised in the same way as vision is organised. If things in different sense layers share the same time, they will integrate on this basis alone; this applies to sound and vision in particular. If a firework explodes overhead with a flash and a bang, the sight and sound of the event will be recorded in separate sense layers but in the same time layers. Because they share the same time, they will create a single space/time region in the integration layer and populate it with datagrams that combine the attributes for the flash *and* the attributes for the bang.

The firework is a very simple example because it is a single event, but the same principles apply when we watch someone dancing to music. Here we have the same two distributions in time occurring in separate sense layers, but they are synchronised so that together they share the same space/time distribution.

The most important integration of all is the merging of the body parts in our private body iconic image layer with the parts of our body we see in the public visual image. This is vitally important because we need to know what our body looks like, as well as where it is and what it feels like.

Earlier, we pointed out that our private bodies are represented in two ways: one that gives us our feeling body, which is located in time but is not located in space; and the other for the articulated mannequin that gives the parts of our bodies their position in space and time. We now need to integrate the visual representation of our body with the private representation so that when we attend a datagram for a particular part of our body, we receive a complete account of what it is, where it is and what it feels like. The key to achieving this lies in attribute codes that are permanently stored in the datagrams in the private body image that tell us what each part is.

To illustrate this, let's use my right index finger as an example. When I look at my right index finger, this will create a region in the visual layer of the public image and I will recognise it as an index finger – but not whose it is. However, the coordinates of the visual image of my right index finger overlap with the coordinates of the region/segment in the stick figure that represent my right index finger. They will therefore fuse together and produce a composite region in the integration layer that combines my finger's visual aspects with where it is and how it feels – a muscle stretch, for example. The integrated datagrams will also incorporate the attribute code (transferred up from my private body iconic image) that says this is my index finger, so I now have a single description for all aspects of my finger – what it looks like, it feels like, where it is and *whose it is*. We do not depend on the precise overlapping of the coordinates of the two sense regions to produce a merger of our visual and body images. If I turn to look at my hand as I move it to pick up a cup, I will download my hand's class/attribute code number from long-term memory into the datagrams of my visual hand because I recognise it from its visual attributes alone. The two representations

of my hand – in my visual and body iconic images – now have the same body part attribute code, so they will form a composite region and position it *on the basis of its visual coordinates* rather than its private body coordinates, because the former are assumed to be the more accurate.

Attended actions

The actions our bodies perform come under three headings. First, there are *reflex actions* that are controlled by local nerve circuits and require no intervention from the brain – knee jerks, for example. Second, there are *unattended actions* that are controlled by the brain but are executed automatically. And finally, there are *attended actions* that we select and execute under our personal control. In this section, we outline a mechanism for attended actions.

We propose that actions are triggered by special class code numbers – action codes – that are embedded in long-term memory. Action codes are classes in the same way that black squares and cats are classes, and they have class/subclass relationships just as squares and cats do. Each action class code is an instruction to move a body part in a particular way, and every part in our body iconic image has in its datagrams the list of action attribute codes it is able to perform.

When a data sequence matches an action class code in long-term memory, this highlights the equivalent action attribute code in the datagrams of the attended body part. If your attention then goes to that action attribute code, this will prepare that body part for that action. However, the action does not execute straight away: only when you attend the Execute attribute in the master datagram at the top level of your body iconic image does the action get executed physically.

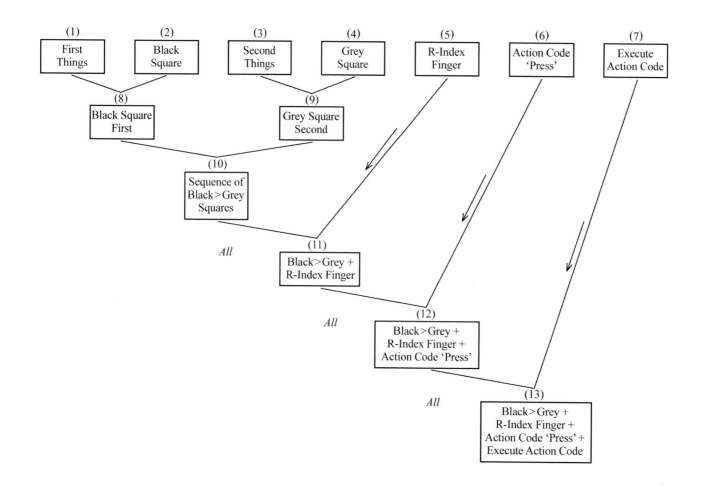

Figure 16.2 How attention builds an action sequence in long-term memory. The instructor has asked you to press a lever when you see a black square followed by a grey square on the screen. Node (10) is your record in long-term memory of seeing the black square/grey square sequence. Node (5) is a record of you attending your index finger, node (6) a record of you attending the action attribute code in your finger readying you to press the lever, and node (7) a record of you attending the Execute attribute in the master body datagram that makes the action 'Press' happen. This sequence of events automatically creates the subclass chain of nodes (11), (12) and (13).

Let's imagine you are taking part in an experiment in which you watch two squares of different colours flashed one after the other on a screen, green/blue, grey/red, blue/yellow and so on. Within the sequence is a black square followed by a grey square, and whenever you see this pairing, the instructor tells you to use your right index finger to press the lever that your finger is resting on. After a number of trials in which you have obeyed the instructor's commands, you will have built up a class/subclass sequence in long-term memory for the black/grey squares – Figure 16.2.

Subclass node (10) represents the black/grey square sequence in long-term memory – the one for which the instructor told you to use your right index finger to press the lever. You reacted to seeing the sequence as follows:

• After matching the squares to node (10) in your long-term memory, you switched your attention as instructed, from the squares in your visual image to your right index finger in your body image, and this matched node (5) in your long-term memory. Node (10) for the squares automatically combined with node (5) for your finger to create subclass node (11).

• Your instructor's command to press the lever created a match to node (6), and this highlighted the action attribute code for 'Press' in your right index finger, you attended it, and this prepared the muscles for pressing the lever. At the same time, node (6) combined in long-term memory with node (11) to create subclass node (12).

- Finally, to execute the action code 'Press', your attention went to the execute attribute code in your master body datagram, and this triggered the primed muscle groups in your right index finger to 'press' the lever. Attending the master execute datagram created a match to node (7) in long-term memory, which combined with node (12) to create subclass node (13), the final node in the chain.

So you have carried out the procedure as instructed, but at the same time you have recorded it as a chain of subclass nodes (11), (12) and (13) in long-term memory. The instructor then says that he will no longer tell you when to press the lever; it is up to you to prove that you have learnt what to do from his previous instructions when you see a black square followed by a grey one. We show this in Figure 16.3.

The next time that the black and grey squares are flashed onto the screen, they match nodes (8) and (9) and, as before, they combine to produce a match to node (10), the class of all black squares followed by grey ones. Node (10) is at the head of a sequence of subclasses each of which has only one subclass, so it will trigger the matching of nodes (11), (12) and (13), one after the other. The nodes (11), (12) and (13) automatically produce matches to class nodes (5), (6) and (7) for your right index finger, the action code 'Press' and the master action code Execute – all things in your body iconic image. The matching of these nodes activates datagrams with those attribute codes in iconic memory, and they form the time-row of datagrams shown in Figure 16.4, which is the sequence of datagrams that your attention should follow.

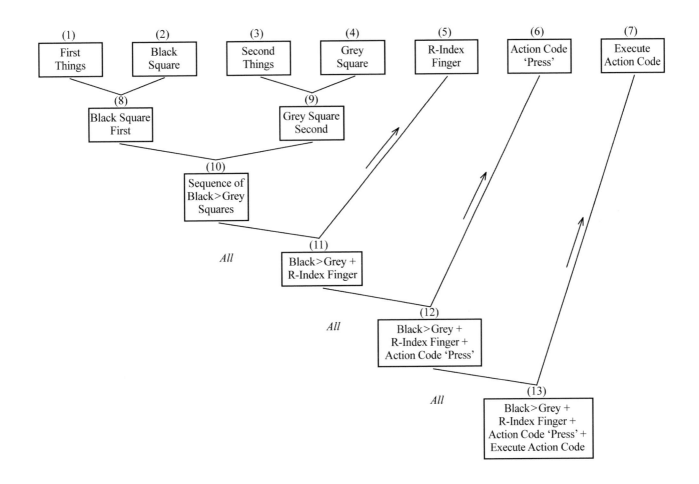

Figure 16.3 How attention executes an action sequence stored in long-term memory. This figure shows how the chain of nodes (10), (11), (12) and (13), set up in Figure 16.2, will automatically sequence nodes (5), (6) and (7) so that when the black square is followed by a grey square, you will know to press the lever without being instructed to do so.

Figure 16.4 The time-row of datagrams that long-term memory creates in iconic memory to press the lever. Datagrams (2) and (4) are in your visual iconic image, and datagrams (5), (6) and (7) are in your body iconic image. To press the lever, your priority system moves your attention from one datagram to the next, attending the highlighted attribute in each one.

The datagrams for the **Black** and **Grey** squares have already been attended. The next datagram you attend is for your right index finger, and the attribute you attend in it is the one that says this is your **R-Index Finger**. You then attend the attribute for the action code attribute **Press** that prepares the muscles in your right index finger for the pressing down action. Finally, your attention goes to your master body datagram and attends the **Execute** attribute, and as a consequence your finger presses down on the lever.

So what holds the datagrams in a time-row together? The answer is that the datagrams of a time-row are overlaid by a group region in iconic memory that covers its extent in space and time. To execute a time-row, you must first attend it at the group level; your attention will then go through the time-row in parent/component sequence, executing any action attribute codes it contains.

It is important to recognise that this is a sequence in time as well as space. When you attend the datagram for your right index finger, step (5), you will attend the attribute **R-Index Finger** and that identifies it. When you then attend the **Press** attribute, step (6), although it too is a datagram in your right index finger, it is not in the same datagram as the one in step (5); instead it is in an identical datagram in an identical index finger region but in the next time layer. The two datagrams are separate in time, but they are within the same attended space/time region. Your attention moves from one to the other via the group datagram that overlays the time-row as a whole.

Comparing the information flows in Figures 16.2 and 16.3 above, you will see that in the training phase, Figure 16.2, the information flows *downwards* from class nodes (5), (6) and (7); the building of the sequence is a *by-product* of the interactions between the iconic and long-term memories that produce the pressing of the lever. In the execution phase, Figure 16.3, the pressing of the lever is achieved by the class node sequence (11), (12) and (13) transmitting information *upwards* into nodes (5), (6) and

(7) so that they can structure a time-row in iconic memory that reproduces the same result of pressing the lever.

We call this type of subclass sequence in long-term memory a chain. Once the first node of a chain is matched, the sequence of subclasses that follows automatically creates a time-row in iconic memory for your attention to follow. The chain of subclasses acts as a template and spins off instructions into iconic memory that carry out the tasks you have been trained to perform.

We will see in Chapter 17 that we can simulate the consequences of implementing action chains before we trigger them, and in this way we can avoid the bad outcomes we might have experienced in the past – provided of course we take the trouble to attend the simulations.

Action modules

All actions are initiated by the triggering of class code sequences in long-term memory that culminate in action attribute codes in the body iconic image being highlighted for execution, depressing a finger for example. The network of nodes that leads us to an action class code are the *pre-conditions* that need to be present for that physical act to take place. The *physical acts* triggered by a particular set of pre-conditions will produce a particular set of *outcomes*, and these are recorded in the chain of *all* subclasses in long-term memory that follow the action nodes. The same physical acts may produce many different outcomes, but for any particular set of pre-conditions, and provided the act has been executed properly, the outcomes should always be the same.

These *pre-condition–physical acts–outcome* sequences in long-term memory are encapsulated into *action modules*, sometimes called 'productions', that are the building blocks for all our behaviours. In order to achieve an overall objective, it is often necessary for many action modules to execute within a single activity.

Action modules are constructed from the chains we described in the previous section. An action module may contain just one chain, but more often than not action modules comprise many chains linked together. All the chains comply with two simple requirements: (a) every node in the *spine* of a chain must only have one subclass; and (b) each successive node in the spine must specify the next attention move in the time-row that has been created by that chain.

Modules are classes like any other. Every module is identified by a unique class code number that acts as the ultimate parent of every class within that module, and every chain within a module is identified by the class code number that is the first parent *all* class in the chain. The last node in a chain is the one that has more than one subclass. Most modules hold a selection of chains that between them perform a range of similar functions. The chains in a module that are selected to perform a particular task will depend on the pre-conditions presented to the module. For example, there could be one module that you would call on to depress – lower – any one of the fingers of your right hand (Figure 16.5).

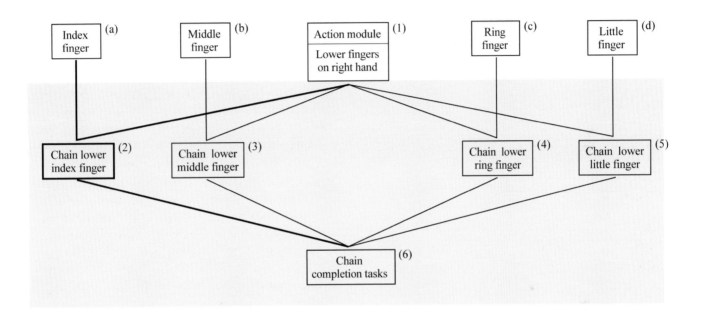

Figure 16.5 A long-term memory module to lower any one of the four fingers of the right hand. To lower your right index finger (a), you must attend one of its datagrams and have met a pre-condition in long-term memory that will trigger the action module (1). When these pre-conditions have been met, chain (2) will download a time-row into iconic memory that lowers your right index finger.

The long-term memory module shown in Figure 16.5 contains the chains of class codes that will lower any one of the four fingers of your right hand. Nodes (2), (3), (4) and (5) are the first nodes in each of the four chains. In this example, providing you attend your right index and the other pre-conditions are met, you will match action module (1) in long-term memory and this will trigger head-of-chain node (2) to download a time-row into the body iconic image of your right index finger that contains the action codes that will lower it.

An attended action sequence to go from my sitting room to the fridge in the kitchen to get a beer incorporates calls by attention to the many action modules needed to do the job. Each module is individually executed, and of course the same action module can be called many times within the overall sequence; however, the choice of modules in the sequence is under the control of attention and its priorities. Attended action sequences of this type leave a memory, a record in long-term memory of the chain of events that have taken place.

Unattended action sequences

It is a rule that we have a single attention stream and it can only process one thing at a time. Yet we are able to perform a wide range of activities in addition to the one we are paying attention to. For example, when I drive my car on a familiar route, I am able to control the car while my attention is engaged in listening to music or talking to the passenger sitting beside me. I will only pay attention to the road if the car deviates from its expected path or something unfamiliar crops up; if either of these things happens, I will immediately switch my attention back to my driving and retake conscious control of the car. We carry out most essential tasks unattended – if we could only do one thing at a time, we would not survive for long in our fast-moving, complex world.

The activities we perform unattended fall into six categories:

- There are those that take place locally and automatically without any intervention from the brain. For example, when we are cut we bleed, and our body forms blood clots to stop the bleeding.

- There are those activities that are beyond our conscious control but are wholly or partially controlled by the brain, for example our heart rate.

- There are complex activities that we carry out by instinct that we have never been trained to do. These are most common in animals and young children.

- There are those activities that we can control and modify if we attend to them, but they will carry on automatically if we do not attend them – breathing and blinking are good examples of this.

- There are action sequences of a complex nature that require our dedicated attention and cannot be carried out unattended. When we switch out of such a complex attention stream, its activity immediately ceases, and we can only make further progress by returning to it. At any point in time, we have many such attention streams on the go. We switch in and out of these, and our short-term memories help us to pick up from where we left off.

- Finally, there are action sequences that we execute under attention but that we can also perform unattended provided we have defined them sufficiently in advance in long-term memory. In this category are most of the routine physical activities we perform

while we are awake, like driving a car or walking over to the fridge without falling over the kitchen table. Here we do not have to authorise every action code or time-row individually – we can pre-authorise all actions in a hierarchy of time-rows by attending and executing just the group identifier attribute in the group region at the top of the hierarchy.

In this section, we describe briefly how we build, execute and supervise unattended action sequences. We process exactly the same action modules in long-term memory whether we are performing an action sequence under attention or unattended – but we execute them in a very different way.

Unattended, there is no attention to control the sequence of action modules involved. Attention sets the pre-conditions for the first module, and after that the modules select themselves. If the pre-conditions for a particular module in long-term memory match the outcomes from the module that preceded it, its chains will download into time-rows in iconic memory and execute automatically. There is no sequencing of any kind, and modules are not connected to each other in any way; they self-select solely on the basis that their pre-conditions match the current data and statuses in iconic and long-term memories. There is no evaluation of future possibilities – the execution path is predetermined and automatic. Unattended sequences are mechanical, and a failure to produce the predicted outcomes at any stage will result in the complete failure of the sequence and a signal to attention to take over. *Unattended action sequences leave no record in long-term memory, and each module executes in complete isolation.*

Context is a vital pre-condition because it allows us to use the same action modules for a range of similar activities in different situations. The way I move around my sitting room is completely different from the way I move around my kitchen – the rooms are different sizes and there are different obstacles to negotiate – but the two basic actions, walking and turning, are the same. I can use the same general purpose navigation modules in these different contexts provided I supply them with the geometry of the scene within which they are expected to operate; in a sense, these general purpose modules are action classes.

So, in addition to the pre-conditions needed to select a module, we need to supply it with pre-conditions, parameters, that describe the particular context at the time of execution. If I am to go to the fridge in my kitchen, the first thing my attention needs to do is download the scene attribute code for my kitchen into the top group layer of iconic memory. From this information, I can tell my position and the positions of other objects in the room. Parameter values are pre-conditions not for module selection, but for the module to perform its tasks correctly.

Unattended action sequences are generally carried out automatically but with intermittent visits by attention. Attention often has to intervene when there is some doubt about the nature of the objects being processed. The problem is that unattended objects do not look like the objects we see under attention as they are in their pre-attentive form of loosely connected shapes (see Chapter 10). For example, much of the practising we do in sport is driven by the need to identify and record simple forms that, as pre-attentive objects, will stand for attended objects in the unattended world.

Although we inherit some action modules, we are constantly building new ones and adapting existing ones. We do this through training, from copying and by trial and error; these are all attended activities because it is only by attending things that we can create a permanent record in long-term memory. When we carry out action sequences unattended, we reinforce the internal structures of the modules we have employed, but we cannot change their structure. Attended and unattended activities share the iconic image but do not overlap, and the partitioning of iconic memory between attended and unattended activities is controlled by statuses assigned to all datagrams across iconic memory.

Motivation

When you are injured, your nervous system triggers an involuntary withdrawal reflex that pulls the injured part of your body away from the source of harm. If, for example, you touch a hot piece of metal with your finger, sensitive nerve endings under your skin will produce a signal that travels along nerve fibres into your spinal cord and then down into muscle groups that will pull your hand away. This is known as a reflex arc. The nerve signals that produce this reflex do not travel via the brain because time is critical – a reflex arc takes only half a second to complete, whereas a response that is controlled by the brain can take 2 seconds.

At the same time as all this is happening, a signal that you have an injury is sent to your brain, where it is recorded as a negative attribute in the datagrams of the injured part in your body iconic image, in this case your finger. You will be forced to attend this attribute because it has a very high priority, and as a consequence you suffer the pain of a burnt finger as a sensation in the physical internal image of your finger. Your immediate priority is to stop the pain. The reflex arc has taken your finger away from the cause of the pain,

but the pain persists because the damage done to your finger has not gone away – the finger has been burnt. The position and nature of the pain trigger a match to a module in long-term memory that contains actions that will reduce the pain; in the case of your finger, this might be by shaking it, or sucking it, or running cold water over it. The action sequence that produces this reaction is downloaded into a time-row in your body iconic memory where it is executed by attention.

If the same circumstances crop up again, you need to be able to avoid being injured again. You have recorded the sequence of events in long-term memory, so if they happen again you should now be able to predict the negative pathway and insert actions to break the sequence so you are not burnt a second time.

To explain how we do this, let's return to our squares and levers experiment. This time the instructor flashes a single-colour square onto the screen for 150 msec. You then have 5 seconds to choose whether or not to press the lever. After 5 seconds, the instructor displays a different coloured square, and so on. The squares are yellow, brown, red and green, and the rewards you receive for depressing the lever when a square is displayed are:

Yellow square	Press lever	No reward
Brown square	Press lever	No reward
Red square	Press lever	A mild electric shock
Green square	Press lever	A £1 coin

Pressing the lever after seeing the yellow and brown squares produces no reward, but also no pain. Press the lever after seeing the red square and you will receive a mild electric shock from the lever. Press the lever after seeing the green square, however, and the supervisor rewards you a £1 coin. In the first pass of the experiment, the supervisor asks you to press the lever with your right index finger after every colour so that you can learn the different outcomes. From then on, it is up to you to decide whether or not to press the lever.

When you see a yellow or brown square, you press the lever as instructed and receive neither a reward nor a penalty. In this case, you simply record a passive sequence of events in long-term memory, which you can follow in future if you choose. Similarly, the green square gives you a modest reward.

The red square presents you with two problems: first, how do you react when you get the shock; and second, how do you avoid getting a shock in the future? The first time you see the red square, you press the lever with your right index finger, as instructed, and you receive a mild electric shock in that finger. This produces the sequence of events shown below:

- The electric shock triggers a reflex arc that pulls your hand away from the lever, and your brain is not involved with this.

- At the same time, the shock produces signals that travel up a nerve pathway into the brain, where they insert a pain attribute into the datagrams of the body iconic image of your right index finger.

- Because of the high priority given to pain attributes, your attention immediately goes to a datagram in your right index finger and attends the pain attribute.

- You experience the sensation of pain in your right index finger.

- Attending the pain attribute creates a match in long-term memory to the action module that controls your response to pain – node (21) in Figure 16.6.

- The pain response module selects chain (30) and it downloads a time-row into your body iconic image that directs your attention to rotate your forearm – node (32).

- Your attention switches to this time-row and executes it. Your forearm rotates so that the position of the pain becomes visible and you can check out the damage.

This pain module might look something like the network in Figure 16.6.

The action module in Figure 16.6 shows how you might be directed to respond to pain depending on which of your body parts has been injured. In this example, you respond to pain in any one of your fingers by rotating your forearm so the site of the pain becomes uppermost in order that you can see it.

The next time during the experiment that you see the red square flashed onto the screen, you must avoid pressing the lever again and avoid being hurt again. However, the memory sequence you left behind in long-term memory is 'red square then press lever' – in other words, you won't know that this is a bad idea until you've

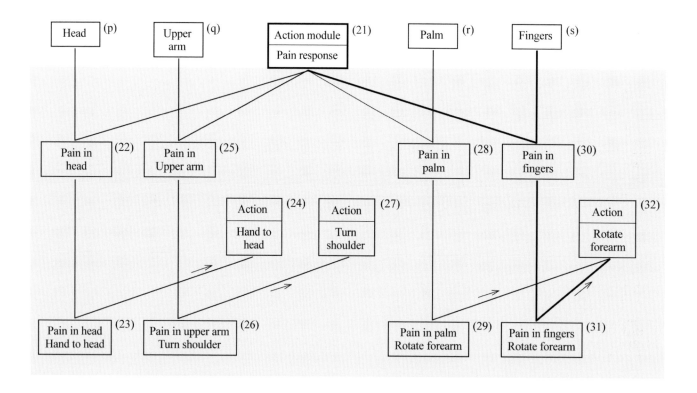

Figure 16.6 Our response to pain. This figure shows a general action module in long-term memory that provides responses to pain occurring in a number of different parts of the body. If the pain response module, node (21), is matched, it will provide a response to head, upper arm, palm and finger injuries – depending on which of these is being attended at the time. In this example, a finger (s) has been hurt so an action chain (30) has been activated, producing a time-row to rotate the forearm so you can examine the injury.

already done it! There is no advance warning in the recorded sequence, so how do you learn to avoid a painful result?

The answer is that the next time you recognise the red square, the sequence of nodes in long-term memory describing what happened before creates a time-row in iconic memory which predicts that executing the action code to lower your finger is followed by a pain attribute in your right index finger. The problem is that we can never access time-row predictions in the future in iconic memory; we can only access things in iconic memory that are happening now, things that are *real*. And if you do attend this time-row, you will simply repeat what happened the last time.

But at the same time as the time-row describing what happened last time was downloaded into your *real* iconic memory, it was duplicated in your simulation iconic memory, where there are no restrictions on visiting the past or the future. The pain attribute in the simulation time-row of your right index finger will give it a very high priority, so you will go to it immediately and attend the 'predicted' datagram sequence in your imagination. The simulated pain attribute code is the same as the real one. It gives an unpleasant but different experience, and it routes you to a different action module in long-term memory, one that helps you to avoid problems rather than to deal with their consequences.

Figure 16.7 is an example of a pain-avoidance module that is designed to help you avoid threatening situations – in contrast to the pain response module in Figure 16.6 that helps you to handle pain when it occurs. Attending the simulated pain of an electric shock in your right index finger will match class code number (51) in Figure 16.7 for the pain-avoidance module. The module downloads the avoidance chain (60) as a time-row and your attention switches to it, this directs you to lift your hand (62) away from the lever and avoid the electric shock.

You have now created two action sequences in long-term memory. The first sequence relating to the aftermath of seeing a red square is a record of you pressing the lever and getting an electric shock, and then of the actions you took in response. The second action sequence records you receiving a warning of the negative consequences of pressing the lever, and in response you lift up your hand, pulling it away from the lever.

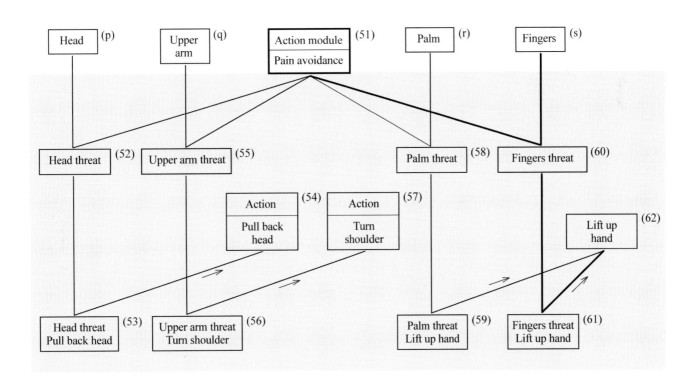

Figure 16.7 The avoidance of pain. The figure shows a pain-avoidance module in long-term memory responding to the simulation of an expected painful event. Avoidance modules are triggered when we attend a simulation time-row predicting a painful outcome. They download time-rows into iconic memory that help us to avoid the action we are planning to execute, and to avoid its consequences. In this example, the module has a chain that directs us to lift our hand away from the lever.

The third time you encounter the red square, you will see, from the memory of the previous sequence, that if you lift up your hand, there are no negative consequences; therefore, the execution of the second chain will be given a high priority. The original sequence in which you pressed the lever and got a shock is still there in long-term memory, it will produce a time-row, and you could still go down that path if you chose – you might think about it if you were promised £1,000 to press the lever and accept the consequences.

Pleasurable sensations that arise in parts of your body are transmitted to the brain by the nervous system in a similar way, and are recorded as positive attributes in the datagrams of the iconic body parts that represent them. Positive attributes generally trigger sequences in long-term memory that work to maintain the status quo, either by doing nothing or by setting priorities so that actions are performed that prolong the pleasurable experience.

When you encounter a past action sequence that led to a pleasurable outcome, the prediction of that outcome will produce a time-row of the actions leading to that outcome, and the sequence will be protected by an attention priority threshold that prevents your being distracted from it.

For example, if you are soaking in a warm bath after walking the dog on a cold winter's day, you will just lie there and enjoy it. Your attention will explore your long-term memory and produce simulations of what else you could be doing, but the positive attributes you are experiencing will create a priority threshold that prevents your attention from finding something to do that will be more pleasurable than a lovely warm bath.

In the datagrams that represent our bodies as a whole, there appears to be something like a well-being attribute that, when we attend it, gives us a sense of how we feel about the world, our general level of satisfaction, whether we are happy or unhappy. Experiencing positive motivational attributes drives this well-being value up, and experiencing negative motivational attributes drives it down. If the value of this attribute is high, we generally feel good about things; if it is low, we generally feel bad about them.

Most pleasurable experiences taper off over time, creating a drop in your personal well-being. This reduction produces negative motivational attributes that trigger action sequences in long-term memory designed to restore your sense of well-being to its former level. We return to the subject of well-being again in the next chapter.

Summary

When we touch things, we create attributes in two separate iconic images: a public one that we share with other people, and a private one that holds a representation of our body. We will merge public datagrams arising from different senses provided they originate in regions that share the same space and time.

The internal body iconic image is segmented into a hierarchy of predefined regions, one for each body part. The attributes generated by our private experience of touching things are recorded in these regions. We have a second private body structure that tracks our body parts in relation to each other and in relation to their positions in public space.

Every body part in our body iconic image holds in its datagrams a permanent list of the action attribute codes that define the actions it is able to perform; the action class code equivalents of these attributes are embedded as nodes in long-term memory. When an action class code is matched in long-term memory, the action attribute code that is its equivalent in the attended datagram prepares the muscle groups of that body part for that action. However, before it can be executed, we must attend the master execute attribute in the group level datagram of our body iconic image.

We build chains in long-term memory that, when matched, produce time-rows of datagrams in iconic memory that execute the sequence of actions the chains dictate. Chains are grouped into general purpose modules so that together they can control activities that have similar characteristics. Unattended action sequences are set up by attention to execute automatically and mechanically. They only require attention if the actual outcomes fail to match those predicted.

Injuries to parts of the body are recorded as negative attributes in those datagrams in your body iconic image that represent your body parts. Negative attributes in datagrams attract high priorities, and when attended, they select chains in long-term memory which download time-rows into iconic memory that, when also attended, produce your responses. The sequence of events contained in your response is recorded in long-term memory so if the same situation arises again, you can anticipate the negative outcome in simulation iconic memory and take the actions necessary to avoid those consequences.

17

What thinking is

Truth is the shattered mirror strown / In myriad bits;
while each believes his little bit the whole to own.

(Richard Francis Burton, *The Kasîdah of Hâjî Abdû El-Yezdî*)

As human beings, we are aware of just two sorts of things. We are aware of the things going on in the world – ourselves included – and we are aware of our own thoughts. We keep these two apart by maintaining them in two separate iconic memories, as described in Chapter 16. One is our *real* iconic memory, which handles all real things, and the other is our *simulation* iconic memory that handles all imaginary things. Simulation iconic memory has all the features of real iconic memory, so for example we have a simulation iconic memory for vision where we imagine seeing things, and alongside it we have a simulation iconic body image where we imagine how we might feel about things.

Although they are separate, our real and simulation iconic memories share the same space and time, and they are processed by the same rules; this means that our attention can switch seamlessly between datagrams in the real world and datagrams in the world of our imagination. All these attention movements are controlled by a single priority system.

At its simplest, perception is being aware of the reality of what is going on around you. If a black object comes into your field of view, it will create a black region in the internal image in your visual cortex, and this will switch on black pre-attentive datagrams in the equivalent region in your iconic image. If you then attend one of those black datagrams, you will physically 'see' the black object because the sensory area in the internal image in your visual cortex outside your mind and the iconic area inside your mind are tied together by the same geometry. Similarly, if you assemble a collection of datagrams that match the class code for a cat in long-term memory, the attribute code for a cat will be downloaded into all the datagrams in the region of the *iconic* image occupied by the cat. If you attend one of these datagrams, you will experience the unique sensation that this is a cat in the *internal* image, not in the iconic image.

When we feel our muscles stretch or we experience pain, it is because we have processed information about our bodies in exactly the same way. So if you hurt your finger, the parts of the brain that records your hurt finger,

but is outside the mind, will switch on pain attributes in datagrams in the body iconic image of your finger. If you then attend one of these datagrams, you will experience pain not in the body iconic image, but in the physical internal image of your finger that shares the same pixels..

These experiences are real because all the datagrams you are attending are in real iconic memory. Thinking, on the other hand, is a simulation; it is the range of sensations we experience when we attend datagrams in simulation iconic memory. The things we are thinking are not actually happening. The attribute code for a cat in simulation iconic memory is the same number as for a cat in real iconic memory, but the imaginary cat and the real cat are experienced differently as the two memories represent different modes of perception, in the same way that vision and sound represent different modes of perception.

But we don't confine our thinking to what is happening in the here-and-now; instead we use our spare mental capacity to speculate about things that are not immediately relevant, things that do not require an immediate response. We spend much of our thinking time in recalling the past, either to eliminate negative experiences in the future or to locate pleasurable feelings that we might enjoy again, and finally we create novel patterns of thought to provide new solutions to old problems. Ultimately, our thoughts have but one aim – to improve our personal well-being.

All these mental activities depend on our long-term memory supplying us with simulations that forecast futures for us to evaluate. These can be replays of recent events, they can be new class structures that have arisen from recent events, or they can be created out of the logical rebalancing of our long-term memory network, a process that is necessary to maintain the integrity and efficiency of its class structure.

To understand how we handle simulations, we must look again at how we control our attention movements. Our attention moves from datagram to datagram across our real and imaginary worlds in a continuous, never-ending sequence. The paths we take, and therefore the choices we make, are controlled at every step by the priority values our internal priority system places in datagrams. The datagram we are attending now may tell us we are looking at a cat, the one after that may deliver the sound of the cat purring, the one after that may trigger the action to stroke the cat, and the one after that may deliver the thought of a dish of cat food. Every step in the attention sequence is dictated entirely by priority values inserted into datagrams in iconic memory, and the datagram with the highest priority value is the one that we must go to next – whether it be in our real iconic memory or in our simulation iconic memory.

But before we explain how we set priorities in datagrams, we must clarify the relationship between the sensation of an injury and the negative nature of the pain it produces, for example between the sensation of an electric shock in your finger and the intensity of the pain you feel as a result of that shock.

Two attributes within the same body part datagram are involved in all painful and pleasurable experiences: the first describes the *nature* of the event, the way the sensation of an electric shock feels or a bar of chocolate tastes; and the second delivers the extent of the pain or pleasure we feel. The negative value of the attribute responsible for a pain will directly reflect the severity of the injury, but of course we will only feel that pain if we attend that pain attribute. These are private attributes because only we can know exactly what an electric shock feels like and only we can know how painful it is. In future, when we refer to *motivational* attributes, we will mean the combination of the two, the attribute that delivers the severity of the pain or pleasure and the attribute that describes the nature of the accompanying sensation, an electric shock for example.

So we propose that two different priority systems work together to set priority values – we call the first of these *impersonal* and the second personal. The rules followed by our *impersonal* system are blind to our personal motivations; they do not reflect our past experiences, our needs or our desires. It is because these rules are impersonal that we tend to see the world in much the same way that others do, and if this were not the case we would find it impossible to communicate. *Personal* priority values on the other hand are calculated from the motivational attributes, positive and negative, that are embedded in the past experiences we have recorded in our long-term memories. Personal priorities values are designed to help us avoid our past errors and to point us to activities that should improve our lives in the future.

Our *impersonal priority system* manages the low-level attention movements that we use to construct objects from their components, for example the movements that help us identify a region as a cat, or that help us understand a verse of a poem from its words and lines. Personal priority values are, on the other hand, held in the datagrams of group regions that enclose lower level activity and, having attracted attention, provide a threshold that protects this activity from interference. Impersonal priority sequences are self-contained, self-regulating and mechanical in nature.

In addition to controlling object-building, our impersonal priority system is involved in other activities, for example the sequencing of attention in time-rows and the comparisons that produce pop-out. In particular, our impersonal system controls the selection of a single datagram for attention from the many thousands of identical datagrams that make up a region. So let's say I have decided to change the time on the clock on the mantlepiece in my sitting room from summertime to wintertime. As I walk into the room, my personal priority system will highlight all the datagrams of the front face of the clock with the same priority value, but my attention can only go to one datagram at a time. So my impersonal priority system kicks in and calculates a different impersonal priority for every datagram within the highlighted region – the highest will be at the centre of the clock face, so this will be the datagram that my attention homes in on.

Impersonal priorities can create immediate responses to potential dangers, for example a car pulling out from a side road. So if there is an unexpected movement in our visual field, our impersonal system will place a high priority in those datagrams, and this will trigger our long-term memory to deliver an unattended response. We will only react consciously to such alarms if they trigger a match in our long-term memory that downloads motivational attributes with high personal priorities into our simulation body iconic image.

The simple objective of our *personal priority system* is to improve our personal well-being. We suggest that personal priorities are set by a well-being regulator that converts motivator attributes into priority values and inserts them into datagrams to attract our attention. The fundamental difference between our impersonal and personal priority systems is that impersonal priority values are inserted into individual datagrams without reference to their motivational significance, whereas personal priority values are attached to group datagrams whose component datagrams have motivational attributes that, if attended, will improve our well-being.

The well-being regulator sets personal priorities through a well-being scale of attribute values held in the master datagram of our body iconic image. Personal priority values range from the worst we can ever feel to the best we can ever feel, with a point of neutral well-being at its centre. The position of our current well-being is always identified on this scale by a single attribute value. For our examples, we will assume that the central regulator scale ranges from −20 through zero to +20. Each negative number on the scale reflects the level of pain or unhappiness we are feeling now, and each positive number reflects level of pleasure or happiness we are feeling now. Every time we attend a pain/pleasure attribute in a body datagram, the position of our current well-being on this scale is recalculated.

To show how the well-being regulator works, we will look at a variation of the experiment we used in Chapter 16 where the act of pressing a lever after seeing a coloured square could produce an electric shock. Suppose, after completing the last trial, that you and your supervisor are having a discussion and suddenly, for no reason, the lever delivers an electric shock to your right index finger. The shock, −8 on the well-being scale, is not painful enough to produce a reflex action, so it is up to you to decide how to react. We suggest the following response sequence:

- The electric shock switches on two motivational attributes in the body image datagrams of your injured right index finger. One describes the sensation of an electric shock, the other the level of the pain, −8 in this example, but you do not feel the pain because your attention is elsewhere.

- Your attention must now be diverted from chatting to your supervisor (current well-being zero!) to dealing with your injured finger. However, the pain motivator attribute, −8, in the datagram in your finger does not itself attract your attention. Instead your impersonal priority system converts the pain, −8, to a priority value of (say) 80, which it inserts into the datagrams of your right index finger.

- Because 80 is now the highest priority in iconic memory, your attention goes from chatting to your supervisor to this high-priority group datagram in your finger. Your impersonal priority system then takes over and directs your attention to the datagram in your finger that holds the attributes for the pain. You feel the pain in your finger, and your well-being is automatically decreased from zero to −8 on the well-being scale.

- Attending the pain attribute produces a match in your long-term memory to the pain response module (see Figure 16.6), which downloads a time-row into your real iconic memory for the action that will rotate your forearm away from the lever. We will assume that this time-row promises to deliver a final pain value of −1, so the well-being regulator calculates an improvement in well-being of 7 (from −8 to −1). The regulator converts this promised improvement in well-being to a priority value of 70 and inserts it into the group datagrams of the time-row.

- This is now the highest priority time-row, so your attention switches to one of its group datagrams and you execute its component datagrams under the control of your impersonal priority system. You rotate your arm, removing your finger from contact with the lever, the pain reduces, and you are left with a well-being of −1.

This example is intended to give you some idea of how a feedback loop might alter behaviour – although we are not suggesting for a moment that our well-being is controlled by a mechanism as crude as the one we are describing here!

The motivational attributes that tell us. how we feel about something, a beautiful flower or an angry person for example, are not held in the datagrams of the thing itself, because they are public objects. *The pleasure we feel when we see a flower or the fear we experience on seeing an angry face comes from motivational attributes in our body iconic image and not from attributes in the thing we are looking at.* How then do we respond to an angry face if there are no motivational attributes in an angry face for the well-being regulator to prioritise?

The answer is that there is in long-term memory a class code for angry faces, and this is in a chain with a class code that downloads the motivational attributes for fear into the group datagrams of your body iconic image. If there is an angry face in your iconic image your impersonal priority system will give it a high priority, you will attend it and this will create a match in long-term memory that will trigger this chain, in turn creating a time-row with a datagram for the angry face followed by a body datagram holding the fear attribute. The well-being regulator will generate a high priority for this time-row, so your attention will transfer first to one of its group datagrams, then to the angry face datagram and then to the fear datagram. Finally, attending this combination produces a match in long-term memory to a module that downloads a time-row to deal with the threatening situation.

At this point, it is worth pointing out that although we say that we 'download' time-rows from long-term memory into iconic memory, no information is in fact transferred; what long-term memory does is overlay existing datagrams in iconic memory with a group region that binds them together so they match the sequence of *all* classes in the matched chain.

In the examples so far, a single time-row has been produced to deal with the position we found ourselves in. In practice, however, our long-term memories generate alternative solutions, each producing a time-row in iconic memory and each assigned its own personal priority value reflecting the well-being improvements that its component motivators promise to deliver. Our attention then transfers to the time-row with the highest priority and executes it step by step. When time is critical, we will execute the highest priority time-row straight away, even though by doing so we may find that there are unexpected consequences.

Most of the decisions we make, whether deciding where to eat or which car to buy, are not time-critical so we have the time to test whether they will deliver the results we expect of them and to consider the alternatives. The simulation of time-rows and the evaluation of alternative courses of action take place in our simulation iconic memory and we experience them as our thoughts.

The content and structure of our simulation iconic memory is identical to that of our real iconic memory, including the projection of moving objects into the future and the retention of immediate past events. This is why, when we download time-rows from long-term memory into real iconic memory, we are able to duplicate them in simulation iconic memory – the scene contents, the datagrams, of the two memories are identical.

We use the same attribute codes in the two memories for the same thing, so the attribute codes for black things, square things and things that are cats are the same whether they are in datagrams in real iconic memory or datagrams in simulation iconic memory – although the sensation we experience when we attend a simulation is always qualified by the mode of perception that tells us that this is not real, it is only our thoughts.

Action codes for the same action are also identical across the two memories, but they perform very differently. When we are doing a simulation and attend a simulated action code, to press a lever for example, we prepare for the action but absolutely nothing happens because we do not attend the master execute datagram.

Instead in this example, the time-row simulates the way your finger would move and the electric shock that would follow if you *really* did press the lever. The simulated outcome delivers an unpleasant warning of an electric shock, which causes the download of a time-row that avoids the shock (see Figure 16.7), and this is prioritised above all other time-rows in real iconic memory.

Our long-term memories present us with many alternative time-rows, each proposing a different solution to the situation we are in. In simulation iconic memory, these time-rows come together to form a group, and the well-being regulator assigns a priority to the group that is greater than the priorities of any of the individual time-rows in real iconic memory. The result is that our attention moves to these simulations and delays the execution of the highest priority time-row in real iconic memory.

We then go through a process of attending and comparing the motivational outcomes for each simulation time-row, and only when a clear top priority time-row emerges do we select that particular one. The process is similar to the selection procedures we described in Chapter 10 and is largely controlled by our impersonal priority system.

There are three very important reasons why we evaluate alternatives in this way. First, the act of simulating alternatives will often trigger our long-term memory into producing additional time-rows that provide better solutions than the ones we already have. Second, this approach provides a check that the activities of the time-row can be delivered and are not threatened by the unexpected positions of things in the scene. Third, by attending datagrams in simulation time-rows before a final decision is made, we leave behind a record of our thought processes in long-term memory. When we encounter a difficult situation in the future, we will now be able to recall (as a time-row) what our thoughts were when faced with a similar situation in the past. This information not only contributes to our personal decision-making, but also provides us with the ability to share our thinking with other people and so draw on the pooled experience of a group.

Finally, after considering the alternatives in the lever-pressing task, we will assume that the simulation time-row to lift your hand to avoid pressing the lever emerges as the highest priority. Your attention goes from this simulation time-row to its real time-row equivalent and triggers it so that you raise your hand and avoid the electric shock. During the execution, you will be aware of the real-world sequence of events and not of your thoughts in the simulation time-row.

The simplest sequences in long-term memory are those that record a single episode, a sequence that has happened just once. The datagram sequences we experience every day are all unique episodes because each has occurred within a unique time frame and each will therefore be represented in long-term memory by a chain of unit classes.

We automatically create generalised chains in long-term memory when chains for similar episodes have class codes in a particular position that can be replaced by a single parent class code. A single generalised chain can then be downloaded and prioritised above the single-episode chains from which it was constructed. In theory, generalised chains should not replace the episodes that formed them – we should retain every episode we have ever experienced – but our brains do not have the capacity for this so we discard old episodes and expect a generalised chain to act reliably on their behalf.

Single-episode chains from the recent past produce simulation time-rows that compete for priority with time-rows that come from generalised chains – this is because often the best thing you can do is to repeat exactly what you did the last time. No matter how many times you repeat exactly the same sequence, you will each time create a new episode chain of unit classes in long-term memory.

So we are in the process of thinking when we attend any simulated datagrams, and in particular we are thinking when we run through the datagrams in a simulation time-row so as to evaluate the future consequences of executing it. This is in contrast to the real experiences we have when we attend real datagrams in real iconic memory, because real things can only exist in an iconic present that lasts for a few seconds. We cannot skip to the far future in a real time-row because the future in real iconic memory is only an extended present.

Let's suppose that in a coffee break in the lab, your supervisor asked you to tell him what would happen if you saw a red square on the screen and pressed the lever. This request would trigger your long-term memory to download a time-row into your simulation iconic memory that sequenced the datagrams for the screen, your right index finger and the lever, so you could run the simulation and tell him that pressing the lever would give you an electric shock. You are able to do this because the screen and the lever are actually present in the room producing datagrams in your simulation iconic memory that long-term memory can bind into a group time-row.

But what if you and your supervisor went to the pub and he asked you the same question? Your simulation iconic memory is a copy of your real iconic memory, so in the pub scene your simulation iconic memory holds datagrams for a pint of Guinness and a dart-board – there are no datagrams for the screen and lever that long-term memory needs to overlay with a group region to create a simulation time-row because there are no screens and levers in the pub.

At this point, we are going to suggest a change in the way we think about how information is transferred from long-term memory into iconic memory. Up to this point, we have said that when our long-term memories recognise a region in iconic memory, as a cat for example, we 'download' the key class code number for a cat from long-term memory into the datagrams of the attended region; here it becomes an attribute code that, when we attend it, delivers the sensation that this is a cat.

What we now propose is that attribute codes are not 'downloaded' from long-term memory into datagrams of regions in iconic memory *because every possible attribute code already exists in every pixel in iconic memory* in the form of a pre-attentive datagram, so there is a pre-attentive datagram in every pixel of visual iconic memory for every possible shade of green, and there is a pre-attentive datagram in every pixel of visual iconic memory that says this is a cat *whether there is a cat there or not*. When we match a region to the class code for a cat in long-term memory, then instead of downloading the attribute code for a cat into its datagrams, our long-term memory simply *switches* on the attribute code for a cat in the pixels of the region where the cat is.

Pre-attentive datagrams for individual sense attribute values, a particular shade of green for example, are switched on directly by signals coming from our senses that have the signature of that attribute code. So as soon as a black cat appears, the pre-attentive datagram for black in every pixel of the iconic region of the black cat is switched on by our internal image *before we know it is there* and before we know it is a cat. If at this stage the cat moves, its black pre-attentive datagrams will be automatically switched off in the pixels of one region and switched on in another. When we attend the components of the black region and recognise it in long-term memory as a cat, then cat pre-attentive datagrams will be switched on across the whole of the black region, and if we attend one of them we will have the experience seeing a cat – not in the iconic image but in the physical world of its internal image.

The reason we are suggesting this way of looking at the relationship between long-term memory and iconic memory is that it allows us think about things in imaginary environments rather than just the one we are actually in at the moment. Back then to sitting in the pub with your supervisor, who is asking you to tell him what will happen if you press the lever following the red square. There are no levers or red squares in the pub, but somehow you are going to have to create datagrams for them in your simulation iconic memory so they can be bound into a time-row sequence that you can then attend and use to respond to your supervisor.

So, to respond to your supervisor, you will think of the laboratory scene, and this will produce *all* matches to the class nodes in long-term memory of the things that are in the laboratory. This memory switches on the pre-attentive datagrams of those things in your simulation iconic memory and creates an imaginary scene of the laboratory.

Of course, the positions and details of the things in this imaginary scene are very crude because we do not hold photographic representations of things in long-term memory, but we can switch on the identity of things, like squares and levers, as token datagrams even though we cannot recreate exactly what they look like. We might switch on a single token pre-attentive datagram for each thing in a scene, so for an imaginary black cat, our long-term memory could switch on a token datagram with the attribute for a cat in just one pixel of simulation iconic memory. In addition, our long-term memory might switch on a token datagram that indicated the size of the cat in the same pixel.

Figure 17.1 We can imagine things happening outside our present environment. You can 'download' an imaginary laboratory into simulation iconic memory using the scene information held in your long-term memory. The simulated scene is constructed from token datagrams that are switched on and then bound into a time-row by the group region that overlays it.

So when your supervisor in the pub asks you to tell him what happens when you see a red square, your long-term memory is able to switch on attributes in your simulation iconic memory and create the laboratory with token datagrams for the screen and the lever. Your simulation body image is also switched on so your right index finger is also within the simulated scene. You now think of the red square, and this triggers a chain in long-term memory that groups together token datagrams producing the time-row shown in Figure 17.1.

You will now attend the attributes highlighted in the datagram sequence (Figure 17.1) in simulation iconic memory and, following the logic but not executing the action, you will be able to explain to your supervisor the consequences of pressing the lever. So by thinking about imaginary actions in an imaginary scene, not only can you anticipate the consequences, but you can also explain to others what might happen.

In the examples above, the things we are dealing with actually exist, and the datagrams in simulation iconic memory that are directing our thoughts are copies of a real thing. But we can also have thoughts about things that do not physically exist – we can imagine a cat by verbally prompting our long-term memory to switch on token datagrams for a cat in

simulation iconic memory because every Pixel in the iconic image holds a pre-attentive datagram for a cat.

Say, for example, someone says to me, 'Wouldn't your cat like another cat to keep it company?' In response, my long-term memory could switch on a token datagram for my black cat and another token datagram for another cat beside it in simulation iconic memory, and together as a pair they would form a group region on the basis that they are both cats. In this way, I create two imaginary things in simulation iconic memory and can then use my attention to create an imaginary relationship between them simply by following the same parent/component rules we use to organise real information in real iconic memory. This simple example illustrates our ability to build classes from imaginary structures and store them in long-term memory so that we can recall and examine them later.

The attributes of every datagram we attend in simulation iconic memory are automatically recorded in long-term memory as subclasses of the class of all imagined things, and the attributes of every datagram we attend in real iconic memory are automatically recorded as subclasses of the class of all real things. Only in this way can we distinguish between the real world and the world of our imagination.

Throughout this and the preceding chapters, we have explained that we identify things, cats for examples, by matching their component datagrams to class nodes in long-term memory. When this produces a unique match, we download (switch on) the matched class/attribute code into the group region of the thing we are trying to identify. The assumption has been that we must make a perfect match in long-term memory before we can attach an attribute code to a region that tells us what it is. But this is not strictly correct, because we can download a match when there is only a probability of it being correct. We can do this because we record in long-term memory the frequency with which each subclass is matched in relation to its parent class, and we are therefore able to calculate the likelihood that a particular thing will turn up when its parent has turned up. Where this happens, we link the datagram holding the possible attribute code into a time-row with a datagram for a motivational attribute that reflects the level of uncertainty.

Things that we have observed in the past are stored in long-term memory, and the time of the observation is recorded alongside the memory itself. When we recall a memory, we do not see it in real iconic memory because, in real iconic memory, we can only see things that are in the here-and-now. Instead we see our memories in simulation iconic memory, and we experience them in the present as events that took place in the past, at the time the memory was laid down. By attending our memories in the present in this way, we create in long-term memory a further record of us in the present recalling the past. Before we can recall a memory at all we must of course download (switch on) token datagrams for the overall scene so they can be bound into the time-row that we attend as the memory.

When we execute time-rows, we generate attributes that reflect how they have performed. These 'tracking attributes' are stored in the group level datagrams overlaying the time-row because they refer to the time-row as a whole. Tracking attributes deliver sensations such as intent, failure and successful completion. Recorded in long-term memory and recalled later, they can provide an insight into our state of mind at the time, one thing that we can share with others if we choose.

Summary

In this chapter, we explain how our long-term memories supply us with alternative courses of action for us to evaluate. These alternatives are ranked by our personal priority system, and we then respond by acting in one of three ways. First, we can simply ignore all the alternatives on offer and just allow events to unfold, accepting the consequences without anticipating what they might be. Second, we can execute the highest priority sequence in real iconic memory but without considering any alternatives. Or third, we can evaluate the alternatives in simulation iconic memory before deciding on our response. The relationship between the second and third of these approaches may reflect the System 1 and System 2 ways of thinking that Daniel Kahneman describes in his book *Thinking Fast and Slow*.

We maintain information in two largely identical iconic memories, one for things that happen in the real world and the other for simulations, our thoughts. Information from our senses and from long-term memory is transferred into the datagrams of both memories so that the two can be kept in line.

Our attention moves seamlessly between the two memories controlled by a single priority system that inserts priority values in both sets of datagrams. The priority system operates at two levels: it sets personal priorities to enhance our personal well-being, and within this personal framework is an impersonal system that translates general personal priorities into priority values for individual datagrams. Our personal priority system is controlled by a well-being regulator that works through a range of well-being attribute values that are held at the group level of our body iconic image.

We simulate alternative courses of action in time-rows in simulation iconic memory, and when a preference emerges, its equivalent in real iconic memory is executed. The evaluation process is recorded in long-term memory so we can recall the reasons for our decisions.

When we recognise something, long-term memory does not 'download' its attribute codes into datagrams. Every Pixel in iconic memory already holds every attribute code that exists in its pre-attentive form. Long-term memory simply 'switches on' the pre-attentive datagrams in the region that hold the recognised attribute code. This makes it possible for us to imagine scenarios in simulation iconic memory when the things we are thinking about are not present.

18

Consciousness and the perfect mind?

Two things fill the mind with ever increasing admiration and awe, the oftener and more readily we reflect on them: the starry heavens above me and the moral law within me. … I see them before me and connect them directly with the consciousness of my existence.

(Immanuel Kant, *Critique of Practical Reason*)

The book has looked at how the mind might function as a conventional information-processing system. Most of us would accept that our minds *are* information-processing systems, but that we have additional qualities that are in a very different category from the ones computers have. We suggest that these qualities arise from the interactions between the abstract information in the mind and the physical biology of the brain.

To help us understand how these interactions work, we have looked to a set of principles that come under the heading of information theory, and although we struggle with its complexity, it may provide the basis for what is happening here.

What information is

Even though information exists in physical stuff, it is not itself made of physical stuff; it is abstract. Information is created in a thing when that thing can take on different meanings without it having to change materially. If, for example, we send an electrical signal representing a cat through a copper wire and follow it with an electrical signal representing a dog, the signals do not alter the 'copperness' of the wire. The same is true of the electrical signals that pass along nerve fibres in the brain – the information in the signals does not alter the biological nature of the tissue carrying them.

Information held in the working memory of a conventional computer is abstract in the same way that the information you hold in your mind is abstract. But if this is the case, how, for example, can the abstract code 65 in a computer's memory cause a physical A to be displayed on a screen? And if information in your mind is abstract, how can it direct the physical muscles in your legs to climb up stairs?

To answer this, we need to be aware that there are two types of information sequence: those that are *predictable* because they always produce the same output from a given input, and those that are *unpredictable* because you can never be sure what any piece of information in the sequence is going to be – for example, in our minds whether a black shape on a chair is a black cat or a black

jumper (and even if you identify it as a cat, whether you prefer to see it as an animal or a pet rather than as a cat).

Computers are programmed with instructions that make them *predictable*. If you hit the letter A on your keyboard, it will send a variable electrical current to the computer's processor that contains a series of high and lows. The first instruction that the processor executes will translate this variable electrical current from the keyboard into a string of ones and zeros, the binary code for the number 65. The second instruction will store the binary code for the number 65 in electromagnetic form in the next position in the text in the computer's working memory, and the third instruction will convert the binary number 65 into a variable electrical current that goes to the screen and displays the letter A. The physical current for the letter A from the keyboard has been interpreted by the processor as information that it stored in physical electromagnetic form as the binary code for the number 65. The processor then converts this information back into a physical current to instruct the screen to display the physical letter A. If, instead of the letter A, you type letter B, the computer will create the number 66, which will instruct the screen to display the letter B – and so on.

No matter how often you hit the A key and display the letter A, the instructions will produce exactly the same physical electrical flows through the computer, even though abstract information is part of that sequence.

This is because there is a one-to-one relationship between 65 as information and the variations in the physical electrical current in the computer that carry the 65. So, in *predictable* systems, abstract information does not have to do anything physical because the physical medium carrying the information does the job on its behalf.

A computer programmed in this way is just like a mechanical carriage clock. You wind up the clock and the energy of the spring rotates the first cogwheel at a certain rate; this rotates another wheel and so on until a final wheel rotates a wheel that moves the minute hand around. Each wheel holds information and passes it on to the next wheel, but it is the physical nature of all the wheels, not the information held in the wheels, that turns the hands and tells us the time.

Information systems that manipulate data in this way are *automata* whether they are mechanical devices like clocks, sophisticated computers carrying out a complicated medical diagnosis or sequences taking place in our brains. They are all, by design, *predictable*. After all, what would be the point of a medical diagnostic system that gave unpredictable results!

Each of our minds is a single information system that can handle both *predictable* and *unpredictable* information sequences at the same time. When we perform *unattended* activities, walking up stairs without thinking for example, we are acting as automata because the actions are all pre-programmed in our long-term memories. Once we have initiated an unattended procedure, it is the electrochemical signals carrying the information in the brain that execute the task, and not the information itself.

However, the attention sequences that lead us through our lives are *unpredictable*. This is because we can never be sure of the exact identity of the information we will come across, and therefore we cannot use the electrochemical signals that carry information in the brain to execute tasks in the same way that unattended sequences do. Instead we must use the information content itself to bring about the changes we want to make in the material world.

But, as we keep pointing out, information is abstract. It cannot therefore generate the energy needed to alter the material nature of things because that would violate the laws of thermodynamics, the fundamental laws of nature that say you cannot create energy from nothing. This being so, how can the attended information in our minds possibly trigger the physical biology in our brains that produces our actions and the sensations of consciousness we experience throughout our lives?

The answer may lie in a line of research and recent experiments indicating that it may be possible for *information to create energy directly at the atomic particle level* without contravening the laws of thermodynamics, but only if we 'sacrifice' a quantity of information that equates to the amount of energy being created. In other words, we must completely erase a quantity of information that we recorded in the past. A report by Stephen Battersby in an edition of *New Scientist* from 14th May 2016, entitled 'The Unseen Agent', provides the background to these ideas, along with a summary of current research taking place in this area.

The interface between the physical world and the abstract world of our minds

We will now consider the structure of the interface between the physical internal image and the layers of the abstract iconic image that overlay it.

The internal image and the iconic image share the exact same Pixel organisation, and the interface between them is a single layer of Pixels that they both share. Every Pixel in the interface holds an attribute code for every possible attribute a thing might have at that point, and every Pixel in the interface also holds a sensation code for every possible physical characteristic a thing might have in the internal image at that point.

So when a black square is captured in the internal image, this will switch on the sensation codes for black and square in the Pixels of the interface where the black square lies; these will then automatically switch on the attribute codes for black and square in the datagrams sharing those same Pixels. If we then move our attention to a datagram in the iconic black square, this will trigger the sensation codes in the same Pixels to produce the chemistry to deliver the physical sensations of black and square in the internal image of the black square. The physical perception of the black square depends on the abstract code for the square and the sensation of the characteristics of the square sharing the same space/time Pixel – the abstract representation of the black square and the black square itself *become one and the same thing*.

We experience sensations for basic forms such as black squares, but we also experience sensations arising from the attribute codes of group regions that represent more complex things, cats for example. Throughout our lives, we continually create new groups for the new things we encounter, and supply each with its own unique attribute code, sensation code and sensation.

But where do these new codes and sensations come from? The answer is that all Pixels in the interface layer hold a stock of unallocated attribute codes, each with its own unallocated sensation code that produces a unique sensation. So whenever a new 'concept' arises, it is allocated the next available attribute code and sensation code on the list.

Suppose a child who has never seen a cat goes on holiday to a country with lots of cats. After seeing a number of cats, he will get used to assembling their parts into a uniquely recognisable group, and eventually its datagrams will be assigned an unallocated attribute code (key class) and sensation code. When the child next pays attention to a cat, he will experience a sensation he has never felt before but that he now understands is what that animal is – and of course he will get this sensation 'in' the cat no matter where the cat appears in his internal image.

A cat is a concept we create in our minds so that it can be assigned an attribute code which we can use to associate it with other things, mice for example. But why do we need to give cats a sensation code and sensation at all when we can do all the processing of a cat we want to do in iconic memory with just an attribute code? The reason is that information cannot exist on its own; information *must* represent something physical, a thing, otherwise it ceases to be information. For this reason, when we create concepts in the mind, and some concepts, unlike cats, have no physical association, we must artificially create a physical presence for them in the brain outside the mind even though they might have no tangible counterpart in the outside world.

Who we are

The last piece in the jigsaw concerns our identities as individuals and our relationship with time.

Our lives are dominated by an ever-changing present that divides a known past from an unknown future. The two time attributes we have introduced do not provide time with a direction. *Dimensional time* attributes only tell us how long a thing lasts, and *distribution time* attributes only tells us the length of the time interval between things. Neither gives time a direction, neither tells us at what point something starts and when it finishes.

In Chapter 13, we suggested that, through our attention movements, we could generate a direction in time, and showed how two squares flashing in succession on a screen would receive the attributes Earlier and Later, respectively. However, this solution raises issues that we have been unable to resolve, and we have been forced to conclude that there is not a time attribute that provides a direction from past to future. So we are left with just two time attributes: one that tells us the length of time between things, and the other that tells us the length of time a thing lasts. But if there is no 'arrow of time' attribute, how do we account for the undoubted fact that we continually experience the passing of time?

We propose that the sensation of moving through time does not depend on a *time attribute*; instead it is driven by a *'life' attribute* that is generated automatically in our minds whenever we attend a datagram. So the life attribute code number '1' is inserted into the first datagram we attend in our lives, the life attribute code number '2' is inserted into the second datagram we attend and so on, up to the last life attribute code number that is inserted into the last datagram we attend in our conscious lives.

The price we pay for this solution is that our minds must become a 'block' world, existing in an endless present with no absolute time or absolute space. In this frozen world, our attention selects things one by one and sequences them as events, points along a single life path. The attributes for extent and interval that describe how long attended events last and the size of the time intervals between events are held within the sequence of datagrams produced by our attention movements, but they do not indicate whether the attention sequence is going backwards or forwards.

So there is no arrow of time. Instead we have an arrow of life that takes us on a journey through an internal world of a present frozen in space and time. Every attention move we make in our minds shines a spotlight into this block iconic world, producing for us a continuous present. The extent of the block world accessed by each attention move is limited by our biology to a few seconds in time and to our local environment in space, but within this extended present, our attention can move in time and space in any direction we choose. Beyond our next move, however, we cannot anticipate which path our attention will take, because we cannot predict *now* the choices we will have once the next attention move has been completed.

In this block world, things do not move. Instead things that occur at regular space/time intervals group together pre-attentively into rows and receive attributes that produce the sensation of movement if attended. The sequences of datagrams we have been referring to as *time-rows* we can now call *lifetime-rows* because, when attended, they are defined by the combination of their life attribute codes and the time attributes for extent and interval that give them their internal structure.

But we have a problem here. In the example of a square flashing twice in Chapter 13, we said that our attention moves from their group parent to each square in turn as a component, and this causes the attribute Earlier to be inserted into the datagrams of the square that happened first in time, and causes the attribute Later to be inserted into datagrams of the square that happened second. This a similar process to that in Chapter 6 where our attention movements produced the Above attribute in the top bar of the **T**, and the Below attribute in the bottom one. But if, as we are claiming, time attributes have no direction, there is nothing in the datagrams of the flashing squares to indicate which should come first and which come second when we attend them. So how then can we tell which of the flashing squares is Earlier and which is Later?

The answer depends, we suggest, on the different states that can arise from the variety of distributions that pre-attentive datagrams can have in this iconic block world. Therefore, we propose that the probabilities of their different states, the Shannon entropy, often referred to in information theory, decides which flashing square gets the attribute Earlier when we attend it, and which gets the attribute Later. In other words, the order in which we describe things is not a time sequence, nor is it the attention sequence; instead it is decided by the way things are distributed in space and time within our frozen block world.

So when we recall a memory, it is not a recollection of something that happened in the past. Instead it is a memory of something that happened earlier in our lives that is separated from us by a quantity of time. Similarly, we do not project things forwards in time, we create potential life paths in a frozen space/time and select just one of them to follow. Everything we know is relative to the life attribute codes in the datagrams on our life paths. They are the only points that are fixed in space and time; they are the context for everything.

It should be clearly understood that we are not proposing here that there is no direction to time 'out there', that we live in a block universe – although that of course may be the case.

We experience awareness every time we attend a datagram on our attention path through life. These individual events are bound into a lifetime row that is overlaid from start to finish by a global group region that is the top region of the mind. This 'life' region is the top *mode* of perception, and is therefore the parent of *all other modes of perception* – vision, hearing, smell, pain and so on. If we attend this region, we experience the sensation of being aware of being aware, in the same way that when we attend a datagram in the top region for vision, we experience the sensation that this is the context for everything we see.

So awareness is the sensation of the top mode, and because it is always at the top of the attention hierarchy, it confers awareness on all the activities of all the submodes that we attend below it. Nothing can depend on you being aware, because we can only depend on things that are components.

In conclusion
In the Introduction, we set out our objectives:

In this book, we have developed a theory of mind using the approach a software developer would use in designing a software application; we are in effect reverse-engineering the procedures that enable us to think. One thing is clear from the outset – that our minds could not possibly handle the variety of information they encounter every day unless the supporting data were held in a standard form.

We believe we have shown in the preceding chapters that a single data standard combined with a small set of rules could underlie our minds in much the same way as the standards we set for digital information systems do for those systems. What then might we get if we were to develop computer software for a vision system that followed these rules? The answer is that we would get a computer system, that mimicked human behaviour. Such a system would not have the special qualities that make us human, the computer would not be aware of anything, and although it would be able to reason in the way we have described, it would not be able to think in the way we do. The reason for this lies in the fundamental nature of information itself and in the way abstract information in the mind combines with the physicality of the brain.

And finally
Although we are suggesting that all intelligent creatures use this model of the mind, the reality of their experiences will be very different depending on the sophistication of their brains. As humans, we feel certain that the way we see the world is how the world is, but cats and bees are probably equally sure that the world is the way they see it, and creatures with superior brains to ours may well be present in a way so foreign to us that we would be no more able to communicate with them than we could engage in dialogue with a bee. Or as Thomas Hardy puts it more romantically in his poem *An August Midnight*:

A shaded lamp and a waving blind,
And the beat of a clock from a distant floor:
On this scene enter – winged, horned, and spined –
A longlegs, a moth, and a Dumbledore:
While 'mid my page there idly stands
A sleepy fly, that rubs its hands…

Thus meet we five, in this still place,
At this point of time, at this point in space.
– my guests parade my new-penned ink,
Or bang the lamp-glass whirl, and sink.
'God's humblest, they!' I muse. Yet why?
They know Earth-secrets that know not I.

Thomas Hardy *(1899)*

Notes on chapters

Introduction to the Notes

In the Notes on each chapter that follow, we provide additional background, fill in some of the gaps, comment on our thinking and occasionally cite some of the relevant research – but there is really nothing here that is not covered by the books by Stephen Palmer's *Vision Science*, or that has not been the subject of an article in one or other of the science journals *New Scientist* and *Scientific American*.

We are looking at the mind as an information system, and therefore the real test of the rules of the mind is their logical integrity. Could such and such an experience be represented in a way that can be coded and processed? Could this or that process be coded as software line by line? Are all the data needed for this process available and in the right form? Could the code produce all the outputs needed for future processing?

We make the assumption that the reader has an elementary understanding of the way information-processing systems work. For those unfamiliar with how information systems operate, this is not difficult to explain because they perform tasks in much the same way that we do things in everyday life.

Essentially, everything in an information system revolves around a *workspace* and the *instructions* that manipulate the things held in that workspace. Instructions bring information into the workspace from outside, from a keyboard or storage facility for example. Instructions then specify how the information in the workspace is to be manipulated, and finally more instructions control how the results of these manipulations are to be transferred from the workspace to the outside world, such as to a screen or some storage facility, for example a disc. In every information system, the instructions and data held in the workspace are the hub around which everything else revolves. In electronic information systems, the instructions are often referred to as code, and the act of writing instructions as coding.

To use an everyday analogy, let's suppose you want to make a chocolate cake. You need just five things: fresh ingredients (direct inputs), stored ingredients (disc memory), a kitchen worktop (working memory), a recipe (the program) and a cook (a computer processor to execute the program). Fresh eggs and cream are delivered to your door and you place them on the worktop. You take the other ingredients, flour and chocolate from a storage cupboard and place them on the worktop too. You then mix the ingredients on the worktop according to the instructions in the recipe, pour the mixture into two baking tins and place these in the oven (the cooker is an extension of the worktop). When it is ready, you take the cake out of the oven, put it on a plate on the worktop, ice it and transfer it to the table for eating.

In computers, direct inputs go into working memory, all data manipulations take place in working memory, and all outputs are sent from it. The cells in a spreadsheet are a good example of working memory – the numbers and characters in the cells are the data, and the formulae in the cells are the program instructions. The computer's processor executes the formulae in each cell and put the results back into other cells in the spreadsheet. We use the term 'iconic memory' for the information workspace of the mind.

In the book, we do not address the support processes that convert the raw data into the form our minds will accept. However, we have a problem here, in that in order to demonstrate how the rules of the mind do their job, we need to show examples of how they operate on information that has originated in the outside world.

In the 1970s at MIT, computer scientist Terry Winograd faced a similar issue. He had developed a conversational language, SHRDLU, that he used to communicate with his computer using a form of conversation, a dialogue. The problem was that he and his computer did not have anything in common that they could talk about. He resolved the problem by inventing a simple imaginary world populated by cones, cubes and spheres, and gave the computer an imaginary robot arm. He then used his SHRDLU language to tell the computer about the objects in this world and how it could use its imaginary arm to interact with them. (Terry Winograd by the way had two notable students at Stanford University, Larry Page and Sergey Brin, who founded Google.)

We have invented here an even simpler imaginary world, comprising a number of black squares, some rectangles, a T shape, a cat, a banana, a lemon and a child's toy block! We presume that preparatory activities in the brain are able to convert the sense data the brain receives from these simple objects into the perfect forms we show in the book's figures. And we presume that post-mind activities will convert the information the mind generates into the appropriate responses.

We have developed a theory of mind using the approach a software engineer might use in designing a software application. These ideas stand or fall on the validity of a single basic assumption, that a mind can only arise in a system if the data in that system are held in a very specific format, a unit of information we call a datagram. The rules that organise and process the data are constrained by this data structure and as a consequence often produce results that are counter-intuitive, even bizarre – for example in the way they handle space and time. We acknowledge that there are gaps and some apparent inconsistencies; nevertheless we believe that the case for a single data standard and a simple set of rules underlying the mind holds up well. Ultimately, however, the model will stand or fall on how well the rules explain our experiences of 'being' in the world.

A final point, we are not for one moment suggesting that the mind is a computer – it clearly is not. Yes, they are both information systems, and yes, they both conform to the universal principles of information theory, but beyond that they are simply not comparable.

Creating an internal world: Chapters 1–4

Chapter 1. The raw data, source of everything we know

In this first stage, the physical raw data are channelled into the internal image, from where they are transferred into the mind and thus become the information we use to control our lives. However, information in the mind is abstract, so the thoughts and intentions we create in our minds must be reversed back into physical form before we can experience and act on them.

To handle the processes taking place outside the mind, we rely on a range of support procedures that supply information to the mind and that respond to information produced by it; none of these processes is part of the mind itself although, like the mind, they all operate within the brain. Support processes capture data from our senses, convert it into a clean standard form and transfer it as information into the mind, where the rules of the mind are applied; the results are then passed back into our physical world, where they become our perceptions, thoughts and behaviours. These support processes can be purely biological in nature or they too can be information systems. However, unlike the mind, they do not work to a common set of rules, and for that reason they are outside the scope of this book.

In Chapter 1, we assume that light intensities transmitted from the retina produce an internal physical image in the visual cortex that is segmented into uniform regions surrounded by edges that separate them from their neighbours. We also assume that all edges are 1 pixel wide. Ideally, there are no gaps between edges, because where one uniform region ends, another uniform region must begin. The internal image has become a mosaic of regions, but no region in this physical image is more significant than any other; there is no order.

This is the structure the mind requires. Our brains, of course, are incapable of producing an internal image in this precise form; our data collection systems are severely limited, and our brains do not have the capacity to manipulate such vast volumes of data. However, the raw data are presented in the mind in a way that *appears* to meet these criteria, and therefore the rules of the mind can be applied – if this were not so, we would not be able to separate the world into individual objects the way we do.

Our retinal receptors transmit signals from our eyes into pathways of nerves that lead into the visual cortex at the back of the brain. Figure N.1 shows how the two nerve pathways that connect our eyes to the visual cortex overlap to produce a single image.

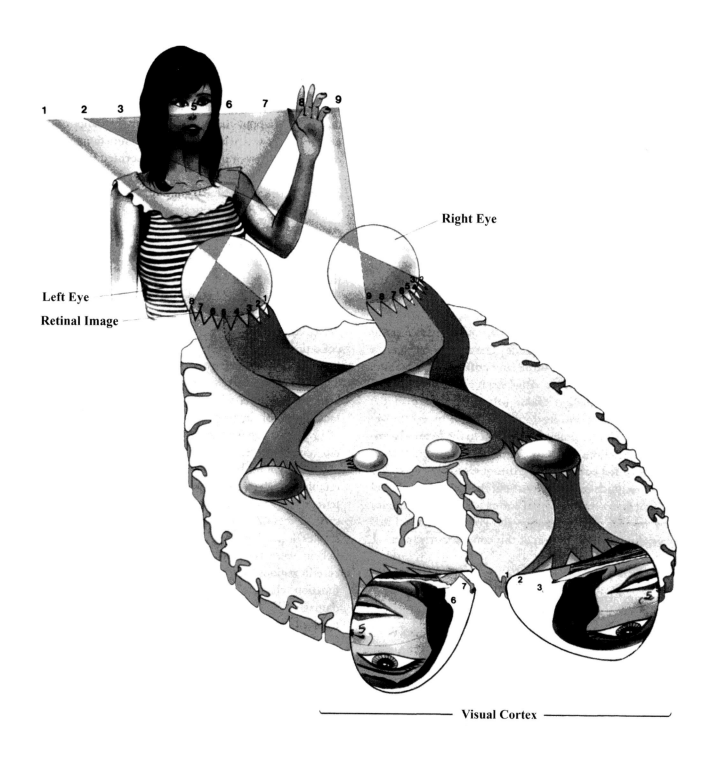

Figure N.1 Transmission pathways from the retina into the visual cortex. (After Frisby and Stone, 2010.)

The nerve pathways in Figure N.1 show how the signals from each eye are split in half so that the two halves of the image from each eye go to opposite sides of the brain. It is because the images from our two eyes are overlaid in this way that we see a single picture.

Our starting point is an internal, two-dimensional, black and white image in the visual cortex in the form of an intensity map. This looks something like the pixelated intensity map at the top of Figure N.2 – just rows of numbers.

Intensities in the Grey Level Map.

	400	401	402	403	404	405	406	407	408	409	410	411	412	413	414	415
432	160	162	158	158	159	160	159	158	156	155	156	157	159	158	160	157
433	160	159	157	160	161	156	157	154	151	150	154	156	157	156	157	157
434	160	160	158	159	158	158	151	148	141	141	142	147	151	155	157	158
435	160	161	159	157	157	156	145	139	131	129	134	143	149	155	158	157
436	161	156	158	158	157	148	138	127	121	119	120	127	140	148	156	159
437	160	158	157	155	150	140	128	120	114	114	114	120	133	145	154	159
438	163	158	158	153	147	132	122	114	111	109	111	113	123	136	151	158
439	159	158	156	149	137	121	113	112	108	109	109	112	119	135	150	156
440	160	159	152	145	132	117	110	110	108	108	111	109	112	126	142	156
441	161	156	151	138	123	111	108	106	106	108	109	109	111	125	140	155
442	161	157	147	134	121	110	109	106	110	109	109	106	109	116	132	149
443	160	154	141	126	114	110	108	109	109	106	107	107	109	117	132	149
444	159	149	135	122	112	111	107	106	107	106	109	105	109	112	125	145
445	156	144	129	116	109	109	106	109	106	106	107	108	109	113	126	145
446	152	138	125	114	108	108	106	106	107	106	106	108	108	111	121	143
447	147	129	118	109	109	106	106	107	104	104	108	109	109	114	123	143

Discontinuities in the Grey Level Map.

	400	401	402	403	404	405	406	407	408	409	410	411	412	413	414	415
432	0	1	1	0	0	0	1	3	3	2	2	2	0	0	0	0
433	0	1	0	1	1	2	4	7	7	6	7	6	3	2	1	0
434	0	1	0	1	1	4	8	11	11	10	11	9	6	3	1	0
435	0	1	1	0	2	8	13	15	14	11	15	15	11	6	2	0
436	1	1	1	2	7	13	17	16	12	8	14	18	16	10	5	0
437	1	2	1	4	10	16	17	14	9	5	9	16	18	14	8	2
438	0	1	3	7	15	19	15	10	6	3	5	11	17	16	10	3
439	0	2	5	11	18	19	11	6	3	1	2	7	16	19	13	4
440	0	3	8	14	19	16	7	4	2	2	1	4	13	19	15	6
441	0	5	10	16	18	12	4	1	0	1	0	2	10	18	18	10
442	1	7	13	18	16	7	2	1	2	0	2	2	9	16	18	12
443	3	11	17	18	12	5	2	1	1	2	1	0	6	14	18	13
444	6	14	18	16	9	4	2	0	1	1	0	1	4	11	18	14
445	8	16	17	14	7	3	1	0	0	0	1	1	2	9	17	15
446	12	18	17	12	4	2	1	0	2	1	1	1	2	8	16	15
447	14	17	15	9	3	2	0	0	1	1	1	1	2	7	16	16

Boundary Elements with Termination

	400	401	402	403	404	405	406	407	408	409	410	411	412	413	414	415
432	0	0	0	0	0	0	0	0	0	0	0	0	0	0	0	0
433	0	0	0	0	0	0	0	0	0	0	0	0	0	0	0	0
434	0	0	0	0	0	0	0	0	0	0	0	0	0	0	0	0
435	0	0	0	0	0	0	127	0	0	0	127	0	0	0	0	0
436	0	0	0	0	0	63	0	0	0	0	0	63	0	0	0	0
437	0	0	0	0	0	63	0	0	0	0	0	63	0	0	0	0
438	0	0	0	0	63	0	0	0	0	0	0	0	63	0	0	0
439	0	0	0	0	63	0	0	0	0	0	0	0	63	0	0	0
440	0	0	0	63	0	0	0	0	0	0	0	0	0	63	0	0
441	0	0	0	63	0	0	0	0	0	0	0	0	0	63	0	0
442	0	0	63	0	0	0	0	0	0	0	0	0	0	63	0	0
443	0	0	63	0	0	0	0	0	0	0	0	0	0	0	63	0
444	0	0	63	0	0	0	0	0	0	0	0	0	0	0	63	0
445	0	63	0	0	0	0	0	0	0	0	0	0	0	0	63	0
446	0	63	0	0	0	0	0	0	0	0	0	0	0	0	63	0

Figure N.2 Pixel maps of intensities in a machine vision application. In computer vision terminology, we would say that the top image had been processed using an edge operator, in this case a modified Sobel function.

The next step is to convert this raw information into the uniform regions and edges that the rules require. These are preparatory processes and take place automatically; they are outside our control in the same way that our liver function is outside our control. These preparatory activities are outside the mind and do not appear to be subject to a single set of rules; their purpose is simply to create uniform regions and edges that can be processed further.

The three pixel maps in Figure N.2 were taken from a computer vision project designed to check the dimensions, after manufacture, of the metal tongues that are inserted into car seat belt buckles. The top pixel map shows intensities recorded by a digital camera directed at the tip of a single buckle.

It is clearly not possible to make out the triangular shape of the tongue from the raw intensities in the top pixel map. The middle map was produced by a program that identified the changes in intensity in the top map that are typically found surrounding edges. This program is similar to an algorithm created by Marr and Hildreth to simulate the edge detection cells in the visual cortex that were identified by neurophysiologists David Hubel and Torsten Wiesel.

In the middle map, the edges of the tongue are not precisely defined, so a final processing step is needed to turn them into the single chain of edge pixels required by the rules – shown in the bottom map. All edges are now 1 pixel wide; anything wider than that is a region that must have two edges, one on either side.

You will see that the program has failed to detect any edges between columns 406 and 410. Although there are programs that attempt to create edge sequences to join up termination points, in practice we always end up with some missing edges and therefore incomplete shapes. Fortunately, attributes in datagrams are coded locally, so *if the geometry of a region looks square from the position of any one of its pixels, the attributes of the datagrams in those pixels will call it a square* even though the region as a whole is not truly square and many of its datagrams will have attributes saying that the region has no shape at all.

If you attend a datagram of an incomplete region that is coded as square, you will believe it is a square; if you attend a datagram of the same region that has a 'no shape' attribute, you will believe that the region has no shape – there is no attribute for 'sort-of-square'. Datagrams that describe a region as having shape are generally given a higher priority for attention than datagrams for the same region that have attributes for 'no shape'.

In Chapter 1, we explain that the first step in dealing with the raw intensities from the black square is to convert them into uniform sequences. For example, we took the raw intensities on line PQ in the internal image of the black square in Figure 1.1 and recorded them as:

P –8898798878653120101120101123568897987898– Q

We then converted them into a uniform sequence:

P –88888888888||11111111111111111||88888888888– Q

To achieve this conversion, a number of intermediate steps had to be gone through. The starting point was the raw intensities in the pixels of line PQ of the black square:

P –8898798878653120101120101123568897987898– Q

Step 1. A formula in each pixel replaced the intensity value in that pixel with the average intensity of that pixel and its neighbours. So in our one-line example below, the replacement for the 9 in the third pixel from the left was $(8+9+8)/3 = 8$ (rounding it to a whole number), the replacement for the 8 in the fourth pixel was $(9+8+7)/3 = 8$, and so on. Therefore the complete line after Step 1 was:

P –8888888887653211111111111123567888888888– Q

Step 2. The uniformly black and white areas are now well defined because they have constant intensities,

1s and 8s respectively, but there are no clear edge points showing exactly where one stops and the other starts. Fortunately, there is a way of precisely locating edges because the sequence of intensity values across an edge has a clear mathematical signature. This knowledge is used extensively in digital camera systems for shape recognition – car number plates, for example – but more interestingly there are centre-surround cells in our visual systems that analyse intensities in a similar way.

This edge-finding formula is in every pixel, and it checks the surrounding intensities to see if this is an edge point. On this occasion in our examples, two edge pixels passed the edge test. and their positions were marked in the line by inserting an || :

P –88888888876||3211111111111123||67888888888– Q

Step 3. A final set of formulae then extended uniform values, 8s and 1s, up to the nearest edge so, for example, 8876||3211 became 8888||1111. The end result, below, is the simplified version of the original line in the raw iconic image:

P –88888888888||11111111111111111||88888888888– Q

The structuring is complete. The final line replaced all the intermediate ones but not the original intensities along PQ, which are retained in the internal image. This example is typical of the algorithms we find at this preparatory stage – acting outside the mind.

We have made edge detection look simple, but it is far from it! To get the best results, edge detectors operate at different scales producing a range of results that are integrated to produce a single edge position. In addition, intensity thresholds are manipulated to produce good figures, and there is a feedback of intensities from the mind to encourage familiar objects to emerge from their background.

However, not all regions in the image are created from edges in this way. Some regions, small blobs and bars for example, are directly identified by neuron groups, and textures and patterns can be identified in the raw data by Fourier-based algorithms – so a tree may be identified before we have identified any of its leaves. In addition, where the intensity level changes at a constant rate across a region, that region is also uniform. Graded regions of this type are the main source of attributes that describe the shapes of surfaces.

Theorists of visual perception have been developing models for over a hundred years to explain how we construct an internal picture of what we see; our model simply builds on their work. The principle of similarity had always been seen as important in building perceptual units, it features strongly in the work of the Gestalt school of thought, it is the basis of Carnap's similarity circles, and it dominates the early processing stages in machine vision. In this project, we have essentially extended this principle, defining similarity of components as the *only* basis for creating any perceptual unit of information.

These preparatory processes cooperate and compete, producing perceptual units, regions, in the internal image with datagrams describing them. These units are then passed into iconic memory as information, giving our minds access to the nature of the world. The activities that take us from the raw internal image to the coded datagrams required by the mind are hugely complex and not fully understood, but they are not part of the abstract world of the mind.

Chapter 2. The emergence of meaning – datagrams
In the second chapter of the book, we introduce the datagram and describe how the attributes it holds are organised. Within cognitive neuroscience, the basic unit of perception is usually called an object file; we have chosen to use a different term here because although the datagram serves the same purpose as an object file, it is structured rather differently. In particular, we insist on describing every entity by two lists rather than one – as both a whole thing and a collection of parts.

The rules governing datagrams apply to regions at all levels in iconic memory. The first four rules are that:

1. Every datagram in a region has the same *Parts* attributes.

2. Every boundary of a region is a complete chain of pixels 1 pixel wide.

3. Every edge pixel contains two edge datagrams that describe the regions on either side.

4. The geometry of a region is defined by its attributes of its datagrams and not by its physical representation.

Attributes in the *Whole* section of a datagram describe the region as a whole and ultimately give us our experience of what a thing is. Attributes in the *Parts* section of a datagram are a list of those attributes that are in every one of the components that make up the region. We cannot access, that is, experience, the attributes in the *Parts* section of a datagram directly because they are mostly ranges, or averages, of the region's components, and because in any case they are not attributes of the whole thing that the datagram represents.

Sense attributes – those attributes created by our senses – generally represent very simple characteristics, such as grey level, colour, size, orientation, curvature and so on. Edges as well as regions have these attributes. Most sense attributes are a continuous range of values that are a measure of some physical characteristic, for example length in pixels or orientation in degrees. Most non-sense attributes are simply code numbers, symbols that tell you what a thing is, a square or a cat for example. Each individual sense attribute is an individual code number, for an exact shade of grey for example, but each code number value is also is in a continuous range of values that represent all shades of grey, so greys with adjacent code number values will always look similar.

In the book, we treat shape attributes, square, rectangle, triangle and so on, as if they were sense attributes, but strictly speaking they are not. The fundamental shape attribute for a region does not actually identify whether it is a square or a rectangle. It only tells us the symmetry of that region in relation to its vertical and horizontal axes. Squares and circles are doubly symmetrical because their vertical and horizontal axes are the same length and cross at their centres, so squares and circles have the same shape attribute. We can only distinguish a square from a circle if we look at its edge datagrams; if the boundary edges of a doubly symmetrical region are straight and at right angles, we insert the attribute 'square' in all its datagrams, if curved we insert the attribute 'circle'. Symmetrical regions with straight boundaries, such as squares, rectangles and triangles, become circles, ovals and pear-shaped when their boundaries are curved.

As mentioned above, the extent of a region is defined by the spatial attributes of its datagrams and not by its spatial representation in the brain because the mind can only hold information – nothing physical persists in the mind. Iconic memory is a logical store of information without physical divisions; everything is encoded in datagrams so that all explicit physicality is eliminated.

We see this clearly in computers. Computers generally store information as it turns up, pretty much randomly. Part of a photograph can be stored alongside part of an audio track with the rest of the photo kept somewhere else. When we instruct a computer to retrieve a photograph, a program locates its elements in different places by using a master list of addresses, and then assembles them in an image buffer before displaying them on the screen. A computer does not need to store all the pieces of the photograph in the same area of disc because its transmission speeds are close to the speed of light; if our brains were capable of such transmission speeds, we too might not need dedicated regions in the brain.

The raw inputs from all our senses are similar to those for vision – they are just sequences of intensity numbers – and, like vision, we have to convert this raw information into regions of uniform intensity with separating edges. So, for example, a uniform pressure applied to an area of skin will produce a uniform region surrounded by edges in the somatic cortex.

Hearing is a little more complicated because we are dealing with a complex waveform. Nevertheless, any uniformity in the sounds we hear will be represented in the auditory cortex by regions that contain strings of related sounds separated from each other by edges. There is also an interesting two-dimensional quality to music if you treat melody as a horizontal dimension and harmony as a vertical one.

Throughout the book, we use black squares as figures to illustrate how we assemble basic forms into complex ones. We choose black squares because they are simple and immediately recognisable and because, in some strange way, black squares are abstract, without preconceptions or associations. (Perhaps this is why Kazimir Malevich's painting Black Square is such a fundamental work of art, and why it made such an impact on artists in the modernist movement.)

Chapter 3. Binding things into groups and the nature of space
In this chapter, we propose a mechanism for binding components into groups. The most important point to understand here is that copies of the distribution attributes that define a group's internal organisation are held in every one of its component datagrams as well as in the datagrams that that describe the overall group. The attributes in the *Parts* sections of group datagrams are not accessible, so the only information available to us about the structure of a group must come from the 'in a distribution' attributes held in the datagrams of the group's components.

This binding principle is the foundation for all the rules of the mind, and is the reason that the datagram holds two levels of information. Unless this rather difficult chapter is well understood, it will not be easy for the reader to appreciate the logic of what follows. Much of the thinking here has its origins in Ann Treisman's feature integration theory and Jeremy Wolfe's guided search.

We have slightly simplified the processes involved in order to give a clearer account, but no fundamental principles have been excluded from the main narrative. The truth is that we do not automatically create datagrams with multiple attributes from the raw data. The datagrams we describe in this chapter are in the form they take when

an object has been attended. Pre-attentive datagrams, those produced directly from the physical internal image, have exactly the same structure as attended datagrams, and obey all the same rules, but each holds just one descriptive attribute in its *Whole* section and one pair of distribution attributes – Black plus iRow/6 for example.

To create a full description of an object, our attention must merge all its pre-attentive datagrams into a single attended datagram that lists all its features. An unattended black square is two unconnected 'free-floating' pre-attentive datagrams, one that says this is a black thing and the other that says this is a square thing. To 'see' a black square as a single object, our attention must bring these two pre-attentive datagrams together in the same region and create a single attended datagram with both attributes, Black and Square, in its *Whole* section.

The reason perception has to start with pre-attentive datagrams with a single descriptive attribute is that an object can only belong to one distribution at any one time. Let's suppose we see a pair of black squares in a row of white squares. Each black square can be seen either as a square thing in a row of squares or as a black thing paired with another black thing. But an attended black square can only have one distribution attribute, so we must see the black square as either one of a pair or part of a row – we cannot see it as both at the same time.

If our attention first selects a square pre-attentive datagram, we will see a square that happens to be black in a row of squares, but if we first select a black pre-attentive datagram, we will see a black thing that also happens to be square in a pair with another black thing. This is all because you can only have one binding attribute in an attended datagram. The attended datagram for the black square can only be in one type of grouping because it is a rule that a datagram can only have one value for any attribute type – the same rule that prevents us from saying that an object is both a square and a triangle.

This is, however, not quite how we have shown the squares in Figures 3.2 and 3.3, as in these figures the attributes Black and Square are *both* highlighted as binding attributes. This is not strictly correct because you can only have one descriptive binding attribute, so the highlighted attribute should be either Black or Square depending on whether your attention created the attended datagram by attending the pre-attentive datagram with Black as its descriptive attribute, or the pre-attentive datagram with Square as its descriptive attribute. The *Parts* sections of attended datagrams can also hold non-binding descriptive attributes provided that they occur in every component of the distribution.

There is considerable experimental evidence that free-floating pre-attentive elements are consolidated into objects by the focus of attention. This forms the basis of Anne Treisman's widely accepted feature integration theory, which provides the foundation for many of the ideas in this book. The two forms information takes, pre-attentive and attended, is a necessary consequence of the way the world is; it is not, as is sometimes suggested, an intermediate step that is necessary because our brains do not have the physical capacity to consolidate information channelled directly from the senses.

In Chapter 7, we go over some of this ground again. In Chapter 10, we describe how pre-attentive datagrams are merged to create attended datagrams. In the chapters leading up to Chapter 10, we are primarily concerned with attended datagrams, so to keep things simple we ignore the role of pre-attentive datagrams up to that point.

To summarise, there are four essential elements to what we are proposing in this chapter:

- When things come together as a group, they form a group region populated with datagrams that exactly overlays the combined extent of the group's component regions and the intervals between them.

- There are three binding attributes that hold the group together: the first binding attribute describes a common feature to be found in every one of the components that make up the group; the second attribute describes the distribution of components in the group – row or pair for example; and the third attribute describes the interval between the group's components.

- These binding attributes are duplicated in the *Parts* section of all group datagrams and the *Whole* sections of all component datagrams.

All group regions must be continuous and *complete*. By *complete* we mean that if something qualifies as a component, it *must* be included as a component. Take, for example, a row of six identical black squares spaced at identical intervals from each other. We *cannot* see this as two rows of three squares, or as a row of four squares plus a pair of two squares. They all have identical binding attributes, so as a group they can only be seen as a row of six squares and nothing else. This reflects the need to limit the number of ways data can combine so that when we see the same thing at two different times, we can recognise it because it is structured in the same way on both occasions. If this rule were not applied, we might see a row of six black squares as two rows of three on

one occasion and as a row of four plus a pair on another. We would not be able to match their attributes and so recognise them as being the same. We are able to assign attributes to individual components and use them to create subgroups, in which case each of those subgroups must be internally complete.

(Note that the intervals between the components of a row will never be exactly the same length as each other, but they will still create a row provided they are all lie within a narrow range of values. However, all the interval attributes in every datagram of the components of a row are given the same value – the 'average' of all the different interval lengths of the row as a whole.)

The common factor that binds things into a group is not always a simple attribute such as colour or shape. A bird flying far away in the sky can be seen as a single object because its parts move at a common speed. All the parts of a pair of spectacles have the same characteristic (attribute) of being mutually connected. A tennis ball and a tennis racquet have nothing in common visually, but seen together they can form a group because our long-term memories will download an identical attribute code into both sets of datagrams that says they belong to the class of tennis equipment.

A final point on distribution attributes. We defined a Unit distribution as a distribution that contained only one element, and gave Queen Elizabeth II as an example because she is the only member of the class of all the living Queens of England. But should we not have called this distribution type iUnit rather than Unit? The answer of course is that the parent and component of something in a unit distribution are one and the same thing so both distribution types are correct. In the book, we have chosen to always describe these as Unit distributions.

We organise data in a way that will facilitate recognition and ultimately our responses; we *do not* create an internal 'photographic' description that we can reproduce as an image, as a drawing. Drawing a picture from memory is a set of modular skills that we use to produce an image from limited recall combined with a general knowledge of how the world works.

We often create group regions that define the extent of the task in hand. So before we recite a Shakespeare sonnet, we will first create a region in our iconic memory to hold all its lines; the region's boundary marks the extent of the poem. All concepts are regions of information held within defined boundaries populated by group and edge datagrams. We have talked about group regions 'overlaying' component regions, but of course they are logical regions and not actual physical regions in the brain. Group datagrams are connected to component datagrams in the brain but they need not be located together physically.

Chapter 4. Minds, brains and rules
We imply in Chapter 4 that any system could become a mind provided that it obeys the rules of the mind, but in reality this cannot be so. Only systems based on electromagnetic transmission can become minds because only those systems can operate at the fundamental particle level, the only place where the rules of the mind could be fully implemented.

Could we program a computer that received information from cameras, audio sources and touch to implement the rules of the mind? Yes, in theory we could produce a mind in a computer based on abstract symbols, but it would not experience the world around it unless we could somehow connect those symbols to sensation-producing elements in the material world – it would be a zombie. And that is the real mystery – not the nature of the mind, but the nature of the physical sense of awareness that the mind triggers within us.

Our physical implementation is poor for a number of reasons. First, we do not possess the sensory apparatus or the powerful algorithms needed to produce datagrams that are truly representative of what is out there. Second, our working memory capacity is severely limited. And third, when biological components fail to perform, due to illness, drugs or trauma for example, the effects can spill over into the mind and effect our mental states.

We have used the word 'information' many times, but what exactly do we mean by information? Information only exists in material things, yet *information is not material*. Being abstract, it is not made of matter and therefore does not combine with matter in the normal way – to produce new chemical compounds, for example. Information is a bit like heat in that both belong in physical things without adding to their chemical composition, and both are transmitted through conductors, for example a copper wire. Information conforms to a very particular set principles, known as information theory, that quantify information in much the same way that the laws of thermodynamics quantify energy; we return to this topic of the nature of information in Chapter 18.

The arrangement of datagrams that describe the cat in Figure 4.1 is slightly misleading because it implies that all its datagrams occupy the same layer in the iconic image when of course this is not so. We have drawn the figure in this simplified way to avoid anticipating how we break down objects into their component segments – a process we deal with in Chapter 6.

Attention-sequencing: Chapters 5–7
Chapter 5. The singular nature of attention
Our model of attention depends on accepting that attention operates in a very specific way as follows:

- Our attention transfers to one datagram in a single pixel at a time.

- It goes to the datagram with the highest priority in iconic memory.

- Only one datagram, the one with the highest priority, is ever attended.

- All datagrams in pixels that surround the attended pixel and that have the same binding attributes as the attended datagram are part of the attended extent.

- Before attention moves to the next datagram, the priorities of all datagrams, attended and pre-attentive, are reprioritised across iconic memory.

- The position of the attended pixel is the position of the attended extent.

The attended datagram defines the single region in the image that is the focus of your attention. This can be as small as a pinhead or it can encompass your entire field of view. If, for example, you attend a datagram for the cat in Chapter 4, you will be aware of the region occupied by the cat, and its attributes will tell you it is a cat and it is black. However, you will not be aware of the cat's ears or tail at that exact moment even though that is how you identified the cat as a cat; this is because the components of the cat are different regions with different datagrams.

It is one of the fundamental rules that the pixel holding the datagram of the thing you are attending defines the position of that thing. However, this definition of position creates a problem because, for example, whenever I look at a particular tree in my garden, my attention will go to a slightly different pixel position on its trunk, and as a consequence I will position that tree in a slightly different part of the garden every time I look at it. The tree will keep moving.

And this is so, but because I recognise it as the same tree and because I believe that trees do not move, I will assume that its position has not changed. To manage this, I hold a class in my long-term memory that is the class of all the positions I have ever seen the tree in (even though it never moves!); and provided, when I look at the tree, that I always attend a position on the trunk that is in the class of all past positions, I will not worry that the tree appears to have moved. Strictly speaking, I have solved the problem by accepting that the tree *can actually be in different places at different times*, but provided I see the tree as the same tree and its position is within a limited range, I will always see it in the same average position.

In Chapter 5, we explain how we represent edge statuses with brackets, and we have listed the various configurations that brackets can have. There is one alternative edge configuration we failed to mention – the edge pair ( ) in a single pixel. If we attend a datagram with these edge pairs, we will see it as an edge that is by itself, not part of a region. This is because the vectors from surrounding edges will always pass underneath them because both sides are closed.

The edge configuration))((describes two regions that are in contact; they butt up against each other but are not connected because they do not share a common edge. The interval between the two regions in this configuration is 2 because together the two edges occupy 2 pixels.

All images contain noise – small image elements that should be ignored because they are meaningless. However, it is against the rules to remove any form of information from the image, so we must find a way of discounting noise without deleting it. We do this by surrounding small image elements with enclosing edges (( )) so that closing vectors from surrounding edges will always pass underneath them. The information is still there, characterised by datagrams, and if prioritised it could be accessed by attention; it is, however, usually ignored.

In setting the priorities that determine the next attention step, we evaluate the alternative paths that attention could take. This evaluation includes looking at alternative interpretations of the same data arising from (1) the existence of alternative pre-attentive space/time distributions; (2) the alternative space and time edge statuses; and (3) the manipulation of intensity thresholds in the raw image. The evaluation process is carried out at the pre-attentive level.

There are of course many more datagram statuses than those we have mentioned in Chapter 5. The vast majority of these come into play when we are trying to find an object's long-term memory identity by scanning its components. We set up a single top parent region in a group layer to represent the object as a whole, and the layers below it hold its component regions. Our attention then moves up and down the layers selecting components and component groups that will lead to a match in long-term memory for the top parent region. In the process, the statuses of datagrams change all the time as their relationship with

attention changes, so for example at one time a part may be a parent, P-status, in relation to its components in the layer below, and later the same part may be a component, C-status, of a parent datagram in the layer above it.

Readers may find it interesting to compare the attention processes we have described here with the philosophical concept of intentionality as presented by Edward Fesser in his book *Philosophy of Mind*.

Chapter 6. Deconstructing objects to find out what they are
In the segmentation of the **T** shown in Figures 6.1 and 6.2, we have assumed that a virtual edge has been generated at the throat of the **T** to divide it neatly into the two rectangles that we need to identify it. This, however, will not happen unless we make it happen.

Having attended the whole figure **T**, our attention is attracted to the two corner edge datagrams at the throat of the **T** because they are symmetrically identical. If we attend them, they will form a pair and generate a group region that encloses them. This group region is a chain of pixels 1 pixel wide populated by edge datagrams. It is a virtual edge closing the throat of the **T**, and its datagrams all have)(status because they now join the two rectangles with a shared edge. The virtual edge region and datagrams of the two rectangles are held in the segment layer, and the parent figure retains the datagrams that describe the **T** as a whole.

We often create virtual or illusory edges in this way to complete simple shapes or to join parts of a shape obscured by something in front of them. Virtual edges can only be created when there are indications of continuity or symmetry in the terminations on either side of the break.

However, we could recognise the **T** even without creating a virtual edge to separate out the rectangles. This is because the parent figure **T** will automatically generate some datagrams with Rectangle attributes in the segment layer *even when no virtual edge exists*. None of these will be generated in the throat area, but there may be sufficient good datagrams to carry out the parent/component sequencing we have described. In this way, we get by with less than perfect figures but still conform to the rules.

At the end of the section on the segmentation of the **T**, we pointed out that, in segmentation relationships, the *binding* attributes in the *Parts* sections of the parent are not duplicated in the *Whole* sections of their components – the normal arrangement; instead they are duplicated in their *Parts* sections (Figure N.3).
Figure N.3 shows two ways in which we can describe the parent/component relationship between the **T** and its component rectangles. The datagrams in (a) represent the parent/segment relationship between the vertical rectangle

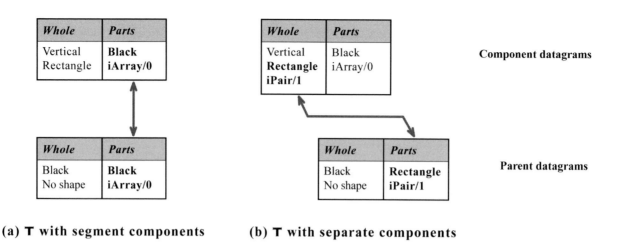

(a) T with segment components　　**(b) T with separate components**

Figure N.3 The datagrams show two ways in which we can describe the relationship between the parent figure T and its vertical rectangle component. The two datagrams in (a) describe this as a *parent/segment* relationship. The black parent figure is *divided* into two black components so the binding attributes, **Black** and **iArray/0**, *are duplicated in the Parts sections* of both parent and component datagrams. The datagrams in (b) show the T as the *coming-together* of two rectangles. Here the binding attributes are **Rectangle** and **iPair/1**, and these are duplicated in the parent *Whole* section and component *Parts* sections in the normal way.

and the parent **T**. Here the binding attributes **Black** and **iArray/0** are duplicated in the *Parts* sections of parent datagram and component datagrams because the rectangle is a subdivision of the whole. The datagrams in (b) show the normal parent/component relationship, where the **T** is constructed from the coming-together of the two rectangles. Therefore the binding attributes **Rectangle** and **iPair/1** are duplicated in the *Parts* section of the parent datagram and the *Whole* sections of its component datagrams.

Two types of figure present us with particular problems. The first of these occur when a regular shape is partly occluded by something that is in front of it, for example a rectangle partly obscured by a circle. We are able to identify the rectangle because pre-attentive edge settings in the occluding figure allow the edge vectors of the occluded figure to pass underneath it, and by making assumptions about the symmetry of the figure, pre-attentive datagrams will be created with attributes for a rectangle as one possibility – remember that it needs only one pre-attentive datagram to have the attributes of a rectangle for us to believe it is a rectangle, provided of course we attend that datagram.

The other difficult figures are holes. In Figure 5.7, when we attended the black faces, the vase in between them became a hole, and through the hole we could see a single white region that extended behind the faces. We could not bring the two faces and the shape of the hole together as a whole. But we can do this if we think of the

three segments, two faces and a hole, as one continuous solid surface *with* the vase segment as a transparent sheet inserted into the hole. In effect we are saying that holes are transparent segments of a continuous in-front surface through which we can see the surface behind. This is one of the alternative edge settings)(that we evaluate and prioritise pre-attentively. There is a good discussion of occlusions and holes in Chapter 6 of *Vision Science*.

The interval attribute tells us the size of the gap between two separate objects but it does not tell us the distance between points on their surfaces. To create this attribute we must move our attention to a point on one object, the one on the left for example, and then (via group) move our attention to a point on the other one. This procedure creates a virtual edge enclosing these points that is populated by datagrams with attributes that reflect the distance between them.

In chapter 3 we emphasized that an interval is an attribute, it is not a thing. Yet, when we see a pair of squares we can attend the gap between the two and experience its characteristics. To achieve this effect we form a row comprising the two squares and the gap as components because they are three rectangles lying side by side. We then create within this parent group a sub group of a pair of squares and this leaves the 'gap' component on its own. We can now attend the gap as a thing and experience its attributes as a description of the gap. Note that the size attribute for the gap produced by this procedure is not a distribution attribute but a dimensional one.

In Figure 6.4, we show a red square in front of a grey square, creating a group on the basis that they are both squares. Yet if the in-front figure were a red triangle instead of a red square, it would still form a group with the grey square, but on the basis that they share the same location in the image. The same principle applies to the grey and black squares shown side by side in Figure 3.4: they will form a group just on the basis that they have a boundary in common – it is not necessary for their shapes to be the same.

Chapter 7. Where we have got to so far
Chapter 7 is primarily a summary of the previous chapters; it is an attempt to put the ideas we have presented in perspective. We covered in a little more detail in the Notes on Chapter 3 how pre-attentive datagrams give a singular view of things whereas attended datagrams are composites.

The retention times we suggest for iconic memory and short-term memory here and in subsequent chapters are rough indications of the length of time each memory retains information. They, like most of the timings we use in the book, are illustrative, although we believe they are of the right order of magnitude.

The big picture: Chapters 8–11
Chapter 8. Scenes and short-term memory
In the example in this chapter, it is assumed that, on entering my living room, the first thing I see is the fireplace, and that from this my long-term memory recognises that the scene as my sitting room, that the mantlepiece is the reference object and that the scene reference point is to be located at its centre. In practice, we do not need our attention to go to the reference object in order to fix the position of the reference point in a scene. Provided we recognise an object that is always in the scene – and it is in its usual position – we can use its scene coordinates stored in long-term memory to deduce the coordinates of the reference point datagram within the scene group layer.

We assume that two things are the *same thing* when we match the one we see now to the memory of one we saw earlier, we know two things belong to the *same class* when we see them together and they form a pair because they have an attribute in common, but how can we tell that one thing is a *copy* of another thing and not the same thing? – that although they look identical, they are made of different stuff. Here we need to be sure that they *are* different physical things and not just two observations of the same thing.

The only way we can be certain that two things are *copies* of each other is if, in the same image, we can bring them together in a pair relationship *and* verify that *all* their attributes are identical. If, however, we see two identical things at different times, we have to depend on our knowledge of the context in which we see the objects before we can decide whether the observations are of copies or two observations of the same thing. We generally assume that if we see an identical thing on two different occasions, we are seeing the same thing twice.

We introduced statuses in datagrams in Chapter 5 that tracked their ever-changing relationships with the attended datagram. Datagrams also hold statuses that track the layer in iconic memory where they are to be found. These identifiers are necessary because the 'layers' of iconic memory are logical constructs. They do not exist physically, and we do not actually hold datagrams in layers (although it helps us to think of them as though we do); instead we give all datagrams within the same conceptual 'layer' the same status code, and we can then can manipulate them on the basis of their logical relationships rather than their physical positions.

When we copy attended datagrams into short-term memory, we include their status codes and we reinstate these status codes into datagrams of the new image. So datagrams in the restored image not only have the attributes of the old image, but are also reinstated in the same logical layers they were copied from.

It is important to understand that, logically, there is no need for a short-term memory; it only exists because we do not have the capacity in iconic memory to retain information in full detail for more than a few seconds. Short-term memory is really an extended iconic memory that is structured in a different way to save space. Our iconic memories for the immediate past are held in a continuous sequence of time pixels, so the time attribute of an event is taken from the time layer that holds that event. We suggest that the past beyond these few seconds is held in short-term memory as a simple list of the datagrams we have attended, and their time attributes are the time they were attended. This turns short-term memory into an extension of the workspace but with the limitation that, unlike iconic memory, it keeps no record of unattended events.

Chapter 9. The seamless flow of perception
The sequences and timings we present in this chapter are based on our interpretation of a paper in the journal *Attention, Perception and Psychophysics* entitled 'The effect of blinks and saccadic eye movements on visual

reaction time' (written by Johns, Crowley, Chapman, Tucker and Hocking in 2009). We suggest that the general reader have a look at this article because, although it was written for specialists, the findings are presented in a way that is reasonably accessible; in addition, the article provides an insight into the type of research that is carried out in this field.

If a significant change occurs in a scene during the image-build phase, we need not wait until the entire build process is complete before we react. It appears that, during this phase, signals from the eye appear to be diverted along a separate channel to a brain region that handles our responses. The new information is not incorporated into the new image but is processed at the pre-attentive level so that long-term memory can provide an immediate reaction if necessary.

Eye movements – saccades – can of course be made to objects in the scene that are outside our present field of view and therefore not in our present iconic image. Even though the priority object is outside our field of view, we can trigger a saccade to its location because we know its scene coordinates, either because we attended it earlier or because we have downloaded them from long-term memory into a token datagram at the target location.

Chapter 10. Things that are the same but different – and what they look like

We create an attended datagram by combining pre-attentive datagrams with different attributes for the shared region. But we do not actually create a separate attended datagram – attended datagrams are simply collections of pre-attentive datagrams temporarily linked together. Things we recognise in long-term memory, cats for example, also create pre-attentive datagrams that produce higher level attended datagrams, such as rows of cats.

Although pre-attentive datagrams only hold attributes for one characteristic and one distribution, they hold supplementary attributes that provide additional information on the distribution they are in. This supplementary information contributes to priority-setting and the sequencing of unattended actions, but is not directly available to us.

The odd one out is actually identified by comparing in each datagram the group's binding distribution with the distributions of its non-binding attributes at the pre-attentive level. Therefore to pop out, an object does not actually have to have a Unit distribution, just a distribution that differs substantially from the binding one. This means that small groups of objects can pop out – pop-out is not confined to single objects on their own.

Each individual sense attribute code tells us what something looks like, and the same time it acts as a symbol for the class of all the things that look like that. But sense attribute code numbers give us something else as well: because they are a continuous sequence of values, the numerical difference between two different code numbers within the same series tells you the relationship between them. When we compare the sense attribute code numbers of two things, the difference not only tells us which one is bigger or smaller, but also how much bigger or smaller. Sense attribute values are not always ordered in a simple number sequence but can be mathematical progressions that give more weight to numbers in one part of the scale than to numbers elsewhere.

The raw values of the sense attributes that we receive reflect the viewing conditions. A black surface will reflect varying amounts of light depending on the intensity of the light falling on it – a grey surface in low light will reflect the same intensity as a black surface in strong light. To solve this problem, we identify the effect of the lighting conditions on grey levels in a scene either directly or by comparing the known grey levels of familiar objects with the actual value we are looking at. We then automatically adjust the actual grey levels we see so that they become what we would expect to see under normal lighting conditions. The result is that what we see is a perceived grey level and not an actual intensity, and it is these perceived values, and not the original intensity values, that determine the attribute code number settings in iconic memory. We maintain these black and white conversion values in the master group datagram for visual iconic memory.

This same issues arise for all the sense attributes, and we suggest that the same solution is applied whenever we need to create a class from a range of values but at the same time retain a connection between what a thing is and what it looks like.

We use the procedures we have described in this Chapter 10 as a general mechanism for ranking the components of any group that hold values for a particular attribute. So we can rank things by how they move or how they are positioned in space or time, and we can rank sequences by their motivator values to determine priorities.

Chapter 11. Three dimensions

We are not denying that there is a three-dimensional world out there, but we can only know *directly* the nature of that world in two dimensions. Our impression of an internal three-dimensional object is a carefully constructed composite made from a real two-dimensional extent plus attributes that describe, or imply, a third dimension using the same units of length; it is not a 'true' three-dimensional representation. We infer a three-dimensional world, but we can only really 'know' things as extents in two dimensions.

The same principle applies to the way engineers produce three-dimensional designs on two-dimensional screens. The designer may conceive of an object in three dimensions, but the only way he can depict it in three dimensions is by creating a series of two-dimensional images on the screen. The same applies to computer-produced animation: animators apply varying textures to flat surfaces to give the impression of curves, and they stretch and distort those textures to produce an impression of movement; they do not create things directly in three dimensions. Oddly enough, Lee Smolin in his book *Three Roads to Quantum Gravity* describes a space based on a two-dimensional hologram that apparently satisfies Einstein's equations.

We insert curvature attributes into datagrams only if the whole of a region has the same curvature. Connected regions each with the same curvature, the faces of a cube for example, come together to form groups in the same way that all groups do. The edge-status rules governing their surface relationships are the same in three dimensions as they are in two, so for example)(and i = 1 are the edge statuses for connecting two adjacent surfaces.

There are three ways in which you can perceive things that occupy three dimensions: as things in a two-dimensional array, as things in a three-dimensional array and as things in a scene. For example, you can see a flock of starlings flying in the sky as an ever-changing region of birds in a two-dimensional array or as a collection birds in a three-dimensional array or as a scene – although to see it as a three-dimensional scene, you must locate your viewpoint inside the flock of starlings.

We suggest that there is a three-dimensional distribution with spokes fanning out from a central point to each of the object's component surfaces – this array structure acts as a form of scaffolding. A fan array's interval is the angle separating its spokes, so for example, the array interval for a cube would be 90 degrees. We could treat the interior (or exterior) of a car in this way, although we are more likely to structure the interior of a car as a scene.

Movement and time: Chapters 12–14

Chapter 12. The way things move

There are only a few points that we wish to make on the ideas presented in this chapter. As in previous chapters, the times, rates of movement and distances are for illustrative purposes only – although we believe that they are of the right order of magnitude.

The cat's change in position is managed separately from its appearance because our brains do not have the capacity to process the whole image in detail with the same frequency we need to track moving objects. The idea of the moving cat figure was prompted by watching dancers performing in the dark wearing black costumes that were painted with a small number of luminous spots. By tracking the 'same' spots from one frame to the next, we create a continuity of identity.

Edges, corners and terminations are the main markers we use for tracking movement. But how do we track moving objects that have curved boundaries, billiard balls for example? What points do we compare from one frame to the next? We suggest that movement tokens are placed in curved boundaries at those points where the curved edge becomes either vertical or horizontal. In this way, a ball should have least three movement tokens in every frame: one on the left, one on the right, one at the top – and possibly one at the bottom. We can then predict the future path of the ball using the distance and time between the positions of these tokens in successive frames, although we are not actually comparing the same physical part of the ball from frame to frame.

We insert tokens predicting future movements for every thing in the image whether or not it is moving. Objects that have an attended identity retain that identity in their predicted tokens, but unattended objects are in pre-attentive form and carry no identity because they represent the many alternative paths that objects might take. These tokens populate the scene component layer. This is a layer directly below the scene group layer that extends over 360 degrees, which means that we can track the movement of an object even when it moves outside our field of view. We probably make predictions for around 3 seconds into the future and retain these predictions for around 10 seconds into the past.

The new set of movement tokens is probably generated in the first 50 msec of the 150 msec image-build phase of a saccade, and the new tokens replace prediction tokens generated from the previous image and extend our view into the future. We retain past prediction tokens because *they tell us how things moved in the past*, so what we 'see' as the past is not the actual movement that took place but the prediction of that movement. If actual token positions have failed to confirm these predictions, the past predictions will be deleted.

We compare predicted token positions with their actual positions for all objects in the image whether or not they are moving, and then we prioritise them for attention. In doing this, we take into account that some objects might appear from nowhere because they have fallen behind something else that is moving. These processes are vital for the performance of unattended behaviours.

Movement needs two components to describe it – rate and direction – and therefore the *Whole* sections of datagrams will have one attribute for speed and another for direction. A directional attribute helps us to match objects from frame to frame but adds enormously to the complexity.

Chapter 13. The attributes of time

We assume that the information workspace, iconic memory, is constructed around two combined extents – a two-dimensional space extent integrated with a one-dimensional time extent – and that in the time extent we represent and organise things in exactly the same way that we do in the space extent. Our attention can move backwards and forwards through time in exactly the same way that it moves backwards and forwards in space – albeit using different reference points. Our time reference point, *now*, moves through time separating past from future just as our space reference point, the image centre, moves through the world changing our spatial perspective.

It is important to be clear that the things we see as happening now are not real but forecasts made earlier of how things will look in the future based on how they looked in the past. Magicians understand this process, which is why they make changes during the blind interval that trick us into believing that the impossible can happen.

We are able to incorporate attributes for time into datagrams alongside those for space because space and time share the same Pixel structure and obey the same set of rules, particularly in the way they handle the statuses (brackets) that define relationships. Time attributes are generated by the brain as physical sense data and are inserted into pre-attentive datagrams as sense attributes so that we can know the positions in time of things and how long they last.

In our examples, we use 1 mm × 1 mm and 1 msec for the space/time dimensions of a Pixel cube. This is for simplicity; the unit of time of our brain 'clock' is probably more like 10 msec, and the unit of space less than 1 mm. It is also conceivable under certain conditions that the pixel units of time and space might need to vary to handle acceleration and mass.

All our knowledge of the world comes from the external data that reach our senses. We record this elemental information internally in Pixels as individual point values, and as we do so we attach to them unit values for time and space. Each point value we record therefore extends for 1 space unit and 1 time unit – a thing cannot exist if it has no presence in space and time. There may be more than one elemental value in a Pixel, but each value will be contained in a single elemental datagram. All elemental datagrams have dimensional attributes that say this value extends for 1 space unit and lasts for 1 time unit.

Whole	Parts
Descriptive attribute value = Black Space dimensions attribute = 1 unit Time dimension attribute = 1 unit Space distribution attribute = *iArray/0* Time distribution attribute = *iTRow/0*	None

Figure N.4 Elemental datagrams carry a representation of a single data type in a single Pixel. They do not have a *Parts* section because they are the smallest data element possible.

Figure N.4 shows the attributes of an elemental datagram in 1 Pixel of a black square. You can see that the datagram has no *Parts* sections because there are no components; these elemental values are the fundamental units of perception – there is nothing smaller.

Figure N.4 shows the attributes in the elemental datagram of a single Pixel of a black thing. The datagram holds a single descriptive value – Black. There are two *dimensional* attributes that tell you that the black extends over 1 space unit and 1 time unit, and there are two *distribution* attributes with zero intervals because there is no gap between the pixel and its neighbours in either space or time; the black is continuous.

Elemental datagrams are how all information received by the mind is initially represented. They are the basis for the pre-attentive datagrams that describe uniform regions and their alternative combinations in time and space. Ultimately, they are also the information source our attention needs to create the higher level datagrams that provide ever more sophisticated descriptions of the world.

Chapter 14. Tracking movement, change and causation

In this chapter, we state that an object must move at a constant speed for it to form a uniform time-row, and that a time-row ends when the constant speed of a moving object changes. Clearly, the full definition of a moving object is broader than this; it requires only that that the speed of an object changes at a constant rate, but there does not have to be a fixed speed. An object moving at a constant speed comes within this definition because its rate of change of speed is constantly zero. A uniformly accelerating billiard ball will create a time-row that terminates when it hits a cushion, and we can group this time-row with the decelerating time-row of the same ball as it moves away from the cushion because they share the same space at the point of impact. We plot the accelerating and decelerating paths by constantly varying the number of 'dwell' Pixels along the length of each time-row.

In Figure 14.7, our attention has to repeatedly attend the same point on the white ball as it moves towards the black one so that we track the ball's path along the same time-row. The point we follow is where the curve of the ball's leading edge is vertical, at right angles to the ball's diameter. These successive points on the ball are not the same physically, but in movement and causal terms they reflect how the ball behaves.

We automatically create many pre-attentive datagrams in the iconic image describing possible time-row distributions that an object could be assigned to, and from the alternatives we select a single time-row. For those who would like to understand more about how alternative time-rows are generated, we suggest they try Shimon Ullman's *The Interpretation of Visual Motion.*

All these predictions of the future are constantly recalculated – and of course we never see anything actually moving, we only 'see' its latest static full image plus a movement simulation. We constantly compare predicted positions with actual positions, and use statuses and priorities in datagrams to signal discrepancies. This is a huge computation that is carried out for every object in the image.

We explain in Chapter 14 why there is a maximum speed that anything can travel at. We call this limiting speed c_{max}, the speed of an object moving across one space pixel in one time pixel; travelling any faster than this, an object cannot find an adjacent space pixel to go to, so it ceases to be the same object. To achieve speeds less than c_{max}, an object must alternate between moving at c_{max} and not moving at all. In other words, c_{max} is not only the fastest speed anything can travel at, *c_{max} is the only speed anything can travel at. There only two speeds, zero and c_{max}, and at any point on its path an object is either moving at c_{max} or is not moving at all.* The speed that we perceive an object moving at is the group average of its time-row downloaded into the individual component datagrams in each Pixel along that time-row. The rules we described in Chapter 10 for group attribute values held in

components of rows in space apply equally to the group attribute values we find in the component Pixels of rows in time – time-rows.

We see the overall speed of an object at any point as the average speed downloaded from the group datagram into the *Whole* section of a component Pixel, measured over a defined (edge-terminated) time period. But this average speed is not the speed of that object at any point along its measured time run because, as we have said, there are only two speeds an object can move at, either zero or c_{max}.

Our time attributes tell us how long things last and the length of the time interval between things, but they give time no direction. How then can things move? The answer is very simple – in our minds, *things don't move*; movement is an illusion. When we see a cat move from A to B, what we really see is a cat disappear at A and another identical cat appear at B.

In this chapter we described the two ways we calculate movement attributes. The first creates pre-attentive movement attributes from the raw input data for every uniform region in the iconic image, this is the only form of movement representation that can be processed in unattended sequences. Apparent motion attributes are confined to attended processing.

Long-term memory and reacting to events: Chapters 15-17
Chapter 15. The way long-term memory is organised
As we have said already, we have no compelling evidence that our brains hold our long-term memories in a class network of the type we describe in Chapter 15. The solution that we present arises from the conviction that all information about relationships must be held in the nodes of the network, and not in the links that connect those nodes. We can only achieve this objective if *all* the links in the network represent just one type of relationship, and the relationship we have chosen to satisfy this condition is that of class/subclass.

Every class node in the network is the unique combination of the two class chains that are their parents. We have restricted nodes to just two parents partly because we like the simplicity of a binary combination, but in theory it should not matter how many parents a class has provided each can be given a unique class code number. In any case, we almost invariably match a key class from its subclasses.

The first time we attend a new region in the iconic image, this creates a match to the Class of Everything in long-term memory. The attributes in the attended datagram then produce matches to subclasses of the Class of Everything until a class code number is downloaded into the attended datagram that tells us what the thing is. The result in long-term memory is a chain of matched key class nodes going all the way back from the last matched node to the node of the Class of Everything. Each matched node stands for a different level of detail, for example the sequence: everything, creature, bird and starling. But only one of these becomes the defining attribute for the attended region representing the object. The defining class/attribute code we finally select will be heavily influenced by the context, the scene we are in for example. If we see an object and have no idea what it is, the class code number for the Class of Everything remains in the datagram to tells us that this thing we are looking at is simply 'something'.

One of the problems we have is that the parent/component relationship we build in iconic memory can produce the wrong class/subclass relationship in long-term memory – they are the 'wrong way up'. On page 91, we point out that if we see a flock of starlings in the shape of a circle, we will process it in iconic memory from the top down, from a group parent circle to component starlings, and as a result we will record it in long-term memory as the subclass of all circles that are made from starlings. However, it is probably better to have the record in long-term memory of what we have just seen the other way up, as the subclass of all starlings that have formed circles.

We can achieve this because whenever we identify something in long-term memory to its class code, a starling for example, it is automatically overlaid in iconic memory by a special group parent that represents every member of that class that exists, so in this case we would automatically create a group region for all the starlings in the world. If we now attend this group region as a parent, the circular flock of starlings becomes a circular segment, and if we attend the circular attribute in one of its datagrams, this creates in long-term memory the subclass of all starlings that are in circles.

Different subclasses of a class occur at different frequencies, so for example the number of occasions on which we see an apple that is yellow is less than the number of times we see an apple that is red or an apple that is green, let's say 10% of the time compared with 30% and 35%. We need to keep a record in our long-term memories of relative frequencies whenever we match the different members of a particular class, but where do we hold this information? We cannot hold it in the links that connect the class node to each of its subclasses because, as we explained earlier, links in long-term memory cannot hold any information other than the relationship class/

subclass. So instead we use another special class, *the class of all relative frequencies* and, in this example, we record the 10% subclass of the frequency class as an *all* subclass of the class of all yellow apples.

We treat the ageing of things over time in long-term memory in a similar way. The times when things happen in our lives are also a class, so when we experience a particular event we can record the instance time that it occurred as an all subclass of that event. The elapsed time since an event in the past is the difference between the time *now* and the *now* time recorded in long-term memory against the event.

When we recall a memory of a particular event for example, we will almost always do so in a context that differs from the original context. When we record a recall event in long-term memory, we will include events that happened during the recall period, which then get consolidated with the original event and effectively modify the original memory.

Logically, our memories do not 'fade', and everything we experience is given an instance time and retained for ever. The reason we do not recall events from the distant past is not necessarily because the memory is not there but because the time that has elapsed since its instance time gives it a low priority. In the real world, our brains are limited in both in capacity and performance, and our memories deteriorate over time, so it is sensible to discard older events in preference to recent ones, but this is a function of how our brains work, not our minds.

In other words, our minds work on the basis that all information in long-term memory is equally available regardless of how old it is, but that what we choose to recall depends on priorities and nothing else. However, *interference* can affect priorities and therefore affect how we recall information from the past. Every new experience produces some interference because they all change the long-term memory record in some way, and therefore change our perspective on things we experienced in the past. We are constantly restructuring, rebalancing and validating the information we hold in our long-term memories (a process called normalisation when carried out in commercial databases). We automatically restructure the memory network to rationalize inconsistencies and to discover hidden logical structures, for example new key classes or parent classes, and we do simulations – dreams – to test new structures so that we do not in future act out undesirable behaviours. As mentioned in the chapter, we also carry out various housekeeping procedures; for example, we carry out mass deletions of subclasses created from insignificant attributes, in particular those created by unattended attributes in attended datagrams.

We use a wide range of special classes to define the relationships between class nodes, and we have mentioned a few of these, but there are many, many more. In particular, there are a range of special classes derived from the algebra of sets that define certain types of logical relationships. You can find a list of the set theory symbols used for these logical functions on the website *rapidtables.com.*

One of the special classes we introduced in Chapter 15 is the *all* class that has same members in its subclasses as it has in its parent class. We have used this device because it simplifies the explanation of the difference between *all* and *some*, but the same result can be achieved based on the principle that nothing can have two values for the same attribute type.

We have not addressed in any detail how we incorporate new information into the long-term memory network. When we attend a datagram, we attend it as a whole, but we also selectively attend individual attributes within the *Whole* section. It is this selective attention to individual attributes in datagrams that drives the matching process, and only attended attributes are fully incorporated into the long-term memory network as new information. Attributes in the attended datagram that are *not* selectively attended will prime nodes in the network, but they cannot directly produce a match. These non-attended attributes of the attended datagram will be recorded as subclasses of the currently matched node but will have a very short retention time. However, by priming unusual pathways in long-term memory, non-attended attributes in attended datagrams can point us to novel solutions and may play a role in providing us with a sense of humour.

Throughout this book, we have insisted that, in the mind, there are only datagrams and the attributes they contain, that the mind is just a collection of datagrams in a single iconic memory and that there is nothing else. And yet we have introduced two memory systems that hold information: short-term memory and long-term memory.

We only need short-term memories because our brains have limited capacity and therefore cannot retain information in iconic form for any length of time, a few seconds at most. A perfect implementation of a perfect mind, however, would have an unlimited iconic memory and would hold past information in iconic form, datagrams, for ever. In this way, a perfect mind would have no need for a short-term memory.

But what about long-term memory, the network of class code numbers we download into the attended datagram, as attributes, that tells us what things are? How can we dispense with this structure? We believe that there is no separate long-term memory in the perfect mind as each class is itself a datagram with class/subclass links to the datagrams of every thing that is a member of that class. For example, in the perfect mind, the class for all cats is a single key class datagram that holds the attribute code for all cats as the single attribute; but it does not just represent all cats – it has class/subclass links to all the unit datagrams recording every time you saw a cat. In other words, in the perfect mind, the subclasses of each key class are ultimately all the things that actually make up that class.

So in the *perfect* mind, the class code number for the class of all cats is not downloaded into a cat's datagrams as an attribute code when you see a cat. When you recognise a cat, a link is activated to the datagram that holds the code number that is, at the same time, the class of all cats and the source of the sensation that delivers the experience of seeing a cat. That is why we insisted we have insisted that the code number for a class and the code number for an attribute are the same.

Key class datagrams, as well as having links to all the things in their class, have links to other class nodes that contain a subset of the things in their class. So, in a perfect mind, the class datagram of all cats would have links to all the unit datagrams of every cat you had ever seen, but the class datagram for all cats would also have a class/subclass link to the class datagram of all Siamese cats, which would itself have links to the unit datagrams of every Siamese cat you had ever seen.

In summary, in the perfect mind, every instance that ever occurred would be recorded for ever, which means that all the instances of all the things that make up all the classes in the network would be retained for ever. In other words, not only would a class datagram in the perfect mind just stand for the class of all things that had certain characteristics, but also each class datagram would have a link to the datagrams of everything that had ever occurred with those characteristics.

To contemplate abstract ideas, we must give them the same type of layered spatial representation in iconic memory that we give to visual objects. If we wish to think about the equation for a circle, for example, we must first create a group region in iconic memory to represent the concept of the equation as a whole and then download information from long-term memory into datagrams in the layers below it to describe the elements it is constructed from. We structure the rules for a circle in much the same way we structured the Alfred Tennyson verse from *In Memoriam.*

Everything in the mind is information represented by regions (concepts) and edges (the limits of those concepts). Regions are logical forms that can represent physical things, but they can also represent abstract notions and ideas – as do Venn diagrams and Carnap's similarity circles.

Chapter 16. How and why we respond to things
We must point out that, as with Chapter 15, we have no compelling evidence for the physical implementation of the logic we propose in this chapter. It is essentially an exercise to see whether we can create structures and procedures that are consistent with the ideas presented in the 15 chapters that preceded it.

It is particularly important in this chapter to be clear on the distinction between recognition and recall. *Recognition* occurs when, by examining the component parts of a thing, you create a match in long-term memory that downloads an attribute code for that thing into its group datagrams. *Recall* occurs when you match a chain of unit classes in long-term memory that produces a time-row of past events in iconic memory. But you can only 'relive' what happened in the past by attending its time-row in *simulation* iconic memory in the present.

We get the impression that all space is visual space, but this is misleading. There is no special visual space but just a single iconic space with a single set of coordinates shared by all the things in all the different sense layers – one of which is vision.

Why do we insist on the need to position anything and everything we can conceive in a single space and time? The answer is very simple. We cannot integrate packets of information arising from different sources unless they share the same value for at least one attribute type, and space and time are the only universal qualities that every piece of information we handle has, every datagram possesses. Iconic regions are essentially three-dimensional extents of information that represent anything and everything.

In the firework and dancing examples in Chapter 16, the vision and sound attributes originate from the same point in space so it is easy to integrate them into the datagrams of a single region. But what if we wish to integrate vision and sound when they originate from different places, when the rule is that we can only integrate two things if they share the same position in both space and time? The answer is that we have to choose the space of one of them to act as the space for both. We hear the voice of the ventriloquist coming from the mouth of his dummy because we choose the dummy's mouth as the single integration space for both sound and vision.

The action sequence shown in Figures 16.2 is complicated enough, yet in this example we have simplified the way we build chains in long-term memory. Before starting this experiment, you would first have to establish the context of the procedure. You would set up a region in the group layer of iconic memory to encompass all the things involved in the experiment, the instructor,

the screen, your index finger and so on, because when your attention moves from one thing to another, from the screen to your hand for example, it must move via a group datagram that encompasses everything that is taking place.

In this chapter, we have made the point that as well as attending datagrams as a whole, we attend individual attributes within the attended datagram. All the attributes within the *Whole* section of the *attended* datagram are individually prioritised, so if we attend a datagram for a black square, the attributes in its *Whole* section, black, square and size, for example will be prioritised individually. As a result, we might attend the black attribute first and the square attribute second, and may not attend the size attribute at all. Yet even though we attend these attributes at different times, we appear to see the blackness and the squareness of a black square simultaneously. This is because they are both given the same *present time*, and it is this that gives us the feeling that that we are seeing the two characteristics at the same time.

Datagrams are prioritised at the pre-attentive level. The highest priority pre-attentive datagram creates the binding that produces the attended region with its attended datagrams, and only when the attended datagram emerges are all its individual attributes prioritised – and of course they will be reprioritised as attention moves from one attribute to another.

It is the sequence in which we attend the attributes in the attended datagram that drives the matching and priming processes within long-term memory. Unattended attributes in attended datagrams can prime nodes in long-term memory but cannot produce matches. Attended attributes leave lasting imprints in long-term memory, whereas attributes in attended datagrams that have not been attended appear to leave a simple subclass record that has a limited lifetime, unless it represents some significant novelty. Attributes in datagrams that are processed in an unattended sequence cannot alter the structure of long-term memory, but they will update the frequency of occurrence of class nodes relative to each other, and this can influence how well an activity is performed in the future.

However, there is one very important exception to the rule that unattended activities are never recorded in long-term memory. If I am walking through my sitting room while talking to someone and I catch my knee on the corner of the coffee table, the pain will switch my attention to my knee in the iconic image. The past sequence of unattended images of my knee and the coffee table are retained by my iconic memory for a second or two, so provided I switch my attention quickly to these images, I can relive what happened and the experience can be recorded in long-term memory.

Motivational attributes in the datagrams of our body parts deal with physical injury, threats of injury, tangible pleasures and the promise of future pleasures – we will call these *physical* motivational attributes. A similar set of *social* motivational attributes is generated from public sense data that help us handle our relationships with other people and our place in society.

Social motivational attributes deliver emotions – fear, shame, approval and pride, for example – and they are downloaded automatically from long-term memory into the *group datagrams in our iconic body image* when particular patterns arise in the public sense data. Two attributes are needed to describe social motivation: one describes the *nature* of the emotion, and the other tells us how positively or negatively we feel about it.

So when we see a disapproving face, our long-term memory downloads two social attributes into a group level datagram of our body iconic image, one to deliver the sensation of guilt and the other to tell us how guilty we feel. If we attend this datagram, we will experience these sensations, and at the same time they will produce a match in long-term memory for our response.

We also use social motivational attributes to implement the cultural norms that are necessary for large populations of people to live together in any sort of harmony. Most cultures have laws that forbid theft, and offenders are punished physically; this acts as a deterrent to stealing, for example, because we anticipate the physical consequences of being caught.

But in many societies, we do not rely entirely on people's knowledge of the *physical* consequences to deter them from stealing. Instead we educate our children to believe that the very *idea* of stealing is *wrong in itself* regardless of the consequences. We use our facial expressions and tones of voice to embed negative social motivators in their memories so that even the thought of stealing produces a negative sensation. A negative emotion engendered by the disapproval of those around us is generally a stronger, more immediate and more efficient deterrent to stealing than is the threat of being caught and punished.

Although social motivational attributes provide a quick, efficient and consistent response to events, the downside of embedding social norms, belief systems, in a population is that they often become counterproductive over time and can eventually produce consequences that damage the society they are designed to serve. There is therefore always a tension between *categorical* and *consequential* morality; we desire to follow the rules and beliefs of the societies we live in, but at the same time we do not want to follow those rules if the consequences –

emotional or physical – of doing so are damaging for us as individuals or for society in general.

The section on motivation in Chapter 16 is of course highly speculative. Pain and pleasure are attributes in datagrams like any other, although they are special in that they generate high priorities. The sensation of pain is not of course generated by the pain attribute in the mind but by physical processes in the internal body image in the brain that share the same iconic location.

Chapter 17. What thinking is
Our priority system directs our attention to things even when there are no strong motivational attributes around, as when we are in the mountains admiring the view, or simply because we are bored. In these situations, our priority system chooses the pre-attentive datagrams of things in the scene on the basis that they possess certain 'gestalt' qualities, they are symmetrical or brightly coloured or large in the context of their surroundings, for example.

The question is which of our two priority systems drives these decisions – the impersonal or the personal? All matched datagrams in iconic memory are linked by long-term memory to datagrams in our body iconic image that have motivational attributes; even things as simple as black squares will produce a specific positive or negative reaction in the group datagrams of our body iconic image if attended. However, these values will be close to zero and will not normally compete on the well-being scale. But our preferences for things based on their intrinsic qualities is driven by our personal priority system, and this is why we are able to modify our preferences.

In our electric shock example, the pain in your finger was -8. The predicted pain value, -1, from your planned response *replaces* the actual pain in your finger, -8, in future datagrams in the time-row. If it did not, your attention could never move away from your finger to rotate your arm because the actual pain would always have a higher priority than the predicted one. If the response module fails to reduce the pain over the predicted period, the pain attribute in your actual finger will return to -8, producing a priority of 80, your attention will immediately return to your finger and you will feel the pain once again.

Note that, at the same time as all this is going on, every other active motivator attribute in your iconic body will generate its own priority value. So if you have lower back pain of -10, the group datagrams for your lower back will receive a priority value of 100 and you will not even notice that you have received an electric shock.

We use another form of simulation to helps us when we have difficulty in recognising things in the world around us when we see them from unusual angles or in unfamiliar positions. To find out what something is, its attributes must produce a unique match to a single key class in long-term memory; only when we have a unique match between the attended region and a single key class can we be certain about its identity, that this is a cat for example. When we attend an attribute in a region that we are trying to identify, or an attribute of one of its components, we automatically prime all the nodes in long-term memory for the things it might be. A primed node is one that has just one matching parent rather than the two needed for a perfect match. The problem is often that the particular parts of the image we need to attend produce a perfect match can be obscured or distorted, making a perfect match impossible. To resolve this problem, we allow primed nodes in long-term memory to switch on attributes in the datagrams of the duplicate region in simulation iconic memory as suggestions for what this region might be.

So, for example, I might not be able to identify a dark shape on a chair in my sitting room, but if the nodes for a cushion, a black cat and a navy blue jumper are primed in long-term memory by the datagram I am attending, this will switch on these alternative attributes in the datagrams of that shape in my simulation iconic memory. If I then attend the 'could be a cat' attribute, this will then prime the triangular corner of the shape as an ear, and if I attend it I will recognise the shape as a cat.

In Chapter 17, we have been vague on the nature of the regulator that converts motivator values in time-rows into priority values. It would make sense for this process to be carried out by the group attributes held in the group datagram at the top of our body iconic image, the one that holds attributes for things that apply to us as a whole person.

Further reading

Ambler, S. (2002). *The Object Primer*. Cambridge: Cambridge University Press.

Barker, R. (1990). *Case Method. Entity Relationship Modelling*. England: Addison-Wesley Publishing Company.

Berkeley, G. (1957). *An Essay Towards a New Theory of Vision*. Everyman's Library, No. 483.

Carroll, S. (2011). *From Eternity to Here*. Oxford: Oneworld.

Challis, B. and Velichkovsky, B. (1999). *Stratification in Cognition and Consciousness*. Amsterdam: Benjamins.

Chalmers, D. (1996). *The Conscious Mind*. Oxford: Oxford University Press.

Dehaene, S. (2014). *Consciousness and the Brain*. New York: Penguin.

Eagleman, D. (2011). *Incognito*. Edinburgh: Canongate.

Feser, E. (2005). *Philosophy of Mind*. Oxford: Oneworld.

Frisby, J. and Stone, J. (2010). *Seeing. The Computational Approach to Biological Vision*. Cambridge, Massachusetts: MIT Press.

Haldane, J. (2002). *Mind, Metaphysics, and Value in the Thomistic and Analytical Traditions*. Notre Dame, Indiana: University of Notre Dame Press.

Harris, S. (2012). *Free Will*. New York: FREE PRESS.

Kahneman, D. (2012). *Thinking Fast and Slow*. London: Penguin.

Lockwood, M. (1989). *Mind, Brain, and the Quantum*. Oxford: Basil Blackwell.

Marr, D. (1982). *Vision*. San Francisco: W. H. Freeman.

Monk, R. and Raphael, F. (2000). *The Great Philosophers*. London: Phoenix.

Miyake, A and Shah, P. (2003). *Models of Working Memory*. Cambridge: Cambridge University Press.

Neuman, Y. (2003). *Processes and Boundaries of the Mind*. New York: Plenum.

Palmer, S. (1999). *Vision Science*. Cambridge, Massachusetts: MIT Press.

Rovelli, C. (2016). *Seven Brief Lessons on Physics*. London: Penguin.

Rundle, B. (2009). *Time, Space, and Metaphysics*. Oxford: Oxford University Press.

Russell, B. (1940). *An Inquiry into Meaning and Truth*. London: Penguin.

Russell, B. (1917). *Mysticism and Logic*. London: Unwin.

Searle, J. (1997). *The Mystery of Consciousness*. New York: The New York Review of Books.

Skow, B. (2015). *Objective Becoming*. New York: Oxford University Press.

Smith, Q. and Jokic, A. (2003). *Consciousness*. Oxford: Oxford University Press.

Vernon, D. (1991). *Machine Vision*. England: Simon and Schuster.

Vernon, D. (2014). *Artificial Cognitive Systems*. Cambridge, Massachusetts: MIT Press.

Ullman, S. (1996). *High Level Vision*. Cambridge Massachusetts: MIT Press.

Ullman, S. (1979). *The Interpretation of Visual Motion*. Cambridge, Massachusetts: MIT Press.

Wolfe, J. Kluender, R. and Levi, D. (2012). *Sensation and Perception*. Sunderland, Massachusetts: Sinauer.

Wolfe, J. and Robertson, L. (2012). *From Perception to Consciousness – Searching With Anne Treisman*. Oxford: Oxford University Press.

Acknowledgements

The authors gratefully acknowledge the permission granted to reproduce the copyright material in this book: Figures: Palmer, S. E. (1999) *Vision Science*, MIT Press, Cambridge, MA (Figures 2.6c, 10.3 and 10.4); Sabada, R. (2002) *Alice Adventures in Wonderland*, Simon & Shuster, London (Figure 11.1); Marr, D. and Nishihara, H. (1978) *Representation and recognition of the spatial organization of three-dimensional shapes*, Proceedings of the Royal Society of London, 200, 269–294 (Figure 16.1); and Frisby, J. and Stone, J. (2010) *Seeing. The Computational Approach to Biological Vision*, MIT Press, Cambridge, MA (Figure N.1).

Epigraphs: Chapter 2, J. K. Rowling, *Harry Potter and the Deathly Hallows* © J.K. Rowling 2007 (with permission from the Blair Partnership); Chapter 3, B. Russell, *An Inquiry into Meaning and Truth* (with permission from the Bertrand Russell Peace Foundation); Chapter 5, From *The Complete Fairy Tales* by the Brothers Grimm, translated by Jack Zipes, published by Vintage. Reprinted by permission of The Random House Group Ltd. © Jack Zipes 1987, 1992, 2002, 2007; Chapter 6, L. Wittgenstein, *Tractatus Logico-Philosophicus* (with permission from Routledge).

Figure 5.1 is taken from Yarbus, A. L. (1965) *Role of Eye Movements in the Visual Process*, Nauka, Moscow. The H. Cartier-Bresson epigraph in Chapter 15 was cited in *Creative Camera*.

Every effort has been made to trace copyright holders and to obtain their permission for the use of copyright material. The publisher apologises for any errors or omissions in the above lists and would be grateful to be notified of any corrections that should be incorporated in future reprints or editions of this book.

Index

downloaded from long-term memory for actions, 109-110
executing time-rows, 120-123
lifetime-rows, 128-129
present time, 67
simulation time-rows, 120-123
time edges, 74-75
time is not a thing, 78
time-rows and motivation, 113-116
unattended time-rows, 112-113
token datagrams
  as predictors of moving objects, 69-71, 79-80
  as targets in a search, 58
  for tracking the positions of
    parts of our bodies, 105
    representing objects outside our field of view, 44-45
  to represent apparent movement, 81
  to represent simulated objects, 123
touch, 103
tracking our performance, 124
training, 113

U

unattended activity
  action sequences, 112-113
  pre-attentive processes, 36-37
unit classes, 34, 91, 102, 122
unpredictable information, 126-127

V

Venn diagrams, 37, 147
verification
  of predicted movement, 71-72
viewpoint,
  definition of standard viewpoint, 66-67
virtual edges, 139
vision
  capturing visual information, 131-133
visual cortex
  holds the internal image, 5
  information structures in the visual cortex, 11
  transmission pathways in the brain, 132
visual iconic memory, 34

W

wellbeing, 119-120
Whole section of datagrams, 2, 7
working memory in computers, 130
workspace
  as the hub of all information systems, 130
  can hold only one attention stream, 27
  iconic memory is the mind's workspace, 34, 35
  in the *perfect* mind short and long-term memories
    are part of the workspace, 37
  the rules assume an infinite workspace, 87

Z

zombie, 138

Index of Authors